Operations Research

for Management

EDITED BY

JOSEPH F. McCLOSKEY

AND

FLORENCE N. TREFETHEN

INTRODUCTION BY

ELLIS A. JOHNSON, DIRECTOR
OPERATIONS RESEARCH OFFICE
THE JOHNS HOPKINS UNIVERSITY

BALTIMORE:

THE JOHNS HOPKINS PRESS

Foreword

D URING the spring of 1952, The Johns Hopkins University decided
—as one means of determining the possible place of operations
research in its academic activities—to sponsor an informal seminar
on operations research. Administration of the seminar was placed in
the University's Operations Research Office.

Happily, in implementing the seminar, ORO decided that each
lecture should be duplicated, primarily for those attending the
seminar, but also to provide unclassified materials to be used in
training new operations analysts joining the ORO staff.

Three important "plus values" soon began to emerge. In one
way and another, persons interested in operations research heard of
the reprints of the talks and began to request them until the mailing
list began to become unmanageable. The Editor of the *Journal of the
Operations Research Society of America* became interested in the
series and urged many of the individual speakers to adapt their papers
for publication in the *Journal*; this created a two-way flow, inasmuch
as some of the speakers were invited to speak before the seminar
because of articles they had written for the *Journal*.[1] And finally,
it became apparent that, more by accident than by design, the
individual lectures represented a sufficient cross section of information
about operations research as to constitute a reasonably complete introduction to the subject.

The actions which have produced this volume resulted. Florence
Trefethen prepared "A History of Operations Research" to pull
together the background materials touched on by the various speakers.

---

[1] Thus, the papers by Magee and Boodman appeared first in the *Journal*.
Those by Goodeve, Pocock, Levinson, Hausrath, and Thornthwaite were given
first before the seminar. A paper by Hitch appearing in the *Journal* and a
lecture by McKean before the seminar were combined to produce the chapter
in this volume.

Dr. Joseph O. Harrison wrote his chapter on " Linear Programming and Operations Research " to round out the outline.[2]

Ellis A. Johnson rewrote his lecture as a general introduction, and Philip M. Morse and Joseph F. McCloskey altered their presentations to serve as introductions to the sections on METHODOLOGY and CASE HISTORIES, respectively. Otherwise, except for minor changes to obviate duplication, the lectures appear in this volume substantially as presented. Vera Riley's Bibliography, originally circulated to the seminar, was brought up to date as of September 1954.

As stated in the title, this volume is addressed primarily to management. The editors and authors know that not all men and women in management have technical training that will enable them to read all parts of this volume with equal facility. Had all mathematical notation been " written around," an erroneous impression of operations research would have been given: operations research does employ highly developed and powerful mathematical tools, and much of its value to management lies in its practitioners' ability to manipulate these tools skillfully.

The important fact for the reader to keep in mind however, is that the concepts which the experienced operations-research scientist (or operations analyst) brings to the solution of complex management problems are vastly more significant than the tools, which are adjuncts of this conceptual knowledge.

The Editors wish to acknowledge the co-operation of the authors; their gratitude to those on the staff of The Johns Hopkins University who made the seminar possible; and their appreciation of the many kindnesses extended by fellow members of the staff of the Operations Research Office.

JOSEPH F. McCLOSKEY
FLORENCE N. TREFETHEN

Chevy Chase, Md.
October 1, 1954

---

[2] This paper was presented as a lecture early in the 1953-54 seminar series.

Contents

Part I

General

Part II

Methodology

Part III

Case Histories

Authors

Ellis A. Johnson is Director of the Operations Research Office, The Johns Hopkins University.

Florence N. Trefethen is a Consultant to the Operations Research Office.

George S. Pettee is Assistant Director of the Operations Research Office.

Sir Charles Goodeve is Director of the British Iron and Steel Research Association, London, England.

Lawrence J. Henderson is Associate Director of the Rand Corporation. He is in the Washington, D. C. office.

J. W. Pocock is a partner of the firm of Booz, Allen and Hamilton, Chicago, Illinois.

Philip M. Morse is Professor of Physics and Chairman of the Interdepartmental Committee on Operations Research at the Massachusetts Institute of Technology and past President of the Operations Research Society of America.

Russell L. Ackoff is an Associate Professor of Engineering Administration and Director of the Operations Research Group at the Case Institute of Technology, Cleveland, Ohio.

Byron O. Marshall, Jr., is a Staff Member at the Operations Research Office.

David Slepian is a member of the Mathematics Research Department at the Bell Telephone Laboratories.

Charles Hitch is Chief Economist at the Rand Corporation.

Roland McKean is a Research Economist at the Rand Corporation.

Walter E. Cushen is a Staff Member at the Operations Research Office.

Joseph O. Harrison, Jr., is a Staff Member at the Operations Research Office.

David H. Blackwell is Professor of Mathematics and Statistics at Howard University and a Consultant to the Operations Research Office.

Joseph F. McCloskey is a Staff Member at the Operations Research Office.

Horace C. Levinson is Chairman of the Board of Tele-Rama, Inc., and Chairman of the Operations Research Committee of the National Research Council.

Seymour T. R. Abt is Divisional Operating Manager, Materials Handling Division, at Stix, Baer and Fuller, St. Louis, and formerly Director of Research of the Giant Food Shopping Center, Inc., Washington, D. C.

John F. McGee is a member of the Operations Research Group at Arthur D. Little, Inc.

Robert H. Roy is Professor and Chairman of Industrial Engineering and Dean of the School of Engineering at The Johns Hopkins University.

Alfred H. Hausrath is a Staff Member at the Operations Research Office.

Charles Warren Thornthwaite is Professor of Climatology and Director of the Laboratory of Climatology, The Johns Hopkins University, at Seabrook, New Jersey, and President of the Commission for Climatology of the World Meteorological Organization.

Vera Riley is Staff Bibliographer at the Operations Research Office.

INTRODUCTION

The Executive, the Organization, and Operations Research

ELLIS A. JOHNSON

I N WRITING this introduction to a volume of essays and reports on operations research, I feel that it is appropriate that I should try to place the operations research function in proper perspective relative to the executives and organizations which it is designed to serve.[1]

Had I been writing this introduction two years ago, when the seminar series on which this book is based was just beginning, I would probably have spent many words attempting to define and, perhaps, "defend," operations research. This is no longer necessary. Operations research has established itself as an activity that can and does bring new attitudes, new concepts, and new techniques of research into the service of management. And, with each passing day, it is increasing its capability of helping management to solve complex action problems and make major decisions.

[1] In writing this introduction, I have felt it to be both permissible and necessary to depart from the talk that I gave two years ago to open the seminar series. Developments in operations research have been far too many for a general introduction to retain much value over so long a period of time. In bringing the matter up to date, I have drawn ideas from many sources and much of any credit that might accrue is due to many individuals. Full allocation of such credit would be impossible, but Dr. McCloskey's assistance in preparing this introduction must be mentioned.

Some terms more familiar to the military than to business and industry are used in the sections that follow, and so it is advisable to define these terms before launching the discussion. By "strategy" is meant the basic disposition of the resources available to the executive. By "tactics" is meant the manner of utilizing the resources which have been committed to a particular activity. By "technology" is meant the physical things which are involved in converting an input into an output of the activity. By an "organization" is meant virtually any identifiable complex of men and machines working toward an objective, whether the complex is military or civilian, industrial or commercial, governmental or private; every effort is made to state broad principles applying to any organization, even though it is recognized that some elements of organization considered in this paper may be absent (or present only by implication) in some kinds of organizations.

The Characteristics of Operations Research.

It may be well to start this discussion by examining a few of the outstanding characteristics of operations research. Basic to all other characteristics is the fact that the majority of the practitioners of operations research were trained in the basic sciences rather than in engineering or administration. It is to be expected then that the methods of operations research are closer to those of the basic sciences than to those of engineering. The dominant attitudes and tools are those of physics rather than of electrical engineering, of psychology and sociology rather than of personnel administration.

At the same time, many graduates of schools of engineering (including industrial engineers) and of schools of business administration have entered the operations research profession and are making important contributions by using the methods and techniques in which they are trained. These methods and techniques are blended with those of the basic sciences, and the resultant synthesis and extension of methods and techniques provides management with an extremely flexible and powerful tool.

This blending of methods and techniques, primarily from the basic sciences, but also from engineering and administration, is not accidental. It results from a conscious and overt recognition by those in operations research of the necessity for having specialists, highly skilled in each field of knowledge having bearing on the particular action problem, work in closely integrated research teams. Because of the scientific training of some members of these teams, systematic development of action models based on fundamental theory (in the manner so well known in the basic sciences) becomes possible, as does a heavy reliance on the more complicated mathematical concepts and techniques of the sciences. Because of the training in engineering and administration of other members of the team, there is sensitivity to the need for exceedingly detailed knowledge gained from experience; these " practical " people help to bridge the gap between theory and application.

The orientation of operations research toward the basic sciences helps account for its deep concern with experimentation. Sometimes the necessary values and " parameters " can be obtained from the study of past or current operations and can be " fed into " the theoretical model of the action. Once the model has been determined to be a valid representation of the action system under study, then values and parameters may be altered in order to predict the effects of adopting new courses of action. More often, however, it is necessary deliberately to design " small " operations in order to obtain the necessary data. These data may then be fed into the model, or the experimental operation may itself serve the purpose of the model in developing new courses of action. Admittedly, design of valid operational experiments is one of the most difficult aspects of operations research. Moreover, such experiments can be very costly. But the difficulty and the cost are insignificant when compared to the adverse results that can ensue when a major operation is entered into without prior experimental determination of its worth.

Thus we see that many of the characteristics of operations research derive from the fact that it is rooted in the basic sciences. But its most distinguishing characteristic stems from the fact that it has been concerned, since its inception, with the overall aspects of action systems. In general, the older professions that exist to serve management have made a sound, healthy application of scientific principles to *separate* elements of action systems. Operations research is more concerned with " optimizing " the operations of the whole organization that with improving operations within one division thereof. Obviously, in order to study and understand the overall system, operations research must study and understand all of the components, and so is interested in serving management at all levels within the system. Only thus can it serve the whole organization.

Because it shoulders this responsibility, operations research has been especially conscious of the necessity for estimating the uncertainties in its predictions of the results of adopting new courses of action. These uncertainties may be introduced by human behavior, by changes in the environment, and by competitor actions and reactions, all of which must be assessed, but all of which are extremely difficult to assess. This estimation of uncertainties becomes especially important when strategic and tactical decisions are involved, because of their fundamental importance to both the short and the long range health of the organization.

From the foregoing, it becomes apparent that an incidental characteristic of operations research is that the kinds of study it makes take more time than those which are usually made by its predecessors in the field of management science. Operations research involves major syntheses and tends to consider new courses of action that have effects over a long period of time. Operations research *is* research and produces *research* studies; these take time for successful accomplishment.

The important characteristics of operations research, then, are:

Research on the operations of the whole organization;

Optimization of operations in a manner that brings about greater assurance of both short and long range health for the organization;

Application of the newest scientific methods and techniques;

Synthesis and extension of the methods and techniques of the older management sciences;

Development and use of analytical models in the manner common to the basic sciences;

Design and use of experimental operations that give an insight into the behavior of actual operations;

Use of integrated and creative multi-disciplinary team research to solve complex operational problems.

The Environment for Operations Research.

If an activity with these characteristics is to function in the best possible manner, two very important conditions must be met. These are the conditions of communication and confidence—and they are incumbent upon both operations research and management.

If operations research is to accomplish major syntheses that will lead to valid recommendations regarding future courses of action, then it must have access to all of the information it *needs* in making its studies; in other words, it must have good communication with all parts of the organization. But this must be two-way communication: The operations analyst cannot expect all of the people in an organization to learn the highly technical language in which he is accustomed to communicating with his colleagues; he must learn their language, however. Most important, he must be able to translate the results of his studies into the language of the executive; that is, into language that sets forth, clearly and simply, the values, effectivenesses, and costs involved in a proposed set of alternative courses of future action.

The second condition—confidence—is interrelated and interacts with communication. If operations research is to have confidence in its results, it must be confident that it has had access to the necessary information. If management is to have confidence in the results of operations research studies, it must be able not only to understand the results but to recognize that realistic assumptions have been made as well. Management must also be able to see that the operations research activity has made decision-making "easier" and that these decisions stand the test of time.

These conditions indicate that operations research is done best by a group that is an integral part of the organization concerned. Further weight is given to this conclusion if we realize that the solutions obtained through operations research must be reasonably compatible with the existing procedures of the organization. This requires great knowledge of internal customs, and this cannot be acquired easily or quickly by "outsiders." Even if outsiders do acquire this knowledge at any given time, they can maintain neither continuous service nor continuous understanding of organizational operations. Development of the necessary conditions of communication and confidence takes time and continuous effort.

At the same time, it is impractical for any but the largest organizations to support an operations research group that includes all of the specialists who might be needed at any given time or on any particular problem. Accordingly, it is wise for internal operations research groups to allocate a reasonable fraction of their budgets to the acquisition of outside *assistance*, as needed. This assistance may be obtained from colleagues in the profession, from specialists in universities and research laboratories, and from the various agencies offering management science services on a consulting basis.

Placed in the kind of environment that has just been described, operations research can do much to assist management. For, advanced though the United States is in science and technology and receptive though management has been to the older management sciences, there is strong evidence that, in many governmental, business, and industrial organizations in this country, management has not been exploiting its capabilities and realizing its full potential. This failure may be due to a lack of co-ordination and communication among the main elements of the socio-economic system of the United States. But it may also be due to an unwise or fatalistic acquiescence in the continued existence of problems that may be the result of habit, custom, and conditioning, all of which *can* be changed if the need for and the possibility of change are recognized. It is important to the nation and to every organization that helps comprise it that we develop and exploit management tools that will make possible realization of full management potential in the quickest and most natural way.

The Elements of Action.

If we are to understand how operations research can help management to realize its full potential, it is necessary to examine more closely the action systems which it is designed to serve.

Action, used in this sense, is produced by the systematic organization of men and machines into man-machine systems—such as industries, business enterprises, military organizations, government bureaus, and combinations of these. Operations research involves the study of possible interactions among men and machines within these systems and is concerned with decision-making, organization (both formal and informal), and internal communications, as well as with the

" operating " elements which effect the physical translation of inputs into outputs of the organization.

These action systems represent accumulated knowledge and experience and require careful preparation to bring them into being. Once in being they are subject to change. Some elements may undergo frequent and violent change, while others may remain stable for long periods. But all of the elements must be co-ordinated to some degree, despite these differential rates of change, if the organization is to maintain its integrity.

This co-ordination has become increasingly difficult in recent years because of rapidly increasing complexity, resulting in large measure from the scientific and technological achievements of the last decade. This increasing complexity affects every element of action systems—but at differing rates. It affects research, development, engineering, production, sales, and distribution. It affects procurement, maintenance, and service. It affects finance, communication and control. It affects the environment and competition. And it makes increasingly difficult those basic decisions that determine organizational strategy and tactics.

In some cases, this growth in complexity is implicit in the nature of the system; in other cases, where the basic principles remain relatively unchanged, alteration in scale of operations has brought a complexity that may be described as quantitative, rather than qualitative. In either case, the details bearing on decisions have become so magnified in number that it has become difficult for single minds, or even for organizational staff groups, to order them in such a way that rational decisions (in which they have a high degree of confidence) can easily be made by executives.

This growth in complexity has made it impossible to start with a fixed plan of action and then proceed with a simple linear arrangement of the various elements that are required to produce that action. Organizational strategy reacts on tactics and on production and on development and basic research. At the same time, basic research is reacting on development, production, tactics, and strategy. The basic research that led to nuclear-generated power has led to a reassessment of its strategic position by every power-using organization on the face of the earth, from governments on down; and these reassessments are leading to new programs in basic and applied research and in development with the purpose in mind of making possible the completion of the still incomplete strategies relating to nuclear power.

This interaction, or feedback, among the elements of the action system requires that management relate the activities within each of the major elements in such a way that not only will the overall objectives of the organization be served, but that the overall national or social objectives will also be served. At the same time, management must be sure that the activity in each element is responsive, without too long time delay, to the changing needs of the organization, whether brought about by technological breakthroughs, discovery in usable form and quantity of new resources, or changed situations with respect to markets or competitors.

Organization of the elements of an action system may be accomplished in various ways. There are frequently good reasons for having basic research carried out as " free research " in universities and foundations, without governmental or industrial support, or with support only of areas of research of particular interest to the sponsoring organization. Similarly, each organization has the option of making or of buying some of the goods and services that go into its final output.

So far as activities carried out within an organization are concerned, experience has established the principle that poor results are obtained if sales, for example, is permitted to control production, or if production controls engineering, or if engineering controls development, or if development controls research. In this chain, the tendency always is for the sales staff to want immediate results from production, and so on down the line, despite the sacrifice in quality and increase in costs that attends such efforts at domination. Each of the steps in the chain, from sales back through research, requires different minimum amounts of time for proper accomplishment of its mission, and each element must be protected from the pressures that may be exerted by another element that has a shorter minimum time requirement.

Equally important are the different requirements for accuracy, for speed in taking action, and for the insight needed best to perform particular jobs within each of the elements of the action system For example, research needs great insight to solve problems that reach into the area of the still-unknown. It is bound to be slow and inaccurate in its results, approaching final accuracy through a series of approximations, each a little closer to the ultimate "truth" than the last. By contrast, sales must be quite exact and timely in the prices (discounts, etc.) set on goods and in the amounts made available to particular sales outlets, if a profit is to be made by the organization. From these simple considerations, it is quite clear that the same organizational structure, personal attitudes, and discipline will not fit both sales and research; in fact, each element of the action system must be organized, staffed, and disciplined in a manner suited to its function.

Thus, management must see that the research scientist is protected from the pressures exerted by the development engineer or sales manager, but it must also provide the scientist with guidance that will assure, to the maximum extent possible, that the results of his work will be useful to the development engineer, and to the production manager, and to the sales manager, and to the ultimate user of the production of the organization.

Operations research is concerned with the heart of this control problem—how to make sure that the whole system works with maximum effectiveness and least cost.

It is recognized, of course, that not all organizations have an equal need for operations research. In small companies, in "stable" industries, and in "safe" monopolies, it may still be permissible to rely on trial and error and on techniques which produce marginal improvements. Operations research may not be of appreciable use to such organizations. Trial and error and marginal improvement were quite adequate even for large and complex organizations as little as a decade or two ago—which may explain why operations reseach has "arrived" only recently in our culture.

Today, however, in those large and complex organizations for whom once-reliable constants have now become "galloping variables" because of the impact of increasing complexity, trial and error must give way to planning, and acceptance of marginal improvement must give way to an organized search for opportunities to make major shifts in the means of achieving organizational objectives. Today, so many industrial and other organizations are so huge, and major operations are so expensive, that a single major "wrong" decision may be fatal; trial and error becomes "trial and castastrophe."

Similarly, adherence to techniques of marginal improvement can place an organization at such a serious competitive disadvantage relative to its competition that a major, healthy enterprise can go into decline in a matter of years.

Operations research is designed to serve these "victims" of rapidly increasing complexity. It is concerned with complex operations which embrace a dynamic technology and which are affected adversely by long time delays in adjusting to change, especially where planned changes must take into account both short and long range futures. In general, operations research is not concerned with techniques of marginal improvement. Rather, it is concerned with major, even revolutionary, improvement. It may be characterized as an improved management tool designed to deal with the non-simple, non-linear, probabilistic, dynamic, conservative, and irrational world in which we live. It is a world in which organizational survival requires planning.

Requirements for Planning.

The first requirement for planning is well known. This is the need for a *mission*. A mission consists of a task and a purpose; the purpose is usually the organizational objective. If organizational policy has defined the objectives of the organization, and these have been made known to those responsible for planning, then the mission of the organization may be derived from the objectives by relating them to the organization's current situation—including its own condition, its relations to its environment, and its position relative to its competitors.

If planners are to make the best and most rational plans consistent with the mission of the organization, then their greatest need is for *information*. They must have past and future as well as current information. Current information must reach them quickly so that corrective action may be taken before a derangement of plan in one element of the system has deranged the whole system.

Timely information of the kind needed for planning is often not readily available in large organizations, possibly because traditional reporting and accounting systems are designed mainly to justify past actions rather than to serve management, except by inference, in current and future planning. The organization must be designed to provide the planners and, through them, the decision-makers, with current information on the status of technical and production programs, training and sales programs, etc.—and special priority must be given to that information which has special implications for the strategy and tactics of the organization. On the other hand, the planners must recognize the dynamic nature of the problems they face and appreciate that there *will* be time delays in the communication of the information needed to control the operation.

Even when the mission of an organization is well defined and the information received by the planners is adequate and timely, there remains the difficult problem of *flexibility* in plans. Some plans, especially those dependent upon the results of basic research, may not culminate in practical results for five, ten, or more years. Other plans, of course, have immediate, short-range effects—and the short-range and long-range plans must be consistent with, and complement, each other. Furthermore, since competition is making *its* plans, provision must be made in one's own plans for flexibility that will permit timely change to meet not only the competitor's changing plans, but the changing environment as well—and all this without compromising the organization's objectives. Plans made now that force the decision-maker of ten years hence to "put all his eggs in one basket" are unwise; *that* executive must be guaranteed the freedom to alter *his* strategy, tactics, and production system to *his* situation, if organizational goals are to be achieved over the long term.

While the short and long range plans of an organization must be compatible with and complement each other, careful distinctions must be made between the two. Thus, short range goals are usually related to immediate production problems that must not be allowed to influence basic and applied research excessively—and planners must plan accordingly. They must provide a set of plans which integrates the various elements under their control in a sensible manner and in such a way that action planned for the immediate future is firm and well defined, both as to procedure and as to objectives. At the same time, the plans must take into account long range goals; these may be much more flexible and much less well defined so far as procedure is concerned, though the ultimate objectives should be stated quite clearly.

Even short range plans must accord subordinate executives some freedom of interpretation so that they are in position to further the objectives of the organization—rather than the plan itself—when a change in environment or in competitor actions necessitates changes in plan in order to achieve objectives. As the plans become longer and longer in range, this freedom for interpretation must be broadened. The limitations on freedom of interpretation must be worked out within each organization in order to accord with the dynamics of the situation and to take into account individual motivation and morale within the overall policies and traditions of the organization.

The Role of Operations Research.

In order to assist the planners, operations research makes use of information coming from all elements of the action system, including those within the organization as well as those related to environment and competition. Operations research uses this information to develop models of the elements of the action system and of the overall system. Then, by examination of the reaction of the model to various changes over future time, a set of possible future courses of action can be developed, and the results of adopting any of the particular courses of action may be predicted. These predictions can then be used in establishing plans for the entire organization.

Here, several points should be made. The studies made by operations research may grow naturally out of the continuing study of the organization; an opportunity for significant improvement of operations may become apparent as a result of systematic analysis. Or, they may result from specific requests arising out of need for information that develops as plans are being formulated. Thus, there is interaction and intercommunication between those responsible for planning and operations research just as there is among all other elements of the action system.

The second point is much more important to an understanding of operations research. *An operations research study is not a plan.* An operations research study results in conclusions and recommendations. These may be accepted or rejected by the planners, who have the responsibility for the formulation of the directives that are to be promulgated by the executive (in most organizations, the distinct functions of formulation and promulgation of policy are combined in the executive; the distinction is maintained here if only to emphasize the point that an operations research study is a *recommendation* for action and is not, in itself, a *plan* of action).

In fact, we may go further and say that operations research must not accept any direct authority or responsibility for action, It must, in every way, stand apart from the action and must arrive at its conclusions with indifference as to whether or not a particular recommendation is adopted. This is necessary if operations research is to maintain its integrity. It must never succumb to pride of authorship, but must accept the decisions of the planners and executives, remaining their agent to carry out studies in the most impartial and scientific way. This role is one that is difficult to fill; it requires the true scientific attitude. Only with such an attitude can operations research arrive at acceptable solutions to the problems it studies.

The final point is that operations research is no magic device that eliminates all uncertainty from decision making. The best assumptions about the future may be found to have departed from actuality when the future has become the present. In constructing models of operations, factors which have been and are "constants" may be included, but the future may prove that these constants have varied. Similarly, factors which vary within well defined limits today may vary widely, or within different limits, in the future. We may add to these sources of uncertainty the virtual certainty that none of the executives or subordinates concerned with the action under study will act perfectly; changes in the factors involved in leadership and morale are, in the present state of our knowledge, unpredictable. Chance events—a fire, a destructive storm—can disrupt the finest of plans. The sources of uncertainty may be catalogued indefinitely.

Operations research does, however, take uncertainty into account, and a good operations research study will frequently include, in the set of alternatives placed before management, predictions of the worst, the most probable, and the best outcome to be expected from a particular course of action. Operations research makes every effort to compensate for uncertainty, *but it cannot eliminate it.*

By way of summary, I should like to give my own definition of what operations research offers to management:

Operations research is the prediction and comparison of the values, effectivenesses, and costs of a set of proposed alternative courses of action involving man-machine systems. To do this, it uses a model

of the action that has been developed analytically by a logical and, when feasible, a mathematical methodology. The values of the basic action parameters are derived from historical analysis of past actions or from designed operational experiments. Most importantly, because all human and machine factors are meant to be included, an estimate of the uncertainty in the predicted outcome and in the values, effectivenesses, and costs of the proposed action is provided.

PART I

General

A History of

Operations Research

FLORENCE N. TREFETHEN

O PERATIONS research began as an organized form of research just before the outbreak of World War II. During the busy years which followed, operations research people on both sides of the Atlantic worked at an accelerated pace to provide state and military leaders with the bases for making such decisions as would hasten an Allied victory. There was then little time for reflection on the progress of research techniques or for looking back to determine how much had been achieved since the start; indeed, in many instances, there was scarcely time for recording day-to-day activities so as to make the later compilation of a history a relatively simple matter.

Once the war was over, histories and reminiscences of several operations research groups were set down, but most have never been published. Enough had been spoken and written about the work of these wartime groups, however, to bring operations research to general notice. Veterans of World War II working in the field began to find themselves almost as busy as during the war years, since not only government, but various civilian organizations as well were seeking to make use of their skills in the activity which had proved so substantial an aid to executive decisions during hostilities. New operations research groups have been established, new kinds of problems have been presented to them, and a wider range of techniques has been tapped to provide solutions. As a result, operations research has become a firmly established profession so quickly that it has lacked the leisure for tracing its own growth and development. There is no special merit in this as the time for gathering up information on the progress of operations research from 1939 to the present. The body of operations research experience and the list of publications about it, however, are building up so rapidly that it seems prudent, without further delay, to present a brief account of the origins of operations research and of its short history.

To describe the numerous precursors of operations research in the history of war and strategy prior to World War II is too extensive an undertaking for any single chapter. Ever since the third century, B. C., when Hieron, King of Syracuse, asked Archimedes to devise means for breaking the Roman naval siege of his city, political and military leaders have consulted scientists for solutions to the problems of war. In many instances, such nonmilitary specialists have been able to assist the military with new ideas about the machines, the tactics and the strategies of war. By World War I, there were clear examples of early operations research on both sides of the Atlantic in the attempts to analyze military operations mathematically. In England, this work was undertaken as a hobby by F. W. Lanchester whose papers on the relationships between victory, numerical superiority, and the superiority of firepower appeared in 1914 and 1915.[1] His efforts to express complex military operations as equations had no effect on operations in World War I. In America, Thomas Edison made studies of antisubmarine warfare for the Naval Consulting Board. His work included the compilation of statistics to be used in determining the best methods for evading and for destroying submarines, the use of a " tactical game board " for solving problems of avoiding submarine attack, and an analysis of the value of zigzagging as a method for protecting merchant shipping. Like Lanchester's, Edison's studies had no actual effect on operations, but were an interesting prelude to similar work in World War II.[2]

[1] F. W. Lanchester, *Aircraft in Warfare: The Dawn of the Fourth Arm* (London: Constable and Co., Ltd., 1916).

[2] William F. Whitmore, " Edison and Operations Research," paper read before the Operations Research Society of America, 18 November 1952, and reprinted in *Journal of the Operations Research Society of America*, Vol. 1, No. 2 (February 1953), pp. 83-85.

British Operational Research in World War II.

In 1939, at the outbreak of war in Europe, there was the nucleus of a British operational research organization already in existence. As Superintendent of the Bawdsey Research Station, A. P. Rowe had, in the late thirties, become interested in using the knowledge of civilian scientists to assist military personnel with radiolocation. Together with Wing Commander R. Hart, he arranged that, when war began, a small group of the station's scientists would form a research section at Headquarters of the Royal Air Force Fighter Command at Stanmore. One of the problems under study at Bawdsey just prior to the war was that of integrating the newly developing radar system of early warning against enemy air attack with the older system of operational control based principally on the Observer Corps, whose members were trained in the sighting, identification, and reporting of planes. · Mr. G. A. Roberts, the scientist assigned to the problem, carried out several investigations into the total efficiency of the communications system, examining it from the position of the executive officer responsible for the entire control network.

Simultaneously, Dr. E. C. Williams was making other studies equally valuable to the R. A. F.; these analyzed the variations in performance among the growing numbers of early warning stations and resulted both in recommendations for improving operator technique and in identifying certain weaknesses in the network. Recognizing the similarities in the work of Roberts and Williams, Rowe, whose organization had since become the Telecommunications Research Establishment, brought the two together in one section under the supervision of Mr. H. Larnder. It was this section which, when the war was declared, moved to Stanmore to study first radar detection and, eventually, a repertoire of other operations. In the period before the Battle of Britain, sporadic incidents of German air activity at night allowed the section to observe the system of Ground Control Interception in action; this work extended into a comprehensive analysis of all phases of night operations, and the report which resulted became the pattern on which other Operational Research Sections' analyses of operations were based.[3]

Since the British Army was responsible for anti-aircraft gunnery,

[3] J. G. Crowther and R. Whiddington, *Science at War* (New York: The Philosophical Library, 1948), pp. 91-94.

it, too, soon became actively interested in operational research. In August, 1940, General Pile, Commander in Chief of the Anti-Aircraft Command, requested scientific assistance in the coordination of the radar equipment at gun sites which gave the slant range and bearing of an attacking bomber with some newly developed apparatus which provided a reading for its elevation. Professor P. M. S. Blackett of the University of Manchester, a Fellow of the Royal Society, a Nobel Laureate, and formerly a naval officer, was recommended to study the problem. The new equipment did not appear to perform on the gun sites as it did at the testing stations, a discrepancy which indicated the need for scientific observation on the sites during actual operations. So that the problem could be examined in several perspectives, Blackett collected for this work men who were scientifically trained, but who were not necessarily radio specialists. The Anti-Aircraft Command Research Group which he assembled included three physiologists, two mathematical physicists, one astrophysicist, one Army officer, one surveyor, one general physicist and two mathematicians. "Blackett's circus," as the group was called, were soon able to demonstrate the value of the mixed-team approach to operational problems.[4]

In March, 1941, Blackett, with some members of his circus, moved from AA Command to Coastal Command. There they became involved in problems concerning the detection of ships and submarines by the use of radar equipment in airplanes. This type of investigation brought Blackett into close touch with the Admiralty's antisubmarine warfare problems, and, in December, 1941, he became Director of Naval Operational Research at the Admiralty. He was replaced at Coastal Command by E. J. Williams.

Meanwhile, the rest of Blackett's circus were joined by others who had just been introduced to radar through a concentrated course at the AA Radio School, Petersham. In May, 1941, they became the Operational Research Group of the Air Defense Research and Develop-

---

[4] *Ibid.*, pp. 95-96. Professor Blackett's is probably the earliest name associated with the literature of operational research. His two papers, "Scientists at the Operational Level" (1941) and "A Note on Certain Aspects of the Methodology of Operational Research" (1943) have been published as addenda to his article, "Operational Research," which appeared in *The Advancement of Science*, Vol. 5, No. 17 (April 1948).

ment Establishment (Ministry of Supply); later, they became a separate establishment known to this day as the Army Operational Research Group. Thus, two years after the beginning of the war, all three of Britain's military services had acquired formally established operational research groups. Later in the war, similar groups were organized in Canada and Australia.[5]

Civilian defense activities also had the benefit of operational research analyses. J. D. Bernal, as a member of the Ministry of Home Security's Civil Defense Research Committee at Princes Risborough, began a comprehensive collection and analysis of damage statistics during the period when Britain was enduring heavy bombing. One hundred and twenty field observers conducted systematic interviews with survivors of enemy air attacks, and the data thus provided were analyzed at headquarters by a team of forty analysts.[6] This is possibly the first instance in which not only observation and measurement but also observers' reports were used in operational research.

The group assembled for this work included several Americans who later became involved in operations analysis for the U. S. Air Force. The indoctrination which they received at Princes Risborough was a valuable experience.

The distinguished British anatomist, Professor S. Zuckerman, did much to scotch popular rumors which magnified the effects of bomb explosions upon human beings. Proceeding from experiments with animals to systematic observations of human injuries incurred during air raids, he was able to arrive at relationships between the number of bomb casualties and the bomb load dropped on a given area. The ratios which he developed were validated in connection with the five-hundred-plane Luftwaffe raid on Coventry; the number of casualties had been accurately predicted in advance.[7]

The numbers of persons engaged in various British operational research activities continued to increase throughout the course of the

[5] Crowther and Whiddington, *Science at War*, pp. 97-98. Army Operational Research Group, Great Britain, " Operational Research in the British Army, 1939-1945 " (October 1947), p. 1. The author is indebted to Sir Charles F. Goodeve for his explanation of the place of the various British operational research groups within the military organization.

[6] Crowther and Whiddington, *Science at War*, p. 98.

[7] *Ibid.*, pp. 98-99.

war. For example, the Army, in 1942, set itself the distant goal of
eventually getting 36 officers into research units in the combat
theatres; by the end of the war, however, some 120 officers had been
attached to these sections.[8] Before V-E Day, a total of 365 scientists
had engaged in operational research for the British Army.[9]

The fact that some of the World War II operations research
investigations have become so well-known among those presently interested in the field as scarcely to bear repetition attests to the degree
of interest which this form of research activity has excited; that
many of these early studies now seem to provide inadequate examples
of operations research demonstrates the progress in method which has
been achieved in the years since. A few will be briefly described here
to illustrate how this kind of approach to operational problems brought
valuable gains first to the British and, eventually, to the American
military forces.

During the winter of 1941-42, Coastal Command was experiencing
disappointing results in its antisubmarine air actions. Variations
in the size of the antisubmarine bomb and in the altitude which
planes attained for drop appeared to effect little improvement. E. J.
Williams, in collecting data on aircraft attacks against U-boats during
the previous spring, observed that most attacks were made against
submarines either on the surface or just submerged; planes sighting
a submarine tended to move in for attack immediately and a submarine
at or near the surface was a more favorable target than one which
had submerged to a greater depth. The charges being dropped,
however, were set to explode at depths of at least 100 feet where they
would be well " tamped " by the water. Since the lethal range of a
charge was approximately 20 feet, it was only on rare occasions that
an enemy sub reached the danger depth in time for the detonation;
the U-boats were obviously not receiving the full punch of depth-bomb
explosions.

Professor Williams recommended that charges be set to explode
at 20 to 25 feet. The " firing pistol " of those bombs in production,

[8] " O. R. in the British Army," p. 3.
[9] O. H. Wansbrough-Jones, remarks at a meeting of the British Association
in Dundee, 30 August 1947, " Operational Research in War and Peace,"
reprinted from *The Advancement of Science*, Vol. 5, No. 16 (February 1948),
p. 322.

however, had a minimum setting of 35 feet. Even that setting increased the hits on enemy submarines to the extent that German crews were reporting that new and more powerful bombs were being used against them. The magnitude of increase in the destruction of submarines was estimated at 400 per cent by the Royal Navy and at 700 per cent by the R. A. F., a discrepancy which is overshadowed by the magnificent gains for the Allies implied in either figure. The study had the added value of calling attention to the need for research aimed toward the development of a new " firing pistol." [10]

The Admiralty was confronted with a problem for which operational research provided an answer: " What size of merchant convoy would be most effective in terms both of minimum losses from submarine action and of minimum escort requirement? " The average convoy in 1942 consisted of some forty ships protected by six escorts, an arrangement which was yielding unsatisfactory results in terms of losses. Evidence suggested that more escort protection would reduce losses, but neither planes nor additional escort vessels were available. Therefore, the only variable with which the research team could experiment was the size of the convoy. The loss records for convoy sailings in 1941, 1942, and part of 1943 revealed that those formations with less than forty-five ships suffered losses averaging 2.6 per cent, whereas those with more than forty-five vessels sustained average losses of but 1.7 per cent. This lighter loss record for larger convoys had obtained even though the number of escort vessels had been roughly the same for all convoys and the size of the attacking U-boat packs had been fairly uniform. The study clearly indicated the advisability of larger convoys; subsequently shipping losses were substantially reduced. [11]

Even the most cursory historian must feel obliged to make further mention of the operational research group at Fighter Command, the first of all such groups. Their work in the detection of enemy aircraft was highly successful. It is estimated that the introduction of radar increased the probability of intercepting enemy aircraft by a factor

[10] Sir Charles Goodeve, " Operational Research," reprinted from *Nature*, Vol. 161 (March 1948), pp. 3-5. Crowther and Whiddington, *Science at War*, pp. 99-100. W. Barton Leach, " Operations Analysis in the Theatres," a talk delivered at the Army Air Force School of Applied Tactics (April 1944), p. 7.

[11] Crowther and Whiddington, *Science at War*, pp. 110-21.

of 10; in addition, the small operational research team's efforts increased the probability by a further factor of 2.[12]

British operational research was originally developed to improve defensive operations, since, at the time, the government was faced with the problem of effectively using relatively small numbers of men and machines to withstand the superior forces of the enemy. As the tide of war changed, however, the data collected and the techniques employed in solving problems related to defense were brought into play for increasing the effectiveness of offensive actions against the enemy. This fact is particularly well illustrated by the eventual use of bomb damage and casualty data collected by Zuckerman and Bernal during the Battle of Britain. Once the Allied Forces were able to conduct systematic bombing raids over Germany, such data made it possible for operation planners to choose the most profitable kinds of targets and to estimate in advance the effect of given bomb loads upon given areas.[13] Just as in the study of convoy losses, operational research indicated that, for bombing raids, larger plane formations suffered smaller percentages of losses. This finding resulted in the first 1000-plane R. A. F. raid over Germany in 1942.[14]

It is virtually impossible to document each stage in the development of British operational research during World War II, since many of the administrative arrangements and advances in method were achieved at crucial moments in the war and have, consequently, become obscured in the history of military events. It is possible, however, to identify certain salient features of operational research which had clearly emerged by the end of the war.

It became obvious at an early stage, for example, that a military operational research organization could function best with both a central office and field units, the central office to maintain contact with such administrative centers as the War Office and the Ministry of Supply, to serve as a planning and data-processing headquarters, and/or to act as a training and recruiting depot, the field units to attach themselves closely to operating elements in order to make those direct

[12] Goodeve, "Operational Research," p. 2.

[13] Crowther and Whiddington, *Science at War*, p. 99.

[14] Herbert Yahraes, "The Mysterious Mission of ORO," *The Saturday Evening Post*, Vol. 224, No. 34 (23 February 1952), p. 75.

observations and measurements essential to the thorough study of operational problems.[15]

The mixed-team approach was, from the start, a feature of operational research. The groups formed in England during World War II consisted of representatives from the physical sciences, mathematics, and statistics. Biologists, probably because of being accustomed to dealing with individual differences within large numbers of cases and to having less than perfect control of experimental situations, contributed substantially to operational research from its earliest days.[16] On the other hand, psychologists and social scientists appear to have been missing from the early groups, even though some of the work could have benefited from their concepts and techniques of research. This was recognized after the war.

The consideration of a problem in terms of its relationship to an entire operation, making necessary the study of additional, operationally-related problems, was, probably, the one achievement which most clearly distinguished World War II operational research from earlier research activities. G. A. Roberts was largely responsible for this expanded approach in England. He was presented with a radar problem primarily because of his experience in communications engineering. He proceeded, however, far beyond the limits of communications engineering and into many other aspects of the operation of the warning network.

The British Army's Operational Research Sections were expressly permitted, from the time of their origin, to initiate investigations which they deemed useful or necessary. Conversely, the Scientific Advisor to the War Office, who was the headquarters director of these sections, had the power of refusing to investigate military problems presented to his office if he considered them inappropriate or beyond the power of the sections within his control.[17] From its beginnings. therefore, operational research has had a continuing responsibility for discerning and selecting operational problems which transcends the mere deference to a customer's order.

[15] " O. R. in the British Army," p. 2. Crowther and Whiddington, *Science at War,* pp. 95-96.

[16] See also Leach, " Operations Analysis in the Theatres," p. 15.

[17] Jacinto Steinhardt, " Operations Research," lecture delivered at the New York Meeting of the Institute of Mathematical Statistics and the American Historical Association (29 December 1947), p. 2.

Finally, the British experience in World War II indicated that the operational research man could function most adequately in the absence of the narrowing restrictions often applied to uniformed personnel. The freedom, either as a civilian or soldier, to communicate directly with all echelons, to mingle with all ranks, and to remain aloof from concerns of promotion and the distractions normal to military life made possible the degree of thoroughness in investigation which is essential to scientific research.

Operations Research in America During World War II.

It is not possible to describe with full accuracy the exact manner in which news of operational research first crossed the Atlantic. Dr. James B. Conant, then Chairman of the National Defense Research Committee, became aware of operational research during a visit to England in the autumn of 1940.[18] Within a matter of months after the United States entered the war, both the Army Air Forces and the Navy had begun work in this new field.

As in the case of early Air Force work in Britain, operations research for the Air Forces in this country grew up around problems arising from new radar equipment. In the spring of 1942, Secretary of War Stimson traveled to Panama to inspect the defenses there. General Andrews, with whom he conferred, suggested that a group of civilian analysts might render valuable aid in coordinating radar equipment with the other defenses of the Canal Zone; several scientists were, accordingly, dispatched to Panama. Shortly thereafter, as a result of Vannevar Bush's description of operational research teams with the R. A. F., Dr. Ward S. Davidson, a scientist, and Major W. B. Leach, a lawyer, were asked by the Committee on New Weapons and Equipment, Joint Chiefs of Staff, of which Dr. Bush was chairman, to investigate the situation in Britain and any similar activities within the U. S. War and Navy Departments. They submitted their report on 15 August.[19]

General Arnold was immediately interested since he had already

---

[18] Col. Edward M. Parker and Lt. Col. David B. Parker, "Trial by Combat—Operations Research for the Army," reprinted from *Combat Forces Journal*, Vol. 1, No. 10 (May 1951), p. 5.

[19] "Operations Analysis, Headquarters, Army Air Forces, December 1942-July 1947," n. d., pp. 1-5.

received a request for an operational research section. This request emanated from General Spaatz, Commanding General of the Eighth Air Force, stationed in England, and was inspired by General Eaker's wish to have within his Eighth Bomber Command a group similar to those attached to elements of the R. A. F. On 24 October 1942, General Arnold dispatched a letter to all commanding generals of Air Force commands, recommending that they include in their staffs operation analysis groups.[20] This letter brought responses from several commands which either requested the assignment of such sections or asked for further information. On the Air Staff, Brigadier General Byron E. Gates offered to have the headquarters of the project within his Office of Management Control, and the Operations Analysis Division was established there on 31 December, with Leach, now a Colonel, in command.[21] Officials of the Office of Scientific Research and Development were, meanwhile, undertaking to train analysts at the Princeton University Station and at the Radiation Laboratory, M. I. T. These trainees were later turned over to the Air Force for service in all theatres.[22]

No resumé of this length can hope to deal adequately with the histories of the several Air Forces Operations Analysis sections. The first of these sections, established in October, 1942, was then attached to the Eighth Bomber Command in England, later designated as the Eighth Air Force; in a sense, it served as a prototype for similar groups attached to other commands. By V-J Day, a total of twenty-six operations analysis groups had been established at Air Force headquarters, including every combat air force and a number of ZI headquarters. Some four hundred officers, enlisted men, analysts and civilians on loan from other agencies engaged in operations research for the Air Forces in the course of the war. The average section consisted of about ten analysts working on the problems vital to the command to which the section was attached. The Operations Analysis Division in Washington served largely as a training and recruiting headquarters.[23]

[20] *Ibid.*

[21] *Ibid.*, p. 6. Charlotte Knight, " Ask Them Another," *Air Force*, Vol. 28, No. 8 (August 1945), p. 31.

[22] James Phinney Baxter, 3rd, *Scientists Against Time* (Boston: Little, Brown and Co., 1946), pp. 406-407.

[23] LeRoy A. Brothers, " Operations Analysis in the U. S. Air Force," a

The growth of operations research in the Navy was equally rapid. In April, 1942, during the early days of intensified antisubmarine warfare, the Commanding Officer of the Atlantic Fleet Antisubmarine Warfare Unit asked the Coordinator of Research and Development to form a group of " outstanding men of reputation with broad vision and receptive minds " who would preserve " the atmosphere of scientific research " to analyze antisubmarine operations. This request was forwarded to the National Defense Research Committee and, on 1 May 1942, a section of seven research men, recruited by Columbia University, was formed with Dr. Philip M. Morse of M. I. T. as its leader. This unit set to work immediately to analyze the results of sea and air attacks against German U-boats and to study means for improving the efficiency of both the Navy and Army forces engaged in these operations.

In July, 1943, the group, now nearly six times its original size, was incorporated into the staff of the Tenth Fleet as the Antisubmarine Warfare Operations Research Group. During the following year, it was transferred to the Readiness Division of CominCh Headquarters and renamed the Operations Research Group. At the war's end, the group consisted of seventy-three scientists who represented a diversity of backgrounds. They functioned as a single coherent central unit attached to the top operational command in Washington; at any time, however, from one-fourth to one-third of the men were on rotation in the field, attached to Theatre, Fleet or Sea Frontier Commanders.[24] The organization has had a continuous history since its establishment and is now called the Operations Evaluation Group.

Before any of the Air Force Operations Analysis Sections or the Antisubmarine Warfare Operations Research Group were established, another operations research group had been organized within the Navy. Its work culminated eventually in the aerial mining of Japanese-controlled waters from Singapore to the home islands. Some

brief description addresesd to the Air Force Officer (September, 1952), p. 1. United States Army Air Force, *Operations Analysis in World War II* (Philadelphia: Stephenson-Brothers, 1948), p. 1.

[24] Ernest J. King (then Fleet Admiral, U. S. N., Commander in Chief, U. S. Fleet and Chief of Naval Operations) " Third and Final Report to the Secretary of the Navy," issued 8 December 1945, pp. 1-2. Jacinto Steinhardt, " The Role of Operations Research in the Navy," *United States Naval Institute Proceedings* (May 1946), pp. 1-4.

measure of the importance of this campaign is provided in Prince Konoye's statement that the 5.7 per cent of the XXI Bomber Command's effort that was devoted to mining the home islands had an effect on Japan comparable to the high-explosive and incendiary bombings that accounted for the remainder of the Command's effort.[25] Japanese industrialists are reported to have told the military that the economic strangulation brought about by the mines made it impossible for the war effort to be supported.[26]

These mining operations were directed by former members of a seminar established during 1941 at the Naval Ordnance Laboratory by Dr. Ellis A. Johnson, then head of the Laboratory's countermeasures section. Finding that there was no doctrine to guide their development of mines for offensive operations, some fifty senior members of the NOL staff set about systematically to study all implications on mine warfare—strategic, tactical, and technological. They used the technique of war-gaming to develop models of possible operations, then "tested" various tactics and weapons.

This work offered sufficient promise to justify the establishment, on 1 March 1942, of the NOL Operational Research Group. By that time, the work going on in Britain had become well enough known to those at the Laboratory so that the organization was identified by name with this new activity. Dr. Walter Michels, head of the group, was assisted initially by Dr. Thornton L. Page and Dr. Laurence E. Hoisington. Their assignment was to study all operational aspects of offensive mine warfare.

During the war, the group underwent numerous organizational changes. It was transferred to the Bureau of Ordnance and then to the Office of the Chief of Naval Operations. For a time, it was headed by Dr. Francis Bitter, but Dr. Michels returned to the group to direct its efforts during the last two years of the war, and up to the time of its disbandment. Dr. John Von Neumann and Dr. J. L. Doob were among those who served with this organization.

Meanwhile, Dr. Johnson and several others from the seminar and the operations research group had gone into uniform. Comdr. Kenneth

[25] Buford Rowland and William B. Boyd, *U. S. Navy Bureau of Ordnance in World War II* (Washington Bureau of Ordnance, Department of the Navy, n. d.), p. 171.

[26] Associated Press dispatch from Tokyo, 13 September 1945.

L. Veth, USN, went to the CBI Theater; Dr. Shirley Quimby went to the Southwest Pacific; and Drs. Johnson and Page, to the Central Pacific, where all became " customers " for the work they themselves had produced earlier in Washington. Although they were responsible for actual operations, they continued the application of operations research techniques to their problems, and the resulting mining campaigns were the products of operations research studies from their inception.[27]

Dr. Johnson later moved to the XXI Bomber Command as Director of Mining. By January, 1945, he had completed plans for what came to be called Operation Starvation, but the operation was delayed because of a lack of mines. His operations research studies had shown that B-29's could be used most effectively in mining if single-sortie raids were carried out at night at an altitude of about 5,000 feet. This tactic had many advantages over the usual high-altitude, formation bombing raids on Japan: ballistic drift was reduced; the engine wear induced by achieving high altitudes was lessened; the strain of formation flying was eliminated; and full advantage could be taken of the weakness of enemy radar and Japan's lack of night fighters. Other factors may have entered into the decision, but it is significant that, after operations research recommendations were submitted to him on 29 January, General LeMay issued orders almost immediately that the proposed tactic be used in all future B-29 raids. This change reduced attrition on missions from about 10 or 15 per cent to roughly one-tenth of that figure.

When Operation Starvation could at last be undertaken (in March, 1945), some 12,000 mines were strewn in Japanese waters in five successive stages; they are credited with a toll of about 1,200,000 tons of enemy shipping. B-29 losses during mining operations were less than one per cent.[28]

In a very real sense, the work done by the NOL group foreshadowed

[27] Ellis A. Johnson, "The Application of Operations Research to Industry," talk delivered at the Fifth Annual Industrial Engineering Institute, University of California, 31 January and 3 February, 1953 (Chevy Chase, Maryland: Operations Research Office, March, 1953), pp. 31-2. The author is indebted to Dr. Johnson and Dr. Thornton Page of the Operations Research Office for their reminiscences of work in mine warfare operations research during World War II.

[28] Ellis A. Johnson, personal files.

the type of strategic operations research which has emerged since World War II, first at the RAND Corporation and, since then, at the Army's Operations Research Office. Military operations research is no longer concerned merely with problems of achieving optimum results with existing systems and equipment, which was all that most wartime operations research could hope to do. It now develops predictions of the results that may be expected from adopting proposed courses of action; these predictions can then be used as guides to the development of future strategies, tactics, and weapons.

Toward the end of 1943, after investigating operations analysis in the Air Force, General George Marshall sent a message to all theatre commanders suggesting that similar analysis teams be formed to study amphibious and ground operations.[29] Army Ground Forces, however, did not make as much use of operations research as the Air Forces and the Navy, although, by the end of the war, they had a few evaluation groups who were using similar techniques in connection with operations in the Pacific.

One of the most important contributions which operations research made during the course of the war was the improvement of techniques for searching out enemy surface ships and submarines. The R. A. F. Coastal Command Operations Research Section had demonstrated, in the Bay of Biscay, that, with carefully scheduled routes and patrolling times, a surprisingly few planes could sight all enemy ships in a given area. In this country, the Navy's Operations Research Group conducted studies which enabled a pattern of planned controlled search patrol operations to be substituted for the more general " catch-as-catch-can " searching activity previously in use. As a result, the number of search planes required to patrol a given area could be reduced, while, at the same time, the area could be more thoroughly covered. In January, 1944, this new patrol system, with four long-range daily sorties of B-24's and PBM's covering the entire South Atlantic, found five German blockade runners. The seizure from the enemy of these ships and their cargoes of raw materials was a valuable gain for the Allies.[30]

The onslaught of kamikaze attacks against Allied ships in the last months of the Pacific war gave rise to a crash project in operations

[29] USAF, *Operations Analysis in World War II*, p. 2.
[30] Steinhardt, " Role of O. R. in the Navy," pp. 2-5.

research. The question to be answered was: "Should the ship under attack maneuver violently to avoid being hit, or keep straight in order to get better aim with its anti-aircraft guns?" The operations research team working on the problem obtained the records of 477 attacks, including 172 hits and 27 sinkings. After analysis, they concluded that a large ship should maneuver violently, whereas a small ship should change course slowly. The group also made recommendations about how ships should turn to receive inevitable hits. Tabulations of succeeding attacks demonstrated the validity of the recommendations. Those ships under attack which observed the recommendations were hit 29 per cent of the time, whereas others were hit 47 per cent of the time.[31]

The problems tackled by the Air Forces' several Operations Analysis sections were as many and varied as the locations of those sections and the missions of the commands to which they were attached.

One section attached to the Fifteenth Air Force in Bari, Italy, studied the problem of destroying with bombs the mammoth Vienna-Lobau underground oil storage depot. Intelligence reports indicated that this oil hoard was practically invulnerable, since it was covered by seven feet of concrete and ten feet of earth. Mr. George Housner, to whom the problem was assigned, began to question the validity of intelligence reports because the concrete protection, as described, was not feasible from an engineering point of view. His inquiries started a careful piecing together and analysis of all available reconnaissance photographs, which led to the conclusion that there was no concrete protection whatsoever. Once this was determined, the analysts turned to the problem of selecting the best bombs and fuses for attacking storage tanks protected only by thirteen feet of earth. Subsequent strikes against the oil storage plant succeeded in rupturing several of the tanks.[32] This illustrates the contribution which the scientifically-trained specialist can make in evaluating intelligence and, indeed, in gathering accurate intelligence.

The most notable operations analysis work for the Air Forces was that undertaken by the OAS attached first to the Eighth Bomber

[31] Horace C. Levinson and Arthur A. Brown, "Operations Research," *Scientific American*, Vol. 184, No. 3 (March 1951), p. 16.

[32] George Housner, "Operations Analysis, Fifteenth Air Force, November 1943 to May 1945," draft (4 January 1946), pp. 14-16.

Command and later to the Eighth Air Force in England. Their bomb-
ing-accuracy studies alone did much both to insure the success of the
aerial campaign against Germany and to enlarge the scope of operations research method. During the initial period of Eighth Air Force
operations over Europe, formations of B-17's equipped with Norden
bombsights were placing less than 15 per cent of their bombs within
1000 feet of the aiming point. For more than two years, a team of
three analysts, William J. Youden, Philip C. Scott, and James A.
Clarkson, worked to improve this record. Their first task was to
devise a means for tracing each air unit's bomb fall by analyzing
thousands of action photographs taken at 6-second intervals during
attack. Once these data were in order, they were able to proceed to
further investigations.

In formation flying, sighting for deflection, which determined
whether the bombs would fall to the right, left, or in line with the
target, was, naturally, done by the lead aircraft for the entire unit.
There was considerable variation, however, in respect to sighting for
range, which determined whether bombs fell short, over, or on the
target; some units sighted on the group leader, some on the squadron
leader, and still others had each plane do its own range sighting.
Analysis of results indicated that groups in which all planes sighted
on the group leader placed more than twice as many bombs within
1000 feet of the aiming point as did those sighting on the squadron
leaders, and three times as many as those in which independent
sighting was the practice. Eventually, sighting on the group leader
became the standard technique wherever formation bombing was used.

Out of this work grew an equally important investigation aimed
toward shortening the bomb pattern in an attack. The analysis team
predicted that, if the length of the bomb pattern could be reduced
from 3600 feet, the average in May, 1943, to 2000 feet, accuracy
would be increased by 20 per cent; further increases of 25 and 35
per cent, respectively, were predicted for reductions of pattern to
1500 and 1000 feet. Eventually, such reductions were achieved and
were attended by the predicted results.[33]

The brevity of this report prevents further description of other
equally important investigations pursued by the Eighth Bomber

[33] Leslie H. Arps, "Operational Analysis Section, Eighth Air Force," n. d.,
pp. 40-63. Leach, "Operations Analysis in the Theatres," pp. 5-7.

Command OAS or by the other sections scattered over the globe. The range of problems presented them extended from those at the weapons level, such as the selection of bombs and fuses, through tactical studies involving bombing accuracy and battle damage, to strategic studies of the best methods for carrying on jungle warfare and amphibious operations.[34] The three levels on which operations research can be conducted had all clearly emerged by the end of the war.

The share which the total operations research effort had in bringing final victory to the Allies cannot be measured. It was, however, an asset peculiar to the Allies and seems to have had no rival or counterpart within the organization of the enemy forces. It represented, in effect, a view of war which was antithetical to Hitler's, bringing measurement, control, and the analysis of complex operations into play against the more romantic and " inspired " moves of the Axis forces.

Postwar Military Operations Research.

Victory found military operations research groups flourishing on both sides of the Atlantic, and the Armed Forces were faced with considerations of how to provide for a continuation of their activity. In the British Army, postwar plans had been considered as early as 1942. In August of that year, at a meeting of the Weapons Development Committee, Sir Charles Darwin had suggested that suitable officers be drawn from the engineering services and thoroughly trained so that they might form a nucleus for later operational research work in the Army. Such a pool was established, and some of its officers served with civilian scientists in the Army's six wartime Operational Research Sections. Officers in those sections which were still in existence at the war's end were absorbed back into the pool which soon expanded, becoming, on 1 November 1945, the War Office's Military Operational Research Unit, functioning side by side with the Ministry of Supply's Army Operational Research Group composed predominantly of civilian scientists. Eventually, the two were amalgamated as a War Office organization under the name A. O. R. G.[35]

[34] USAF, *Operations Analysis in World War II*, pp. 11, 29-32.
[35] O: R. in the British Army," pp. 2-3, 8. The author is indebted to Colonel John Shirley of A. O. R. G. for his explanation of the transformation of operational research units from wartime to peacetime organization.

The provisions made for postwar military operations research in this country varied from service to service. Continuation of the Navy's Operations Research Group was requested by CominCh, and this request was approved by the Secretary of the Navy. In 1947, it became the Operations Evaluation Group, its responsibilities outlined in a contract drawn up between the Office of Naval Research and M. I. T. At present, the group, directed by Dr. Jacinto Steinhardt, includes about fifty scientists who advise the staff of the Chief of Naval Operations and the various field commands, such as those in Hawaii, Tokyo, and the Mediterranean. The subject areas in which they conduct research include anti-submarine warfare, guided missiles, radar, and atomic energy warfare.[36]

The Army Air Forces faced a somewhat more complicated problem in continuing their operations research efforts. As the war drew to a close, the Air Force Commands were shuffled in response to changing conditions, and the OAS's attached to them were either moved or disbanded. This resulted in some disruption of the Air Forces' operations research activities.

The war had scarcely ended, however, when new problems emphasized the need for the continuation of operations research. LeRoy A. Brothers, who had been chief of two OAS's during the war, became the Chief Analyst of the Air Forces' operations analysis organization, a Division under the AC/AS-3, in October, 1945, and, in April, 1946, was named Assistant for Operations Analysis. A regulation dated 11 October 1946 established Operations Analysis in the peacetime Air Forces and authorized an OAS to each command where the Commanding General desired one. After the establishment of the United States Air Force as a separate service, operations analysis underwent various organizational changes. Mr. Brothers has continued as Assistant for Operations Analysis and his organization now consists of an Operations Analysis Division, within the Office of the Deputy Chief of Staff/Operations, and Operations Analysis offices assigned to many Air Force commands. These offices engage in operations research on the problems of their own commands, many of these being the

---

[36] Steinhardt, " Operations Research," pp. 17-18. C. M. Stearns, " Operations Research in the Navy," *Research Reviews* (Office of Naval Research, Department of the Navy, October, 1952), p. 11.

immediate and practical problems arising in the operations of the commands.[37]

In 1946, General Arnold, sensing the need for an organization which would provide scientific assistance in formulating Air Force decisions with respect to research and development persuaded Donald Douglas of Douglas Aircraft to manage Project RAND. (The name is an abbreviation for Research and Development.) Ten million dollars were provided from Air Force funds to finance this project. The original nucleus of the staff was drawn from industry, but was soon augmented by academic research people, first physical scientists and later social scientists.[38] Postwar operations research for the Air Force was, from the beginning, more closely allied to industry than were operations research activities for the other services, possibly because the Air Force is unique among the services in having most of its procurement problems concentrated within one industry. This necessitates intimate contact with airplane producers and with their developmental research and production problems. RAND and the aircraft industry have developed this sort of close cooperation; RAND is probably the only group conducting operations research for the military which holds as many industrial as military secrets.

In 1948, Project RAND became the RAND Corporation, a non-profit organization initially financed by the Ford Foundation. It moved from Douglas Aircraft to its own establishment in Santa Monica, California, where it remains. This group combines research personnel from both the universities and industry, maintains close liaison with the aircraft industry, and works under contract to the Air Force, reporting to the Office of the Assistant for Development Planning, Deputy Chief of Staff/Development. RAND's operations research, in contrast to the work of the Air Force's several Operations Analysis offices, is largely theoretical and requires considerably less investigation in the field.

At the end of World War II, the Army was also interested in

[37] "Op. Analysis, Hq., AAF, December 1942-July 1947," Annex, pp. 1-4. "History of Operations Analysis in the United States Air Force, July 1947-June 1950" (30 May 1950), pp. 1-5. Parker and Parker, "Trial by Combat—Operations Research for the Army," p. 6.

[38] John McDonald, "The War of Wits," *Fortune*, Vol. 43, No. 3 (March 1951), p. 147.

setting up a permanent operations research unit. General H. S. Aurand, Director of Army Logistics, emphasized the need for civilian scientific advisors to the Research and Development Board and called attention to the unavailability of operations research assistance for the Army and for the Joint Chiefs of Staff. In the budget for the Fiscal Year 1949, one million dollars was appropriated for Army operations research. In April, 1948, Major General McAuliffe, then Deputy Director of Logistics for Research and Development, selected The Johns Hopkins University to administer the research group, and, in September, the General Research Office was established at Fort Leslie J. McNair, Washington, D. C., with Ellis A. Johnson as Director. Three months later, its present name, Operations Research Office, was adopted.[39] In June, 1951, ORO moved to what was formerly the Chevy Chase Junior College, in Chevy Chase, Maryland. ORO also maintains field offices at FECOM Headquarters in Tokyo, USAREUR Headquarters in Heidelberg and at the Office of the Chief of Army Field Forces, Fort Monroe, Virginia.

Meanwhile, the National Security Act of 1947, which had created the National Military Establishment, clearly indicated the need for an impartial evaluation of various weapons and weapons systems at the level of the Joint Chiefs of Staff. Both the Hoover Commission and a special committee appointed by Secretary Forrestal recommended the establishment of a body which could perform this function. Subsequently, in a directive dated 11 December 1948, Mr. Forrestal authorized the Weapons Systems Evaluation Group which would serve the Joint Chiefs of Staff. The directive called upon the new unit to provide the National Military Establishment with " rigorous, unprejudiced and independent analyses and evaluations " of present and future weapons under " probable future combat conditions." Shortly thereafter, Lt. General John E. Hull, Commanding General U. S. Army, Pacific, and over-all commander for the Eniwetok atomic bomb tests, was appointed Director of the new group. Dr. Philip Morse was its first Technical Director. The staff was composed of armed services officers, civilian scientists, and other technicians. WSEG receives the reports developed at ORO, OAD, RAND, and OEG; the

[39] Parker and Parker, " Trial by Combat—Operations Research for the Army," pp. 5-6.

conclusions of such reports become data for WSEG in optimizing solutions to problems at its own level.

The creation of WSEG completed the provision of operations research organizations within the defense establishment. The Army and Navy each have under contract a research group administered by a university, and including a central headquarters and field offices. The Air Force is served by the Operations Analysis Division at headquarters, by its Operations Analysis offices attached to the various Air Force commands, and by the RAND Corporation reporting to the Deputy Chief of Staff/Development. Finally, the Joint Chiefs of Staff have a research group of civilian scientists and military officers who are able to apply the same sort of analysis used by the services to interservice problems, leading toward the formulation of coordinated plans for war. These five military operations research organizations participate in informal Joint Operations Research Group seminars held periodically for the exchange of information on methods. Four members of the Group, WSEG, OEG, OAD, and ORO, jointly maintain a representative in the United Kingdom for liasion with comparable operational research organizations there.

Most of the military operations research which has been conducted since the war's end is under security classification and cannot be cited to illustrate the progress of the art. Some information concerning the areas in which work is proceeding, however, is available. Those engaged in operations research work for the British Army devoted their first postwar year largely to the exhaustive study of data gathered during the war. Once this analysis was completed, the group set to work within four general areas: (1) the soldier with his weapon, equipment and clothing, with a view to improving efficiency; (2) requirements for new weapons and equipment; (3) military training, its content and methods; and (4) problems of supply, maintenance, etc.[40] Whereas most of the wartime problems which were studied for the military predominantly involved "hardware," this short list demonstrates that men, together with machines, weapons and equipment, have become clearly identified as an important field for future investigation.

In the United States, operations analysis for the Air Force has,

[40] Wansbrough-Jones, "Operational Research in War and Peace," p. 323.

in addition to various other projects, been conducting a series of studies aimed toward estimation of the combat attrition of war plans. In 1946, the war planners, faced with the task of estimating the requirements for attaining certain military goals and the capabilities of certain military forces, asked Operations Analysis to assist them by extrapolating from World War II to hypothetical future wars. A team of people from Intelligence, Operations, War Plans, and Operations Analysis were assembled to answer the question: " What could we accomplish with a certain number of groups of certain types of aircraft if we were attacked by a certain enemy nation at a specified time?" The intensive effort devoted to this question produced a reasonably reliable answer. It also succeeded in evolving a method for producing quantitative estimates for war plans, involving attrition models which describe air battles in mathematical terms. The earliest of such models were tested by use of combat data from World War II; World War II data, however, have become less and less useful with the passage of time. Combat data from the small number of battles between B-29's and MIG-15's in Korea have made it possible to determine that the model designed to describe the air battle between B-29 type bombers and jet interceptors is reasonably reliable.[41]

Of the various Operations Analysis offices, that attached to the Fifth Air Force has been closest to operations in Korea. When war began there, the mission of this office changed immediately from a study of the air defense of Japan to studies essential to the Korean offensive. The analysts of this office worked on the selection of targets and of weapons for attacking those targets. They examined targets of early Fifth Air Force actions to evaluate the effectiveness of attacks and to suggest improvements in operations. They were also able to analyze the experience of the Fifth Air Force in using equipment untried in combat prior to the Korean hostilities.[42]

Much of the work for the Air Force in progress at the RAND Corporation involves the evaluation of various bombing systems and recommendations for the best system so that Air Force budget can be properly allocated. In order to do its job effectively, RAND extends its operations research thinking toward future weapons, tactics, and strategies. In studying bombing systems, RAND researchers take

---

[41] Brothers, " Operations Analysis in the U. S. Air Force," pp. 12-15.
[42] *Ibid.*, pp. 17-18.

into account such factors as the social effects of bombing the enemy. This interest leads naturally to studies of Russian capabilities, particularly predictions of future capabilities. One result of this type of research has been the codification of those principles of action which appear to underlie the Politburo's calculations; such codification is now available as one factor to be considered in making analytical predictions of Russia's future actions.[43] The emphasis on human factors in military operations has resulted in drawing social scientists into the operations research family of disciplines. Both the RAND Corporation and the Operations Research Office have engaged psychologists, sociologists, economists, political scientists and anthropologists for their staffs.

One of the studies conducted by the Operations Evaluation Group during the postwar years involved the scheduling of activities of seaports heavily taxed by the demands of war. The mathematical technique brought to bear on this problem produced two interesting results. It revealed that a large system could operate closer to its capacity than a small one before running into the risk of tie-ups; that is to say, a 10-berth seaport might break down under a 6-ship-per-month load, whereas a 100-berth port might be able to withstand a 90-ship load quite well. Secondly, the research results indicated that it was possible to predict, given the size of the seaport and its operating load, the length of time until it would become tied up.

Like the Air Force, the Navy has also used operations research in the gathering and analysis of data provided by hostilities in Korea. One of the studies concerns the interacting results of enemy anti-aircraft fire and the fire from U. S. Navy planes. The narrative and photographic histories of hundreds of airplane flights, many of which include hits from anti-aircraft fire and dogfights with enemy planes, have been subjected to analysis so that less vulnerable planes can be designed, and so that pilots may learn where to expect the most danger to themselves and how to wreak the most destruction upon enemy planes.[44]

Although the Operations Research Office has had a much shorter history than the Navy's Operations Evaluation Group or the Air Force's Operations Analysis Division, the range of problems it has

[43] McDonald, "The War of Wits," pp. 148-50, 158.
[44] Stearns, "Operations Research in the Navy," p. 10.

studied has been remarkably wide. One of ORO's earliest assignments extended into the field of international relations. The research staff was asked to ascertain whether the Army should recommend economic and military aid to Western Europe. The extensive report which resulted formed the basis of the Army's recommendations on this question.

Shortly after the beginning of hostilities in Korea, Dr. Johnson, ORO's Director, led a team of four into the battle area. Other teams followed and, throughout the years of war, operations in Korea provided a laboratory for Army operations research.

On one occasion, FECOM General Headquarters asked ORO to investigate the problem of close air support for infantry operations. The question to be answered was: " How can the Air Force best help the infantry by doing most damage to enemy front-line infantry troops? " After a study of the possible alternatives, the team suggested that B-29's be used for close air support. The recommendation caused a general lifting of eyebrows, since the B-29 is a large plane intended for long-range missions against strategic targets; it appeared that its special attributes would be wasted on a job such as close-support bombing. The research people pointed out, however, that, since the Communist forces were in the open mostly during the hours of darkness, the most profitable time to strike them from the air was by night; and that the plane with the most navigation and radar equipment, namely the B-29, would be the most effective striking weapon under such conditions. The result was that the strategic bombers began to take on a tactical job.[45]

Military security has, by and large, prevented public knowledge of the activities of WSEG since its establishment in 1948. Occasionally, the Press has given some indication of the kinds of problems under consideration, but non-classified reports have not been forthcoming. Newspaper reports appearing during the period November, 1949-May, 1950, indicated that the Group was considering a complicated problem concerning the character of the nation's air forces. According to such reports, the investigation covered the entire problem of strategic bombing, beginning with a historical analysis of B-17 and B-29 bombing data from World War II, and including experiments and calculations involving newer planes.

[45] Yahraes, " The Mysterious Mission of ORO," pp. 36-37.

Operations research for the military has, since 1939, developed from its original state, in which scientists informally pooled their hunches on new problems then followed through with observation and measurement, to a degree of organization in which techniques for the collection and analysis of data are highly developed and for which a body of tried method is constantly expanding. *The Small Back Room*, immortalized by Nigel Balchin, has now become a sizeable establishment, complete with its own computing laboratories, libraries, subcontractors, and a network of essential channels for communication with various government and private agencies. It has, however, retained much of its original spontaneity: it is improbable that an activity for which research in the field, be it battlefield, fleet, or testing ground, is an essential will ever bog down into uninterrupted paper-shuffling; nor is it likely that research teams representing such a diversity of disciplines and environments will ever reach the stage of " taking things for granted."

Nonmilitary Operations Research.

The preceding description of the development of operations research gives the impression that it is exclusively a military enterprise. Although the military services in World War II brought operations research through its birth pangs, civilian activities had their influence on its development in embryo and have, since the war, been hastening its growth. Once hostilities were over, there was a wish, on both sides of the Atlantic, to " get down to business as usual." In Britain, this desire was intensified by the precarious economic situation which the war had caused, necessitating increased production and vastly increased visible exports; in this country, the need to make up for lost time put fever into the activity of reconverting industry from wartime activities to production for private consumers. The concept of analyzing business operations, therefore, found a warm reception in both countries.

The beginnings of postwar nonmilitary operations research, however, differed on the two sides of the ocean. In this country, with its highly competitive economy, there had long been a great deal of effort expended to make business and industrial operations more efficient and, therefore, more profitable. Many of the techniques employed toward this end later formed part of the operations research *modus operandi.* Horace C. Levinson, one of the first proponents of operations research in the United States, began his work during the 1920's. Having given up a career in astronomy for another in merchandizing, he proceeded to apply some of the trained scientist's methods to the problems of his employer. His work for L. Bamberger and Co., included studies of customers' buying habits, the effect of quick response advertising on sales, and the relation of neighborhood environment to types of articles sold. His value to the firm is demonstrated by the fact that he was made Vice President; the value of his work, by the fact that much of it is still a company secret.[46]

Levinson's investigations provide what is probably the best example of preliminary operations research in American business and industry before World War II. There were many others. The whole field of management consulting, which has much in common with operations research, had its beginning in the last decades of the nineteenth century, when such pioneers of scientific management as Taylor, Gantt and Emerson started their work.[47] Time-and-motion studies, long the anathema of labor unions, were widely undertaken in the 1920's and the analysis of markets was a solid concept before the beginning of World War II. Techniques for quality control and industrial engineering and various other management consulting services, such as those offered by Booz, Allen and Hamilton and Arthur D. Little, Inc., were available to management in the interwar years. All of these activities helped to pave the way for operations research, and some personnel previously engaged in them later found it easy to make the transition to operations research.

What, then, did this new activity developed during the war add to the previously established techniques? For one thing, it broadened the point of view from which problems were approached. Whereas the time-and-motion study treated both the machines and operators as mechanical components of the total complex and attempted to make measurements as though both were equally predictable, the psychologist on an operations research team, faced with a similar problem, would add such variables as motivation and morale to the factors

[46] Herbert Solow, "Operations Research," *Fortune*, Vol. 43, No. 4 (April 1951), p. 105. For further information concerning Dr. Levinson's work, see Chapter 16.

[47] See Chapter 5.

for consideration. Examination of every pertinent aspect of the operation, with "pertinent" interpreted very loosely pending further study, is one of the new and dominant features of operations research.

Secondly, management consulting services, although they were able to make valuable contributions toward improving the efficiency of their customers' interests, were usually incapable of bringing to bear the sophisticated mathematical ability required for the solution of complex problems involving many variables. Levinson, with his scientific background, may have been the exception. Those mathematicians and physicists who tackled operational problems during the war clearly demonstrated that mathematical solutions could be attained for extremely complex problems. Once the war was over many of these men began work in nonmilitary operations research, bringing with them both their wartime experience and their highly specialized mathematical abilities.

The situation in Britain was vastly different. British industry and trade, more traditional, more dependent on artisan skills and personal services, and less likely to become intrigued with new gimmicks, had not experimented so extensively with improving operations during the prewar years. An interesting exception was the protracted efficiency investigation conducted in the British cotton industry from 1926 onward. Proceeding from crude stop-watch measurements of the behavior of looms and tabulations of the causes of loom stoppages, the study expanded to include observations of all machines and operators. The work was essentially self-generating at the Shirley Institute and did not proceed from a problem posed by management. Consequently, the results, while of interest from a research point of view, did not influence any significant managerial decisions for many years. Eventually, however, the data collected became the basis for such decisions as changes in the hourly wage scale.[48] In general, postwar nonmilitary operational research in Britain proceeded directly from wartime experience and did not pick up a thread of related business activity from the prewar years.[49]

In one sense, this was an advantage. The American industrial

[48] L. H. C. Tippett, "Operational Research at the Shirley Institute," *Operational Research Quarterly*, Vol. 1, No. 2 (June 1950), p. 20.

[49] See C. H. Waddington's article, "Operational Research," *Nature*, Vol. 161, No. 4089 (13 March 1948), p. 404.

manager, having previous experience with management consultants and efficiency experts of all types, could and did say to the operations research man, " What's new about this? " Unconvincing replies, in many instances, deterred management from encouraging the activity; American nonmilitary operations research, consequently, got off to a slow start after the war. The British industrialist, on the other hand, immediately recognized operations research as a new and valuable instrument. Impetus was provided by the economic and political situation in which Britain found herself at the end of the war: the battle for exports with which to buy food was nearly as desperate a problem as those faced during hostilities; the nationalization of a few industries offered the opportunity for new experiments aimed toward increasing production. For these reasons, nonmilitary operations research in Britain has accelerated rapidly since the war.

In 1946, the Special Research Unit of the Board of Trade was established " to apply to some of the broader problems of peacetime industry and trade the statistical and scientific methods, which, in the form of Operational Research, have proved so valuable to the Services in war." At the close of the Unit's first experimental year, it was decided that the experiment should be extended. Among the problems which this unit has studied are the effects of variety and standardization on the production and cost of various items, and the selection of the most profitable cotton textiles, in terms of value added to raw material, to be earmarked for export channels.[50] Operational research has also been used in Britain in the boot and shoe industry, in railroad and street transportation problems, and in road building, to name a few examples. There are now over forty operational research sections in Great Britain.[51]

In the United States, examples of operations research in industry are less likely to be published. Whereas, in Britain, operations research often serves an entire industry, consisting of a family of competitors, in America, it usually serves a particular enterprise which is not eager to share the results for which it has incurred considerable

[50] " Reports on the Principles and Practices of Operational Research by the Working Party of the Committee on Industrial Productivity," Office of the Lord President of the Council, 21 July 1948, retyped 9 August 1949, copied by ORO 26 March 1952, pp. 63-64.

[51] See Chapter IV.

expenditure with other firms trying to attract customers for the same goods or services. Macy does not tell Gimbel on this side of the Atlantic. Operations research is being conducted in transportation, communications, agriculture, merchandising, and various kinds of manufacturing. There are now, in this country, at least half a dozen firms which are employed by industry to work on operations research problems. Some two dozen firms (in addition to the military services' own operations research organizations) undertake operations research contracts for the military departments. Several business enterprises, including such large interests as the U. S. Rubber Company and the Sun Oil Company, have their own groups, and many others are interested in establishing an operations research program.[52] Firms of management consultants, such as Booz, Allen and Hamilton, and Arthur D. Little, Inc., have added operations research to the services which they are willing to provide for management.

One problem area, not heretofore mentioned, but which seems admirably susceptible to operations research methods is that of government social and economic planning. In the United States, where the aim is a free economy, the opportunities for such research are relatively infrequent. Britain, however, has made extensive use of operations research in this area during and since the war. One prominent example is the Government Social Survey, organized during the war years and now a permanent government research unit. The "Survey of Sickness" which this group conducted during wartime provided the first really comprehensive picture of the general health of the population. For the Ministry of Food, the unit performed extensive surveys on food consumption and expenditures so that the effects of government food and price policies on the nutrition and family budgets of the public could be estimated in advance.[53] It seems reasonable that, in any crisis situation where policies involving wage control, price control, and the rationing and control of materials are under discussion, operations research would be able to provide useful, quantitative predictions of the results to follow from various alternative measures or combinations of measures. In this connection,

[52] Johnson, "Application of Operations Research to Industry," p. 49.

[53] Louis Moss, remarks at a meeting of the British Association in Dundee, 30 August 1947, "Operational Research in War and Peace," reprinted from *The Advancement of Science*, Vol. 5, No. 16 (February 1948), pp. 329-330.

it would become a tool for the legislature as well as the executive in cases where the two are discrete bodies.

The most dramatic evidence that operations research can make an effective contribution to national planning has been provided by the rapidly changing situation in Puerto Rico during the last ten years. Early in the forties, the imbalance between the paucity of natural resources and the undependable nature of the labor force on the one hand, and the astonishing growth of the population on the other, could no longer be regarded tolerantly. Three alternatives seemed to promise some alleviation of the falling standard of living: a change from agriculture to industry; birth control; or large-scale emigration. Preliminary considerations indicated that the first was the most acceptable alternative, and an island-wide program of changing the economy in successive stages was begun. Centered in the Puerto Rican Industrial Development Corporation, acting under the advice of Arthur D. Little, Inc., this inclusive effort, which took into account social, economic, and political factors, has already brought about a more efficient use of labor, a higher standard of living, increased capital investment and a more broadly-based economy. " Operation Bootstrap " has, in fact, transformed Puerto Rico from an impoverished agricultural island to a thriving, semi-industrialized community with a standard of living which compares favorably with that of other Latin American countries.[54]

The Study of Operations Research.

It was inevitable that a research activity which had attracted increasing numbers of personnel and excited wide interest within government circles, the military services, and industry should eventually find its way to the universities. In 1948, the Massachusetts Institute of Technology established, in collaboration with the Navy, a course in the nonmilitary applications of operations research. At University College, London, a course of ten lectures was given in the autumn of 1949, and Birmingham University conducted a summer course in July, 1950, on " Work Study and Operational Research." The Case Institute of Technology held a conference in November,

---

[54] Stuart Chase, " *Operation Bootstrap* " *in Puerto Rico: Report of Progress, 1951*, Planning Pamphlet No. 75, prepared for the NPA Business Committee on National Policy by the National Planning Association.

1951, on the applications of operations research to the problems of business and industry and has since become the first institution of higher learning to offer a curriculum in operations research leading to the degree of Master of Science. In the spring of 1952, Columbia University presented its first course in operations research, and The Johns Hopkins University initiated a graduate seminar in the autumn of that year. These early efforts are largely exploratory, for the status of operations research in relation to other disciplines is still in dispute. There are those who regard it as a new discipline for which a specialized course of training can and should be developed; others prefer to think of it as a combination of existing disciplines and recommend a specialist training in some one of the sciences or in mathematics, supplemented by operations research indoctrination, as the best preparation for an operations research career. As experience with courses, seminars, and on-the-job research accumulates, the position of operations research will undoubtedly become clearer.

To speed the process and to provide a clearing house for the exchange of unclassified information, operations research societies have been established in both Britain and America. In London, in April, 1948, a few of those scientists who had been active in operational research during the war years formed the Operational Research Club, which, since that time, has been holding about six meetings each year in the rooms of the Royal Society. The word " Club " was chosen pending a clearer understanding of what was meant by an operational research worker; it is now being changed to a " Society." The Club organized the University College course to which reference has already been made and launched *The Operational Research Quarterly*, the first periodical in the field.[55]

In America, a Committee on Operations Research, with Dr. Horace C. Levinson as chairman, was established in 1949 by the National Research Council; its purpose was to foster interest in non-military operations research and to disseminate information about it. In April, 1951, the Committee published *Operations Research with Special Reference to Non-Military Applications*, which briefly described operations research, the area of its problems, and its personnel requirements. In January of the following year, the nucleus of an

---

[55] Sir Charles Goodeve, private communication.

American society, consisting of ten interested persons, met in Cambridge, Massachusetts. After a second preliminary gathering in March, to which additional research people were invited, a Founding Meeting was held at Columbia University in May, and the Operations Research Society of America was formally established with its own constitution and officers, headed by Dr. Philip M. Morse as President.[56] The first number of the quarterly *Journal of the Operations Research Society of America* was published in November, 1952, the month of the first regular meeting, which attracted more than twice as many members and prospective members as the most optimistic founder had anticipated.

In May, 1952, the Chief of Naval Operations convened The Decennial Conference on Operations Research on the occasion of OEG's tenth anniversary. The variety of backgrounds and organizations represented in the speakers and the wide area covered by their papers made this conference an important episode in the history of operations research.

Operations research appears now to be in an intermediate stage. Its usefulness has been vividly demonstrated and it has passed through its first efforts to cope with widening problem areas and to employ a growing variety of methods. Yet it is still developing with such speed that even the most experienced among operations research workers would hesitate to mark out all those problem areas susceptible and not susceptible to an operations research approach or to place it in exact relationship to other disciplines, techniques and activities. Such achievements belong to the future of operations research and not to its history.

---

[56] Philip M. Morse, "The Operations Research Society of America," *Journal of the Operations Research Society of America*, Vol. 1, No. 1 (November 1952), p. 1.

Operations Research
as a Profession

GEORGE S. PETTEE

TO DESCRIBE operations research as a profession is to express, in
another language, many of the same things that one must say
to define operations research, or to speak of it as a science, or to
expound on its philosophy, or to deal with any of the various facets
through which it can be approached. If operations research is really
a live discipline, it can, like any other live discipline, be described in
terms of its content, of its doctrine, of the people who practice it, or
of its institutional shape and pattern. When one describes a production general staff, the Communist party, the Catholic church or the
A. F. L. in any of these ways, one says substantially the same thing
as in describing it in one of the other ways; so it is with operations
research. The institutional description, the description of the people,
the description of what they do, of what they think, say, write and
store in their files, are all complementary descriptions of the same
living action pattern.

There is no mystery about the word "profession" as it is used
here. A profession is an identifiable group of people who earn their
livings in a common manner. It is something for which people can be
trained. If it is an old and established profession, young people in
college can decide that they want to belong to it and can prepare for
it accordingly. A profession is a classifiable special skill, and its
members can be readily identified by prospective clients. If it is a
real profession, it is a career which a person can enter, where he can

36

earn his living, and from which he can eventually retire with a sense of accomplishment.

Sociological Characteristics of Operations Research.

Operations research is not an old and solidly-established profession; consequently young people have not, in the past, planned to enter it, shaping their academic careers with that intention. Now, one hears of a few students, mostly in graduate school, who are thinking in terms of operations research careers. Experimental training courses are just getting started in a handful of institutions scattered throughout the country. The people now doing operations research, however, have been enticed into it or have drifted toward it from other fields.

The questions which next arise are: " Is operations research a profession at all? Is it the real thing or merely a pretender? " Among all the candidate movements, fads, fashions and intellectual false starts which have cropped up in American life in the last twenty years, giving rise to such questions as " Is technocracy a profession? " etc., many have fallen by the wayside. How can one determine whether operations research will turn out to be a profession? Some of the criteria which reveal and more or less test whether a profession is indeed a profession are related to an analysis of which type of profession it most resembles.

The sciences, such as physics, chemistry and biology, have certain distinct characteristics. The loyalty of their practitioners is primarily to the advancement of knowledge. The source of pay of scientists, however, is not directly related to what they contribute to such advancement. A scientist is likely to get his living by teaching, but to get very little or no money for his efforts in adding to existing knowledge. In general, there has been no direct relation between the pay that a man like Lavoisier received and his contribution to learning; he was paid far more for the by-products of his main effort.

Engineering as a profession differs from science in two major ways. First, an engineer is paid for doing a direct, specific job of performance for a customer. Secondly, the problem on which he works is a specific, concrete, *ad hoc* problem, at a specific point in time and space, in contrast to that of the scientist who seeks general solutions to general problems.

The legal profession is marked by an interesting dichotomy. There are two ways in which to make a living in the courts; as a judge, or as counsel. The counsel deals with specific cases and directly serves his client; the judge also deals with specific cases, but makes general law in the process. The judge publishes everything he does, with such occasional exceptions as the proceedings in a child custody case. Normally the judge never keeps a secret; the counsel, on the other hand, never betrays a secret.

Medicine is difficult to classify: it is a science, in that it concerns itself with research for the advancement of knowledge; it is like engineering too, however, since it is applied to specific cases for specific customers. It cannot be categorized as a scientific profession or an engineering profession, but lies between the two and overflows to some extent into each.

These, then, are some different types of professions. To which type, if any, does operations research belong? To begin with, does it have the characteristics of a science? From the point of view of the history of science, all sciences have a certain kind of historical genesis. No one will deny that there was a considerable body of physical knowledge floating about in the tenth century; people knew how to use a crowbar or a pulley. But physics, in the current sense of the word, did not then exist. In the eighteenth century, however, physics did exist; therefore, it must have originated sometime in between. It would be fruitless to argue whether Galileo or Newton was the first physicist; it is sufficient to say that, within the course of a few generations, the transition from pre-physics to physics had been achieved, and that physics, ever since, has had a different character.

The same may be said of chemistry. People may argue about whether Boyle, Priestley or Lavoisier was the first chemist, but all will agree that there was a time before and there is a time since the genesis of chemistry as a modern science. Operations research, during the past fifteen years, appears to have experienced this sort of historical genesis; something catalytic has occurred and those now working in operations research seem to be able to distinguish clearly between pre-operations research of which there was a long history, and operations research, which is relatively new.

One of the characteristics of a science, after it gets well started, is what may be called, if jargon is permitted, the unification of the three " therefores." In ordinary English usage, the word " therefore " is employed in three distinct senses. There is the " therefore " of natural causation: " The steel was corroded, and *therefore* the boiler has sprung a leak "; or " The support was removed, *therefore* the body fell "; or " A cold front came in last night, and *therefore* there will be frost tonight." There is also the " therefore " of logic: " A equals B, and B equals C, *therefore* A equals C." This is, in part at least, an arbitrary matter of linguistic structure. Everyone is familiar with examples in which the logic is absolutely faultless, but the premises are wrong and the conclusions equally wrong. Finally, there is the " therefore " of purpose: " I was hungry, and *therefore* I fried an egg." In the ordinary conditions of life, the consequences of actions are very often entirely out of accord with intention. Also, logic is frequently out of accord both with natural consequence and with intention. The scientist, however, when doing a job on which he is a scientist, obtains a result of his action which is in accordance with his intent. When he wants a particular effect, he goes after it, except when he is on the fringe of experimental knowledge and happens upon an effect different from the one he is seeking. Insofar as a science is a science, causality, logic and purpose are in harmony. And within the structure of knowledge which constitutes the science they have been harmonized; when applied in action, they work out according to plan. The strongest and most provable thing about operations research today is that the three " therefores " are becoming constantly more unified. This process has been going on from the time of its beginning and has been progressing ever since.

After a science really becomes a science, there is also a new rate of originality. There was a spurt of young chemists making interesting new discoveries after Lavoisier, and the rate of accumulating chemical knowledge was markedly accelerated; the same might be said of physics after Galileo or Newton. This phenomenon, which is characteristic of a science after its genesis, is now evident in operations research.

The communicability of knowledge also changes, once a science becomes a science. Before Lavoisier, there was a vast amount of chemical knowledge: people were able to smelt all kinds of ores; they could make porcelain and glass and soap; they knew a great deal about handling dyes. How did a man learn this before Lavoisier? He learned it the way a man learns a dozen languages—by painstaking memory work. How did he learn it after Lavoisier, or, to be more accurate as to time, after Avogadro's hypothesis was finally accepted? By that time, the complete set of equipment which makes chemistry so easy to classify and organize in one's mind, valence, atomic weight, the atom, the molecule, the compound, etc., had begun to take shape, and it was a much simpler task to communicate information about the subject and to teach it. It became possible to teach Tom, Dick, and Harry enough so that they could go out and be good chemists and so that an increased proportion of them could become original chemists. It required genius to be a Priestley; but it required no genius to be a good chemist in 1900. And, by that time, the learning of chemistry no longer consumed a lifetime of the drudgery of memorizing arbitrary and unrelated facts.

Operations research, in this respect, is still in a somewhat crude state. It bears a closer resemblance to chemistry at the time of Lavoisier than to the chemistry of 1880. As yet, classification has not been fixed, nor theory neatly combed out. The degree of confusion which remains seems fairly typical of a discipline that is still only fifteen years old, if, in fact, operations research is a new discipline.

Once the genesis of a science has occurred, training in that science takes on a new character altogether. The maintenance of unity within the subject comes fairly readily and rapidly. The settlement of a controversy may require ten years, but settlement is reached, in contrast to controversies in religion or law. Disagreements between the Roman Law and the Canon Law, disagreements between Lutheran theology and Catholic theology never get settled. Differences within a science, however, are settled fairly rapidly in historical terms. In operations research, the fact that doctrine is taking shape is clearly observable. On some of the questions that were extremely controversial five years ago, there has been distinct progress toward agreed settlement and toward agreement on the value of the evidence on which settlement could be reached.

After a pure science is born, a field of associated engineering application ordinarily develops. In the field of operations research, as in medicine, the two seem to be inseparable. They do not divide into a pure science of operations analysis and an applied operations analysis, and it seems likely that they will be permanently interwoven. The closest thing to operations research which is entirely divorced from research on the operational problems of the customer will probably be the teaching itself. In answer to the question, "What kind of profession is operations research insofar as its social characteristics are concerned?" one might describe it as one in which characteristics of the science and engineering professions are closely intermixed.

Ethics in Operations Research.

With the development of engineering applications of any science there arises the problem of relationship to the client. This introduces the subject of professional ethics, a second aspect which must be considered in evaluating operations research as a profession. The main ethical basis in the pure sciences is the advancement of the science; there is free communication and the fundamental purpose of the work is human welfare and the growth of the culture. Most of the recruits to operations research have come from the sciences rather than the engineering or client-serving professions. Operations research, however, was begun as a service to the military, which requires severe restrictions on the life of the intellect. The operations research recruit, therefore, endures a fair measure of strain and stress in stepping from the freest possible intellectual life to that which is probably the least free. It is not intrinsic to operations research that it serve the military; it must, however, serve some customer.

Most personnel in operations research keenly feel the impact of the switch from the ethics of the advancement of learning to the ethics of service to the customer. If, however, the ethics of some of the other professions are considered, it becomes apparent that operations research is in no unique position. Its ethics will probably resemble those applying in law or medicine rather than those of pure science and the university. In both law and medicine, the privacy of a client's business is fundamental to the profession's ethics. And in each, the client confides in the practitioner of the profession. Even a good lawyer cannot serve his client or save a man from the gallows if the client does not give the lawyer his full confidence. It has been established in the law for many years that the lawyer has the right to preserve the privacy of this confidence.

Specific action problems nearly always involve opposed interests. The manager of a retail clothing store which is proposing to run a mark-down sale does not want his nearest competitor to learn of it before the advertisement appears in the paper. Similarly, for almost every other action problem there is some kind of opposed interest. Disclosure of the problem's solution has a very curious effect. If the solution to an action problem is achieved and then disclosed, what has happened? It has ceased to be a solution in the presence of opposed interests and in the absence of absolutely definite intelligence concerning the nature of the opposed interests. If one knows what the opposed interest is, one can play the game theory and work out a new solution. If this is not known, however—which is the normal situation in private commercial life—one cannot anticipate what arguments may be raised against the solution. Suppose a person were to devise a new traffic plan for Baltimore. He would not know which real estate interests, which commercial interests, or which citizens' groups would come forward to oppose it. When the nature of the opposed interests is not known and when there is no clear and easy way for discovering it, the disclosure of a plan of action destroys its character as a solution to a problem.

Operations research deals with action problems. Like some other professions, it must, therefore, respect the privacy of its clients' interests. In fact, the need for this respect is probably more pronounced in operations research than in any other profession. Operations research produces results for a client on the basis of which that client acts. There is not necessarily an opposing interest who would interfere with the person following a lawyer's advice. There is rarely an opposing interest who would interfere with the advice given to a client by a doctor; such interference would only occur in an exceptional situation, such as the family entanglement of *The Little Foxes*. It would be most unusual, however, if there were no opposing interest who would, if possible, interfere with the advice given by operations research to its clients. Where the military is the client, the enemy is the opposing interest; when business or industry is the client, competitors are " the enemy."

Professional ethics, therefore, are fundamental to operations research. In its work for government agencies, the ethics are those of national service and are called security. Although it has a military emphasis, it is not confined to military information. The security of crop reports in the Department of Agriculture is just about as tight as that for any top secret military plan and for good reason. Since speculative private interests might take enormous advantage of any leak in such information, it would be scandalous and unfair if such leaks occurred. If such a misdemeanor should be committed, a speculator could make a fortune overnight.

One member of the British Cabinet was deprived of office some years ago for a security breach. J. H. Thomas naively let information leak concerning the government budget a few days before it was presented in the House of Commons. The advantage to speculators resulted in someone's making something on the order of $40,000 out of the information. The size of the scandal, however, was in no way reduced by the smallness of the speculative gain. Mr. Thomas went out of office so quickly that there was no doubt in anyone's mind as to the impropriety of his action. Something similar happened to Mr. Dalton in the postwar Labour Government of Britain, though it is doubtful whether any speculative gains resulted from his indiscretion. There was nothing military about either case, though both men were guilty of violating professional ethics. What happened to each is what one would expect to happen to a lawyer who leaked a client's business secrets to a competitor, or to a doctor who gossiped about a patient's illness to the neighbors.

This raises some interesting problems. If operations research is a profession like medicine, that is, both a science and an engineering client service, how is the science to grow if everything is bottled up in privacy or security? The ethical ramifications of this question are and will undoubtedly continue to be the subject of much thinking and of much argument. How can the ethical loyalty to the advancement of science be reconciled with ethical loyalty to the client's privacy? Obviously, some rules will have to be devised which could, possibly, take the line that the application belongs to the client, whereas the methodology belongs to the art.

This division is not without precedent in another profession. Doctors quite frequently publish cases in which the ailment, method of treatment, or response to treatment is in some way unique or important. The patient in such a case might expect to see it reviewed in a medical journal; he would expect, however, that his name be omitted. While requiring that his privacy be respected, the patient generally has no wish to deprive medical science of information which would advance it is a science.

So it is in many operations research cases. Frequently, the concrete data, the concrete results of a study, must be private for many years, regardless of whether or not the client is military. It might be possible, however, for the methodology to be published promptly and without damage to the client. Methodology should be published without unreasonable delay, so that students can study it and so that other operations research people can apply it elsewhere. Neither the doctor nor the patient in the first successful appendectomy should have a patent to the technique whereby success was achieved. Similarly, the use of a new method in operations research should be shared with other practitioners.

⑤ Basic to the ethics for any profession is the definition of malpractice. In the case of operations research, this will be simple to do in some instances, more difficult in others. One would assume, for example, that it would be malpractice, almost prima facie without further discussion, for an operations research agency to serve two clients having related interests. The agency should probably not work for two railroads, and certainly not for two competing railroads. False pretenses will probably be another aspect of malpractice in operations research. If operations research becomes really interesting and attractive and acquires prestige, there will undoubtedly be charlatans. The danger of charlatans may, in fact, be fairly close at hand. It will be necessary to develop some definition of what constitutes false pretenses.

There will also be a need for sanctions on the professional ethics and against the malpractice. Ordinarily there are three levels of sanctions for any profession. There is the informal sanction of bad reputation. If a lawyer or doctor becomes known as a gossip, people can punish him by taking their custom elsewhere or by saying that he is loose-tongued. This can result in an informal boycott, and boycott or loss of business is one of the normal sociological penalties on breaches of ethics in any profession. There are, secondly, those sanctions at the disposal of the profession itself, as when the bar disbars a lawyer for malpractice. Finally, there are those sanctions at the disposal of the government, as when it jails people who practice medicine fraudulently. There are parallel sanctions, jailing for espionage, deprivation of security clearance, etc., which can be applied against operations research people who work for the military, since a real breach of ethics vis-à-vis the military is subject to penalty under law.

The application of ethics to operations research is one of the reasons why operations research needs to be organized as a profession. There is a need for those who practice it to meet and to discuss some of the ethical problems involved. It is to their interest to protect the honest practitioner against the charlatan. The problem of developing a set of professional ethics will apply to operations research as it does to law and medicine, but as it does not to the academic sciences.

The Operations Research Professional.

The sociological characteristics and the ethics of operations research have been briefly discussed. A third way in which to describe and identify a profession is to identify a " pro," an example of what a professional is in that profession. What kind of person is the operations research professional? Many of the descriptions convey a feeling that a " pro " in this business is a jack of all trades and a master of none. If that were so, this would not, of course, be a profession. Other descriptions refer to operations research principally as interdisciplinary teamwork, in which a physicist, a biologist, an economist, a sociologist, etc., get together, pool their resources, and do something startling. If this is an accurate summation of operations research, every faculty committee in every university is doing operations research.

Operations research requires something more. Is it just tact and common sense? This is a possibility. One happens upon occasions where tact and common sense and accidental concatenation of personalities produce what might be called operations research, assuming that the term were known to the group in question. A good example within the writer's own experience was a committee on rubber for the War Production Board. The committee consisted of a former leather merchant, a former rubber buyer, a Canadian lawyer, an English economist, several rubber industrialists, and the writer as secretary of the committee, a political scientist with sufficient knowledge of rubber to put on a pair of rubbers in the event of rain. By the accident of a wonderful meeting of minds, the language problem easily unraveled itself, and the combination produced something far beyond the capability of any single man in the group. The whole was greater than the sum of its parts.

Such occasions as these, rare as they are, are examples of a kind of accidental operations research. It isn't the real thing, however. Suppose a group had participated in this kind of productive teamwork; if the group members were separated and scattered into other groups, could they repeat such performance? Could any one of them catalyze any group? The ability to catalyze a group, any group, is one of the attributes of the real operations research professional. This catalytic phenomenon has for operations research groups become more than just a happy accident; it is conscious and applicable and systematized. The " old pro " in operations research can usually take four new and assorted competent scientists, sit down and work with them and make the results jell. He cannot, of course, always achieve this, since personalities are very refractory materials with which to work. He can generally, however, repeat the performance with different subject areas and different groups.

One might next ask what characteristics make it possible for the " old pro " to achieve this skill. He would, it seems, have a heightened degree of consciousness and awareness of systems analysis and experience in using it. He has, so to speak, the kind of attitude according to which the old, conventional systems are fundamentally arbitrary. The seventeenth, eighteenth and nineteenth century scholars carved up the body of learning into subjects like physics, economics, biology, literature, a division still reflected in college faculties and college catalogues. The division, however, could have been made in another way. If civilization were begun anew on another planet, would the same arrangement result? Possibly and, then again, possibly not. It is logical for man, in studying the universe, to come up with such subject divisions as physics, chemistry, etc. These hang together as subjects. But action problems don't emerge in such neat packages; they are, rather, a mixture of subjects. Physics and chemistry can be thoroughly intermixed in the problem of studying why the sun is hot.

The action problems that face an organization such as the Army do not come neatly catalogued as sociology problems, economics problems, military problems, physical problems, and so on through the range of possibilities. The problem is usually a complex one with many facets. When analysis results in the identification of the most effective weapon, the problem is not wholly solved. Other questions arise such as whether dollars are available so that the weapon can be produced, or whether material resources are available from which the weapon is to be made, or whether manpower is available to manufacture the weapon, etc. The problem remains a human one.

The solution to the problem, furthermore, must never demand of the human element more than it can perform. It must never recommend to the executive a solution of which he is patently incapable. It must never provide " cockroach " solutions, as described in one of the few operations research jokes to have appeared. It is the story of an ant and a grasshopper. One frosty night, the grasshopper went around to see the ant and complained, " Oh dear, oh dear, I've been living the life of Riley all summer, but now I'm getting hungry and will probably freeze before long. Give me some advice. You've been industrious and farsighted and have made some wonderful plans. For gosh sake, give me some advice about how to get ·through the winter." The ant promised that he would write a report on the matter. A few days later, the ant presented the grasshopper with a handsome memorandum, complete with conclusions and a recommendation which read, " Turn yourself into a cockroach and live in somebody's kitchen all winter." The grasshopper read through the report and remarked, " This is a marvelous solution. That is certainly worth many times the fee I am paying for it. Oh, by the way, how do I turn myself into a cockroach?" The ant replied, " Oh, that's an executive problem. I'm just giving you expert advice."

" Cockroach " solutions are not characteristic of real operations research. If the solution solves every physical factor in the problem but omits checking for feasibility in respect to the human element, it is no solution by operations research standards. It is easy to fall into the pitfall of neglect for the human factors: a " good " plane from the point of view of mechanics could be designed in which it would be impossible for the pilot to remain conscious. A more usual example is the presentation of a " good " economic solution to a politician who sees immediately that the solution is far wide of the mark of political feasibility.

The " old pro " in operations research has a feeling for systems analysis and he always includes the human element in the system. He has a sense of semantics, for, without the saving catalysis of semantics, it would be difficult for a sociologist, a physicist and a biologist to get together and share a common language about a common problem.

The operations research professional must have a sense of feasibility and must not neglect any factor which effects the feasibility of a solution. He must have a sense of organization context, since that is the significance of the statement, " Operations research is for the executive." " For the executive " means for the man who is making decisions in a large social organization. It does not distinguish the executive from the legislator. The executive is always part of an organization and, in serving him in his decision-making function, operations research is in compliance with all the exhortations which have been going on in this country for the past thirty or forty years regarding the need for interdisciplinary understanding and the integration of modern knowledge in order to counteract the trend to

overspecialization. In operations research, science is, by necessity, a
social activity; scientific investigation depends on teamwork because
no single scientist has the competence to pursue the investigation
alone. The results of operations research are not only achieved *by* but
also *for* a social group, in that they are tools which the executive of
the organization uses to make decisions.

Conclusion.

These then are some aspects of operations research as a profession:
its sociological characteristics, its professional ethics, and the characteristics of its professional people. These three types of description
do not, of course, fully treat operations research. But, just as three
dots on a blackboard might be used to give an impression of a circle,
these three aspects of the profession enable the uninitiated to form an
impression of operations research; the picture in detail, of course, can
only emerge from one's own experience in doing operations research.

Operational Research as a Science

CHARLES GOODEVE

MUCH HAS been written about the wartime efforts of a group of scientists,[1] particularly in England but also in America, who were largely responsible for the development of operational research, and about the profound effect which this had on the outcome of the war. In the postwar years, the use of operational research has been extended to a number of industries. In England, some of its first applications were to road traffic, civil aviation, railway and bus services, the distribution of electricity, agriculture, and house-building. Various government departments used operational research in solving many of the social and economic problems facing Britain. Before long, the method was being used in the manufacturing industries, particularly the textile, food, electrical, light engineering, and metal industries.

A recent survey [2] has indicated that there are more than forty operational research sections in Britain. These range in size from one qualified man with an assistant to organizations of over fifty people; the most typical section includes between five and ten people. Three of the forty are in the headquarters of the Army, Navy and Air Force, respectively; eleven, in such large public utilities as roads

[1] See also Goodeve's article, "Operational Research as a Science," *Journal of the Operations Research Society of America*, Vol. I, No. 4 (August 1953).

[2] Goodeve and G. R. Ridley, "A Survey of O. R. in Great Britain," *Operational Research Quarterly*, Vol. 4, No. 2 (June 1953), pp. 21-24.

and electricity; seven, in cooperative research associations; and the remainder, in a variety of industrial firms. Although all these groups are performing work which can be classed as operational research, rather less than half of them now use that term in the name of their group. The same survey indicates that, in addition, about forty companies in British industry conduct operational research at some time or other. This is probably an underestimate, since the survey questionnaire was distributed only to about two hundred selected companies and organizations.

One might well ask what justification there is for the development of one branch of science to run through so wide a range of apparently unconnected fields. The answer is threefold. First, the methods of attack which have helped to solve one problem can very often be used to solve another in a quite dissimilar field. Secondly, the characteristics of phenomena found in one system repeat themselves again and again in other systems. Finally, the underlying causes of action in fields as widely separated as agriculture and railways are much more common than might, at first, be obvious, simply because one is always dealing with systems involving people.

There have been several attempts to classify operational research studies, but these are always liable to be artificial. The following subjects for study reappear frequently in the programs of work of British operational research teams. Although they can be grouped under the headings indicated, this should not be looked upon as a classification, since there is much overlapping.

I. *To do with people alone.*

    (a) Organization and management
    (b) Absenteeism and labor relations
    (c) Economics
    (d) Decisions of individuals
    (e) Market research

II. *To do with people and machines.*

    (a) Efficiency and productivity
    (b) Organization of flow in factories
    (c) Methods of quality control, inspection and sampling
    (d) Accidents
    (e) Organization of technological change

III. *To do with movement.*

    (a) Transport
    (b) Stocking, distribution, and handling
    (c) Communications

The development of operational research in the United States has been along very similar lines, despite the independence of the growth in the two countries.

The Tool—The Scientific Method.

In using the tool of scientific method to assist management, operational research has shaped its own particular "edges" just as biological science has shaped its own. In any branch of science, one must begin by clarifying the problem or the objective and by defining precisely the terms to be used. One follows this by a series of observations to determine the facts, by a mental process of imagination or intuition to build up an explanation of the facts, and, finally, above all, by testing and retesting the conclusions that are derived from the explanation. The more quantitatively the facts are expressed, the more rigorously can the testing be done; the quantitative approach, therefore, is dominant in the scientific method.

The operational research worker must use both ingenuity and discrimination in seeking out his information and he must find some means of assessing the degree of certainty or the significance of every piece of information. He then submits this information to an exhaustive series of analyses to determine whether any patterns can be identified, or whether there is any interdependence or relationship between various quantities; here the mathematical methods of statistical analysis are frequently used. Given enough observational data to work on, one can find out not only that an action A occurs at the same time as an action B, but how frequently and to what extent. It is also important to know whether there is a time lag between actions A and B.

The story is not complete, however, unless one has information on the nature of the coupling between A and B. Elementary science teaches that there can never be action at a distance without some form of coupling. The various kinds of couplings lie between two extreme types. The first, or positive, type is such as occurs between two parts of a machine, where the force or energy for one or other of the actions is transmitted through the coupling. In the second type, energy is provided locally, and the coupling consists merely of a signal which is a trigger to the second action. A parallel operational example for the first type might be the use of a strong economic pressure to force a group of people to do certain things; for the second type, the action of colored lights at a road crossing which calls forth some particular action on the part of drivers.

It often happens that government authorities try to offset the force of an economic coupling by means of a weaker coupling such as propaganda or legislative action, usually with little effect or with effects other than those intended. For example, the imports and exports of any country are positively coupled [3] as described by one of the "laws" of our present economic system. In recent years, however, several countries have attempted to import less than they export. The coupling prevents the achievement of such a goal, yet some governments persist in their efforts only to produce an unintended general reduction in world trade.

Balancing Opposing Factors.

The objective of many operational research problems is to find the best balance between two or more opposing factors, in short, to optimize a given system. A simple type of problem to be found in almost any manufacturing works may be illustrated by the example which Passano has described. [4] The company with which he was associated frequently received orders for steel bars of a standard length with only a small tolerance. Each bar was rolled from a billet of as nearly as possible constant weight; because of the fluctuations in the size of the billets, however, the actual as-rolled lengths of the final bars varied over a range of several feet. A bar exceeding the required length had to be trimmed to size, and the pieces cut off were usable only as scrap; a short bar had to be scrapped altogether.

Passano investigated the situation by measuring some hundreds of bars and plotting a frequency distribution of their lengths. If the bars were required in 40-foot lengths, for example, their actual

---

[3] Gifts should be looked upon as a slipping of the coupling and loans as a take-up of part of the elastic capacity.

[4] R. F. Passano, *Yearbook of the American Iron and Steel Institute* (1949), p. 192.

lengths, as rolled, were likely to vary from a little over 40 feet to about 43 feet, as shown by the solid curve in Figure 1.

The top part of the diagram illustrates how one hundred bars might look if they were laid side by side in order of their lengths.

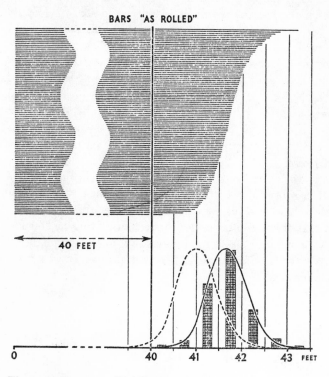

BARS "AS ROLLED"

40 FEET

0   40   41   42   43 FEET

Figure 1—Frequency Distribution of Bar Lengths. The dotted curve illustrates the result of reducing the average length by 8 inches. One per cent of bars are now short of 40 feet but the loss due to overlengths is much reduced.

The histogram below shows the number of bars in each length interval: 40 feet to 40 feet 6 inches; 40 feet 6 inches to 41 feet, etc. This histogram is not unlike a normal distribution curve.

In this example, there is an average waste of 1 foot, 8 inches arising from the trimming of over-length bars; in other words, a

4 per cent loss. Passano showed that the total waste could be reduced if the average billet size were reduced so that the distribution curve moved to the left to the position illustrated by the dotted curve. The minimum loss in this case corresponds to a position of the curve where 1 per cent of the bars are short and are scrapped but where, simultaneously, the loss in trimmings is reduced to about 1 foot per bar, or 2.4 per cent. The total loss, then, would be 3.4 per cent as against 4 per cent; the bringing of the billet-cutter's settings to the best position makes possible a valuable increase in yield (0.6 per cent) without there being any other changes in the process. Of course, it would be better still if it were possible to obtain greater precision in the weight of the billet and, thus, in the length of the bar; this, however, is a separate problem and one which is not easy to solve.

This illustration provides an example of the failure to balance regular losses against the much more *sensational* losses involved in an occasional short length; the foreman of the bar mill made such a fuss when a bar came out short that the cutter of the billets played for safety and erred on the long side. This might well point up the lesson that the man who prides himself on getting no losses on one account is probably causing unnecessary losses in another. It is possible to balance these losses only by a quantitative analysis of the entire situation.

Similar phenomena have been met in the steel industry and elsewhere. For example, a foreman of a cogging mill is very conscious of those rare occasions when an ingot comes to the mill either too hot or too cold. He insists, therefore, on margins of safety in the soakingpit which cost the industry considerable annual sums in fuel. The foreman is, of course, justified in arguing that the improvement should come from a narrowing of the distribution of errors; at the same time, however, he should contribute by allowing a proper balance between the fuel consumption in the soaking pit and the costly but rare disruption caused by ingots which are too hot or too cold.

Another similar problem has recently been analyzed, namely the lack of balance between the time patients at hospital out-patient clinics must wait to receive attention and the time lost by the doctor when the next patient is not immediately available. Even if the doctor's time is assessed as being many times more valuable than that of the patient, the present balance is extremely far from the optimum.

The reason for the excessive waste of patients' time is that the procedure is entirely governed by the doctor's wishes.

Self-Coupling.

Earlier mention was made of couplings between two separate actions. In many systems, however, one action is coupled either directly or indirectly back onto itself. Such systems are analogous to feedback circuits in electronics.[5]

This type of self-coupling can be of two kinds. In the first type, the back-coupling tends to *oppose* the initial action or change; this is called "self-compensating" coupling. In the second kind, the tendency is to *enhance* the initial action, and this is called "self-aggravating" coupling. The first type leads to an equilibrium condition, whereas the second leads to a catastrophic change or, at least, to violent oscillations. Physicists will recognize the first as another description of the well-known theorem of Le Chatelier: "If a change is imposed on a physical system in equilibrium, there are automatically generated other changes which tend to reduce the effect of the first change." This theorem follows from the second law of thermodynamics and is of general application.

The field of economics provides many examples of the self-compensating phenomenon, one of which is the so-called "law of supply and demand." If the rate of supply is changed to a lower level under conditions of constant demand, prices rise; this stimulates an increase in supply, thus reducing the original change. There is, however, often a time lag between the cause and effect which may lead to an overshooting of the equilibrium position. Just as in electronics, this would produce oscillations unless good anticipatory couplings were also introduced. Self-compensating couplings, except when a lag exists, are, however, of limited interest because one seldom wants to change them; the equilibrium position to which they lead is generally what is desired.

Self-aggravating couplings, which also occur frequently in operational problems, are of great interest and great importance. The scheduling of buses provides a good example. The schedule may be organized so that buses depart at regular two-minute intervals from

[5] This analogy has been developed extensively by A. Tustin in his book, "The Mechanism of Economic Systems," Heinemann, London, 1953.

a depot and pass along a route through a large town to another depot. Under normal loading and with no special obstacles, the two-minute interval can be retained fairly evenly throughout the entire schedule. If, however, a small delay takes place with one bus during the " rush hour " when the load is near the maximum designed value, this bus will find itself faced with the problem of picking up a larger number of accumulated passengers and making more and longer stops than would otherwise be necessary. This aggravates the delays for this particular bus. The process is repeated with the next and following buses, the total delay becoming steadily worse until the buses get through the heavily loaded part of their route. This phenomenon is the basic cause of the " convoys " of buses which are frequently seen in large towns.

In this example, there is no time lag between cause and effect. In other instances, however, some very severe results can be obtained. Suppose, for example, a military convoy of some thirty lorries were traveling through a town, and that it began the trip at even speed and with equal separation between each two vehicles. Something happens to cause the leading vehicle to slow down ever so slightly. After a short time interval, the second driver becomes conscious of the narrowing separation between his and the first vehicle, and he slows down, rather more rapidly than did the first. The third driver does the same, but brakes quite vigorously. Down the line of the convoy, the rate of deceleration increases until, finally, some of the vehicles come sharply to a full stop. The converse of this procedure occurs if the leading vehicle accelerates slightly; a wave of increasing acceleration passes down the convoy until, finally, the vehicles at the rear are racing madly to catch up with what they believe is a rapidly growing gap. Observations of this " concertina " effect in military convoys have shown that very small changes of speed of a few miles an hour in the leading vehicle can cause the last vehicle in a convoy to come repeatedly to a stop and then race up to forty-five miles per hour.[6]

A third example of self-aggravating coupling is taken from the field of economics. There are, in Great Britain, two systems of pensions. In the first, the accumulative system, a man or his employer

[6] D. F. Bayly-Pike, Note in *Operational Research Quarterly*, Vol. 4, No. 1 (March 1953), p. 14, and private communication.

puts aside a certain *percentage* of his income each year until he retires. In the second system, which is operative in the British Civil Service and in many companies, the amount of pension a man receives is worked out as a fraction of his *final* income on retirement. In times of inflation, wages and salaries are high and the man who is on the final income scheme is obviously in the better position for retirement. This involves, however, serious self-aggravating effects as compared with the accumulative system.

In times of inflation, there is an excess of jobs over available manpower; to bring things into better balance, people should be dissuaded from retiring early. The accumulative pension system has exactly this effect. A man approaching retiring age will find his pension small and will want to remain at his job a few more years in order to accumulate a pension more commensurate with the standard of living he wishes to enjoy. In times of deflation, on the other hand, there is unemployment, prices are low, and his pension will be relatively high; he will find it to his advantage at such times to retire early, thereby creating a job vacancy and beginning to spend his savings. In short, the normal pension scheme is part of a self-compensating coupling in the economic system and is well suited to help in reducing trade-cycle oscillations. It encourages saving in time of inflation and spending in time of deflation.

The final-income scheme has exactly the opposite effect. In times of unemployment, those with pension rights tied to their final incomes will not want to retire, but will wait for a time when wages and salaries are higher. They will continue to save rather than to begin spending their savings. This scheme, therefore, provides a self-aggravating coupling in the economic system.

The real situation is, of course, more complicated, if only because most people retire at an age limit fixed by contract made many years earlier. Furthermore, to be accurate, one should take into account anticipatory or lag effects. There are many other couplings in the economic system, most of which are more important than the example just cited. Their isolation, however, and an analysis of their characteristics would be a step toward getting them under control.

A better-known example of a self-aggravating coupling in the realm of economics is the tying of wages to the cost of living. Here the direction of the coupling is always the same, i. e., to aggravate the inflationary spiral. If, however, the coupling is kept weak, as in Great Britain, by use of a formula in which wage changes are much less than cost of living changes, the aggravating effect is not very serious; a strong coupling, as in Australia, can lead to extremely difficult problems for a community.

Fluctuating Loads.

Problems arising from fluctuations in the loading of a particular part of a system are among the most important and common problems in the various fields served by operational research. Such fluctuations may arise from a number of causes, of which the following are a few types:

(a) One or more of the steps in a series of operations may be subject to random interference in its scheduling, or have inherent randomness.

(b) A system may have in it self-aggravating or time-lag elements which lead to oscillations.

(c) A batch process may be feeding into a continuous part of a process.

(d) Individual cyclical operations working in parallel may get in phase or may "bunch," thus leading to abnormal demands for servicing, etc.

In the first type, one can recognize a number of patterns. For example, the arrival of babies in a population (during any short period) is almost as completely random as the production of alpha particles from a piece of radium. The arrival of ships bringing ore to British ports or of long-range airplanes at an airport has a high element of randomness, but there remains the background of a schedule. In both of these examples, there is little or no direct coupling between individual events.

The intervals between random or uncoupled events, when plotted as a frequency distribution, always give a curve of a characteristic shape. Figure 2 shows a plot compiled from the London telephone directory, a plot which could be reproduced by anyone. The first telephone number ending in the digit 2 on a randomly chosen page has been taken as a starting point, and the intervals between this and successive 2's up to 250 have been counted and sorted into groups. The results have been plotted as a distribution curve in the form of a histogram. The solid curve shows the result one would expect to get from the well-established theory of random processes, and represents a " Poisson distribution." The *average* interval was found to be ten, as might be expected, but intervals of less than ten are the more common. The average is maintained by there being a few intervals much larger than ten.

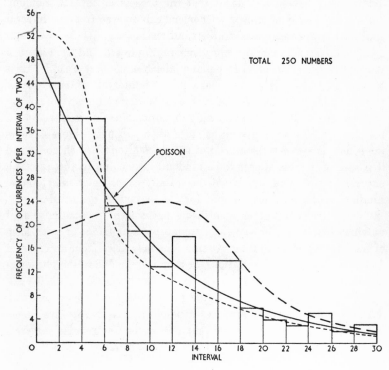

Figure 2—Frequency of Intervals Between Telephone Numbers Ending in " 2 "
—London Directory.

Coupling, if present in a process, may be one of two opposite types, one tending to group events and the other to separate them. No actual examples come readily to mind, but they can be predicted. If, for example, the occurrence of one accident tended to make people more nervous and jittery, small intervals between accidents would appear more frequently than in the random case; one would get a curve rather like that described by the dotted line in Figure 2. If, on the other hand, one accident tended to make people more careful and more likely to avoid accidents, one would get a converse curve, rather like that described by the broken line in Figure 2.

Both of these are examples of couplings between events; if one finds either type of distribution curve, one knows that a coupling exists. On the other hand, a curve like a Poisson distribution is not in itself sufficient evidence that the process is, in fact, random. All sorts of highly organized phenomena can emerge from an interval analysis as apparently random distributions.

Two practical examples are given in Figures 3 and 4. Figure 3 shows the intervals of cars passing along a country road.[7] It is obvious that there is a very sharp peak of intervals of only one or two seconds. All the rest of the distribution follows the normal random curve. This sharp bunching of intervals is due to interference between vehicles, since passing is not always possible. Figure 4 shows the intervals between the arrival of ore ships at one British port [8] and it is seen that these appear to be random. Bunching in this case is a natural phenomenon and is not due to any coupling or interference. Similar results have been found for the arrival of ore trains.[9]

There are many other identifiable patterns of fluctuations, most of which include either some background periodic factor or some form of marshaling or scheduling. Oscillations may arise from an external factor, such as diurnal variations, or they may be due to the phenomenon described in (b) above.

Fluctuations arising from batch processes are extremely common. An open-hearth furnace produces a batch of, say, twenty-five ingots which, in due course, must be sent one by one at regular intervals into the cogging mill. A retailer must buy a batch of a given variety of goods from the wholesaler, but he sells more or less continuously, except, of course, with a random variation according to the arrival of customers.

Having identified the type of fluctuation which occurs in a given system, the operational research worker commonly tries to discover

[7] R. J. Smeed and G. T. Bennett, "Research on Road Safety and Traffic Flow," Institution of Civil Engineers, Road Paper No. 29 (London, 1949).

[8] D. G. Owen, Berthing Delays to Ore Ships, PE/F/70/51.

[9] M. D. J. Brisby and R. T. Eddison, *Journal of the Iron and Steel Institute*, Vol. 172 (1952), p. 171.

whether it is possible or worthwhile to reduce that fluctuation. Several
methods might be tried. Usually it is important to cut down the

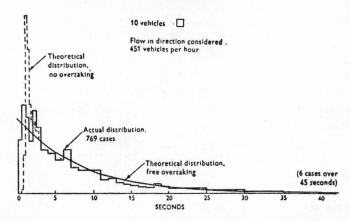

Figure 3—Frequency Distribution of Time Intervals on a Dual Carriageway.

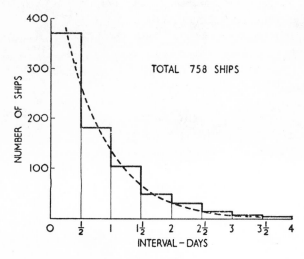

Figure 4—The Distribution of Intervals in the Arrival
of Ore Ships at a British Port.

peak loads, and this may be accomplished through some restriction
in the flow line. More commonly, one imposes a marshaling or

scheduling factor on the system. In the case of fluctuations arising from batches, the only recourse is to reduce the size of the batch as much as possible. This, however, usually involves a serious economic disadvantage, and a balance must be found.

Capacity.

Most problems of fluctuating loads are dealt with by the intro-duction of capacities at strategic positions. Three types of capacity are found in physical systems. First, there is the holding capacity, say of a pint pot; here the capacity is a measure of an extensive property. The second type, the rate capacity, is less common in physics, but an example exists in the cathode of a radio valve, which has an emission capacity in coulombs per second; here the capacity is the differential of an extensive property with respect to time. The third type, the elastic capacity, can be illustrated by the movement of a spring under a force, or by the charging of a condenser with electricity under a voltage; in this case, the capacity is the differential of an extensive property with respect to an intensive property, i. e., one signifying an intensity, not a quantity.

In operations, there are the same three types of capacity. In the first type, there is the capacity of a bus, the lifting capacity of an elevator, or the holding capacity of railway sidings. Most of these quantities are easy to specify and measure, since they are the maximum that a container, in the broad sense of the word, will hold. Of course, there will generally be some flexibility, as in the number of people that can be put into a bus.

Rate capacities are measures of abilities to do things and they are the most important and the most prominent in operations. The capacity of a man to perform so much work per day, or of a plant to produce so much output per day are illustrations; these are related to productivity by the equation $P = UC$, where U is the "utilization" of the plant or of the man. Thus, the rate capacity of a plant is its productivity when it is fully utilized.

It is rather difficult to define rate capacity accurately, for the output can, in theory, be pushed very high under exceptional con-ditions. It is often necessary, therefore, to introduce qualified terms, such as short term or maximum capacity, economic capacity, or a capacity associated with a given product mix. Once the conditions and the objectives are specified, however, it is usually possible to measure the rate capacity with reasonable accuracy. If conditions and objectives are not specified, an accurate measure is impossible.

The third type, elastic capacity, has not yet really come into operations, largely because the quantities concerned are very difficult to measure. Prices and incentives are examples of intensive properties or can be defined as such. The supply of a given commodity is said to be elastic and depends upon the price. When this relation is a linear one and both quantities can be measured, then one can define and use an elastic capacity for this system. One can predict that the capacity, in the case of the change of supply in steel scrap in relation to a change in the price, will be very low; in other words, the market is inelastic. On the other hand, the supply of a mineral can commonly go up rapidly with prices, and this system could be considered elastic with a high capacity.

Capacities of all three types, but particularly the first and second, come into systems where an attempt is made to offset the effects of fluctuating loads. Problems of finding the optimum balance, i. e., the size and types of the various capacities and the most strategic positions in which to place them, account for a large part of operational research work, no matter what the field. Usually it is required that the optimum be sought on an economic basis; all the components, including the costs of occasional failures to deal with peak loads, must be taken into account.

In the flow lines of a large manufacturing process such as steel making, the soaking pits are used as holding capacities to change a batch into a continuous process. To deal with the peak demands for scrap caused by the bunching of open-hearth furnaces, a steel plant has a surplus in the rate capacity of the equipment and men loading and charging scrap and also of the holding capacity of scrap loaded and ready to charge.[10] Various types of capacities can be used for dealing with grouped train arrivals.[11] In the case of military convoys, the introduction of extra-large intervals after the sixth, twelfth, etc., lorry provides a holding capacity in space or time and will almost completely eliminate the worst of the fluctuations.[12] Gas manufac-

[10] R. Solt and R. W. Davis, unpublished report.
[11] Brisby and Eddison, *Journal of the Iron and Steel Institute.*
[12] Bayly-Pike, private communication.

turers use both holding and surplus rate capacities to deal with fluctuating loads, but electricity undertakings can use only rate capacities.

Analyses of problems of this kind must take account of the probable interval between the peak loads themselves. In some cases, the peak loads are randomly distributed and can bunch, thereby presenting difficult problems. In other cases, such as in the bunching of open-hearth furnaces, a peak is always preceded by a "valley"; accordingly, holding capacities are often the solution since they can be replenished during the valley period.

Queueing.

Almost every operation within the social and manufacuring fields can be considered as a "gate." Each unit of material or person arriving at that gate requires a certain service time before it or he can be passed on and the next unit or person can be accepted. The rate capacity of this gate is obviously the reciprocal of the service time. If the demand on the gate or the input to the gate exceeds the capacity for a short period, material or people will be kept waiting; in other words, a queue will develop in the holding space before the gate. This space itself might be considered to have a holding capacity, but commonly it has unlimited capacity. The use of this capacity, however, might be very costly, as in the case of ships or airplanes waiting to be accepted at a port or of vehicles at a red traffic light.

It has already been noted that certain improvements can be effected by the marshaling of arrivals at the gate to make the demand or input more uniform. This is obviously always the first approach to such a problem; frequently, however, there are severe limitations to what can be done.

The theory of marshaling and queueing has advanced greatly.[13] Problems may be attacked from either a theoretical (mathematical) point of view or by model experiments, the former depending on the possibility of describing the fluctuations by simple equations, such as a Poisson distribution for demand or load.

Most fluctuating loads, however, depart significantly from the

---

[13] See the report of the Meeting of the Operational Research Club in London, 17 March 1952, in *Operational Research Quarterly*, Vol. 3, No. 1 (March 1952).

Poisson distribution and, therefore, other methods must be tried. An example involving the arrival of planes at an airport has been studied by research workers at the Massachusetts Institute of Technology and will be described in a later chapter which deals with queueing theory in more detail.[14] The techniques used in that study can be applied to a wide range of problems. The Road Research Laboratory near London, for example, has conducted a similar study on the lengths of queues that develop and the delays to the vehicles as a function of the rate capacity of a road junction.

Conclusion.

The selection of these few from the numerous themes in operational research should be sufficient to show that operational research is a branch of science which can claim a wholeness in its own right. Through the work of operational research sections, the scientific method is increasingly being brought to bear on the problems of executives in both industry and government.

[14] See B. O. Marshall's chapter, pp. 134-48, below.

Organization for
Operations Research

LAWRENCE J. HENDERSON

WHETHER IN operations research or in any other sort of activity, the function of organization is to permit groups of people to work together effectively. It is a service function, a means to the end of effective group work, and not an end in itself. Organization deals with relations among human beings. Because human beings are characterized by wide ranges of individual difference, detailed principles of organization are difficult to develop. Most good organizers and administrators carry on their work "by ear" through trial and error, relying on their observations of the capabilities and limitations of particular individuals and on their collection of experience with human behavior. Such experience yields some principles, but beyond the obvious ones of leadership, responsibility, and authority, these are for the most part general principles of individual or group behavior, and not of organization as such.

Reference to the literature on organization provides only limited assistance in sifting out principles. One of the important books on the subject is Chester I. Barnard's *The Functions of the Executive*.[1] It is abstruse and difficult, so sophisticated that many people find it unreadable; nevertheless it is one of the few essays on organization or administration written by a successful administrator. Only rarely have students of human affairs who were not themselves executives,

[1] Published by the Harvard University Press in 1938.

66

administrators, or politicians been able to produce useful material. One exception is Pareto's *Sociology*.[2] Although this book does not deal explicitly with the problem, or at least does not purport to do so, it contains a vast amount of general sense on the subject of human behavior, and hence on organization. Most conventional books on organization, for example on the functions of corporate directors, describe formal differences among various organizations, attempting to point out those organizational patterns which, on the whole, work well. Such explanations often lose sight of the fact that organizations vary because people vary. There is, in effect, considerable attention paid to form without sufficient recognition of the confusion between form and substance.

An example from the last war may help to illustrate this point. An Army major in the European theatre, in charge of a unit which performed what was, essentially, a service function, managed to get the unit functioning well without any particular regard to regulations and red tape. In short, he saw to it that the right people were in the right places doing an effective job. Late in the war, a new colonel, reputed to be an expert on organization, arrived from Washington. He requested the major to draw up a block-diagram organization chart, and to prepare a series of statements concerning the functions of the people in the organization.

When the chart was produced, the colonel pointed out one block with the comment, " Look, this is wrong. Don't you see that you can't have this man here? He must be over there." He criticized several other sections of the chart and finally said, " I want you to change this."

The major asked, " You mean change the diagram? "

The colonel answered, " Yes."

"All right, I will," agreed the major, and the colonel went away happy and satisfied.

Unlike some people who concern themselves with organization, the colonel really did little harm. He made no attempt to change the actual organization, but simply accepted a change in the formal description of the organization. Unfortunately, many so-called experts are too prone to interfere with efficient real organizations which

[2] *Trattato di Sociologia Generale*, Torino, 1916. Translated into English in 1935 as *The Mind and Society*.

happen not to meet the currently fashionable pattern of schematic organization. Yet it seems that the freedom of people to vary organization, within the rather broad limits set by society through the law and by regulatory bodies, has been to a considerable degree responsible for the success of the American free enterprise system. Many organizations of various forms have, in competition with each other, been equally successful. " Equally " must, of course, be read to mean " more or less equally "; where one has been more successful than another, the difference has almost certainly been due to the qualities of the manager and members of the working group, rather than to the form of the organization. There are occasional pathological cases where an organization strait jacket stifles people of great ability; such cases can be spotted in government and in some very large businesses, where the worshippers of form and organization as an end have set up road blocks which sometimes make it virtually impossible for groups of good people to work effectively.

This is not to be construed as propaganda to the effect that organization should not be studied, but as a plea for studies of people working together rather than of organization as a supposed entity in itself. Neither should one infer from this that the characteristics of a human group are the same as the sum of the characteristics of its members. The important characteristics of the group are, however, determined by the behavior of group members and their interrelationships rather than by any formal description or organizational block diagram. This has been recognized by a few logicians and mathematicians, some of them working in the field of operations research. They like to think about everything in precise terms, and it is extremely difficult to conceive of realistic thinking about human relations in terms which are mathematically precise. Nothing daunted and quite properly recognizing that organization block diagrams and the like describe nothing but the diagrams themselves, they are seeking to develop " organization theory." To date, such development has involved attempts at mathematical formulation of the process of decision-making in small human groups—in other words, mathematical formulation of certain types of human behavior. One can only admire and wonder at the courage of these pioneers in view of the pitifully elementary state of empirically or experimentally derived generalizations concerning human behavior.

Variety in Operations Research Organizations.
In examining some of the existing operations research agencies
from the organizational point of view, one should recognize that the
organizational *details* of such groups differ little from those of many
other organizations. This chapter, will, therefore, treat general, or
policy, matters, ignoring the details. One fact is readily apparent.
The great diversity in form of organization and method of dealing
with the customer together with the unquestioned success of most
existing operations research groups seems to support the premise posed
earlier about organization in general, namely that it is often the
freedom to vary organizational forms which leads to success.

Operations reseach organizations can be classified along various
lines. First, there are the contract, or independent types, where the
research group, as a separate organization, sells its product or services
to the user or customer. At the other end of the spectrum are the
integral types, where the operations research group is actually a part
of the customer's organization. Among the latter category, one finds
groups which are permanent organizations and others which are
temporary task forces, formed to tackle a specific piece of work and
disbanded when their mission is completed. An operations research
organization can be either centralized or decentralized: its work may
be done largely in one unit at one place or by a number of small
units scattered geographically and performing various tasks. Operations research, in name at least, began as an aid to decision-making
in the military services and is still heavily concentrated on military
problems; but there is the dichotomy of military and nonmilitary
operations research, the former concerned with the problems of the
Armed Services or of the Department of Defense, the latter with
business and industrial problems. Finally, there are those groups
which deal with immediate, emergent operational problems, and others
which deal on a longer term basis with problems of broader scope.
Each of the operations research groups now in existence seems to
represent a different combination of these various characteristics.
Such variation has prevented the fixing of a rigid organizational
pattern, and has helped to establish a precedent for organizational
adaptation aimed toward increasing the effectiveness of operations
research work. It might be well here to describe a few of the principal operations research groups in order to demonstrate the variety
they display.

The Operations Analysis Division represents an integral organization; that is to say, it is basically a part of the organization of its customer, the Air Force, and of course it deals exclusively with military problems. Futhermore, it works principally on immediate operational problems arising at Air Force Headquarters and in the various Air Force commands. It is primarily a decentralized operation: most of its work is done in the commands in this country and elsewhere throughout the world. The headquarters in Washington does consist of a fairly large group which, however, is in reality one of the working groups and does not function as a centralized agency concerned with all Air Force operations research problems.

The Weapons Systems Evaluation Group in the Office of the Secretary of Defense is also an integral organization, working for the Secretary of Defense and the Joint Chiefs of Staff. It studies military problems, but at the inter-service level; it is concerned largely with broad systems matters. The Weapons Systems Evaluation Group is centralized; all of its work is conducted in the Pentagon.

Among integral operations research groups in industry are those at Glenn L. Martin in Baltimore and Consolidated-Vultee in San Diego. These are permanent organizations which perform operations research of a sort largely associated with military design problems. Similar permanent groups in other organizations deal with non-military problems. The General Electric Company has, for many years, made use of the integral task force type of group. Teams of people are formed to study specific problems as they arise; these are usually combined management and operations research problems.

Senior among the contract or independent organizations, and, in fact, oldest of all operations research organizations in the United States, is the Navy's Operations Evaluation Group. This group is administratively part of the Massachusetts Institute of Technology, under contract to the Navy Department, and physically located within the Department. It deals with military problems, most of which are of an immediate operational nature. It is at once a centralized and a decentralized organization, with a main section in Washington and smaller groups or representatives spread through the major Naval commands. Functionally, this group is almost integral to the Navy, but, from the standpoint of formal organiaztion, it is the product of a Navy contract with M.I.T.

The Army counterpart is the Operations Research Office, administratively a part of The Johns Hopkins University and under contract to the Army. ORO studies both broad and immediate operational problems. It is both centralized and decentralized, with working groups in the Far East, in Europe, and at Headquarters Army Field Forces, besides the main headquarters in Chevy Chase, Maryland. It is not integral to the Army in the same sense as is OEG to the Navy; several miles separate the Pentagon from the Maryland site of ORO. And, since ORO is prepared to tackle either broad or immediate problems, it is more nearly like the independent type of operations research group.

The RAND Corporation is another contract group and is entirely independent of the military. Although most of RAND's work involves Air Force problems, it is also engaged in studies for the Atomic Energy Commission. Many of RAND's studies are not properly described as operations research—they are more in the nature of research on planning, rather than operations. RAND is entirely centralized; except in special cases, it does not send people out on permanent assignment to various Air Force Commands, though very close contact is maintained through visits. The operations research problems of the commands are, of course, studied by the Air Force Operations Analysis sections which specialize in more immediate problems. Because RAND is interested in the broader aspects of future weapons systems, it concerns itself in large part with development problems. Unlike OEG and ORO, RAND is not a contract with a university. It is an independent non-profit corporation specifically established for the purpose of conducting broad planning studies. Consequently, it differs organizationally from the groups serving the Navy and Army.

One type of independent contract organization which is rapidly increasing in number is exemplified by Arthur D. Little, Inc. This is established as a business, selling its services to customers, either military or commercial. The organization works on specific tasks; a problem is posed by a particular customer and, once this problem is solved, the contract is fulfilled and is terminated. Management consulting and engineering consulting firms have been engaged in similar work for years. At Arthur D. Little, however, are many people experienced in military operations research who have brought with them a new flavor not present in previous consulting work.

These examples are sufficient to show that it is impossible to draw up inflexible rules concerning the type of organizational arrangement with the customer best suited to the conduct of operations research. In some instances, the nature of the problem may determine which kind of organization is most suitable. The integral operations research group has an advantage in providing intimate acquaintance with the customer's problems. In some instances such acquaintance is important to efficient work, and its absence can impede success. For example, some recent study contracts sponsored by the military, which verged on operations research, were not entirely successful because the research people did not have the opportunity to become fully familiar with the real problems calling for military decision. In other cases, however, integration between the research people and the customer may have the effect of delimiting the problem area. That is to say, the customer may direct the studies his way, thereby losing the advantage of the independent view of his problem. The integrated situation also raises problems of personnel and of time pressure. When the operations research team is in close juxtaposition to its customer, it can be subjected to almost constant nagging for results. For this reason such a research group usually tends to concentrate on immediate rather than broad, long-range problems. Furthermore, the people who do the research in an intracompany team remain in the company after the study, living with the people whose activities they have studied and competing with them for jobs; this, naturally, is potentially disruptive to smooth interpersonnel relations.

Despite the varying points of view of how operations research should be organized and despite many of the difficulties encountered in the administration of operations research, the existing organizations appear to be working with some measure of success. Fortunately, there seems to have been sufficient flexibility of approach to organizational problems and sufficient variety of organizational forms to preclude the kind of rigidity which might impede the introduction of new ideas and the progress so necessary in any kind of research.

Internal Organization—The Mixed Team.

So much for the external aspects of organization—the relationship between the operations research group and its customer or customers. The internal aspects may now be considered briefly. How should the work and the people within an operations research group be organized? Here again, it would be foolish to draw up a series of rigid requirements, since, in this area more than others, procedures are necessarily dependent on the task rather than the task on the procedures. In considering internal organization, differences in philosophy about the scope of operations research become important.

In order to examine this problem even superficially, it appears useful to review very briefly the history of operations research. It seems clear that the type of work done by military operations research groups in the last war, a type still being effectively continued, raises organizational problems which are familiar in many organizations, such as management consulting firms, and which are fewer and different from those which arise in groups studying broad problems, such as the Weapons Systems Evaluation Group, ORO, and RAND. It is with the origin and development of the latter that I should like to deal.

When the first military operations research organizations were formed in England and the United States during the last war, those who took the lead in such formation did not have a free choice of the types of people they wanted to employ and to assign to military problems. By the time operations research organizations were taking shape, many other wartime agencies had picked over the rosters of scientific and technical personnel. Furthermore, many scientists and engineers were actually in uniform. Though it was a closely guarded secret, in the United States the Manhattan District had begun to take those physicists who had not already been put to work at the Radiation Laboratory on radar or with the Radio Research Laboratory on countermeasures. In short, trained scientists and engineers had practically disappeared from the labor market. Had a newly appointed chief of a wartime operations research group decided that he wanted physicists and chemists to do the work, he would quickly have learned that these were unavailable. With a very few exceptions, there were no competent people left in these fields. Those responsible for assembling operations research staffs soon realized that they would be obliged to assign work to categories of people which orginally they would never have considered.

Actually, they made the most of the situation. Interested people were found, some with backgrounds which did not seem in the least

appropriate for the job in hand. Yet practical accomplishments began
to materialize, largely because there were so many problems to be
solved and because many of these were gross problems. Those in
charge of these groups immediately began to attribute the productivity of their organizations to the fact that the "mixed-team"
approach was used. As a matter of fact, they felt obliged to offer
some explanation for staffs of assorted biologists, lawyers, economists,
etc., and the "mixed-team" seemed a convenient label. At the present
time, there is frequent reference to "mixed-teams" and "task forces,"
and it is sometimes easy to forget that such phrases really came into
being primarily as morale builders. Lest this evaluation appear
ungrateful, it might be well to state categorically that groups for
which biologists, statisticians, a very few mathematicians, a chess
player or two, economists, lawyers, and so forth were picked up along
the way turned out a large volume of analyses of military problems,
most of them of real merit. Their sucess convinced the Armed Services of all the free nations that operations research is indispensable.

Why was it, though, that biologists, lawyers, astronomers, and
economists could perform successful analyses when faced with problems having nothing to do with biology, law, astronomy, or economics?
These people were able quite adequately to substitute for the engineers,
mathematicians, and physicists, whom any right-thinking person would
have preferred for tackling the jobs at hand, because bodies of knowledge no more abstruse than algebra, freshman physics, and elementary
statistics, plus the ability to reason abstractly for at least short spans
of time, were sufficient intellectual equipment for the solution of
many of the immediate operations research problems then facing the
military. In the case of the biologists, of course, the experience
of dealing with messy data and individual differences within large
numbers of cases proved extremely useful. It should be repeated
that the problems examined at that time were largely gross problems.
If one examines the much-quoted study of the depth-bombing of
German submarines and continues through to most of the reports
which established operations research as indispensable to the Armed
Services, one rarely finds reference to more sophisticated techniques
than those just mentioned. Some rear-area operations research organizations, such as the Applied Mathematics Panel of the National
Defense Research Committee, then used and continue to use various

elegant analytical techniques. Those reports usually cited to demon-strate how operations research has paid off, however, describe much more practical problems of the type under consideration when the term " mixed-team " came into use.

It would seem that, within the practice of conventional operations research, the team aspects have been more frequently encountered in metaphor than in actuality. It is true that, when great masses of data had to be reduced for analytical study, as in bombing accuracy studies, gunsight-aiming-point motion picture film measurements, or studies of damage inflicted on friendly aircraft, Air Force Operations Analysis sections assigned from two to seventy people, both profes-sional and clerical, to the task. These groups were, of course, " mixed " in the sense that the operations research men in them had taken their degrees in diverse departments of colleges and universities ; they were "mixed " in the sense that civilians and military personnel worked on the same projects. The word " team " is an excellent word to use in employer-employee relations, particularly when much of the work to be done is tedious and not likely to lead to rapid advances in grade. In actual fact, however, wartime operations research assignments were frequently solos, in which an analyst worked alone ; actual tabulation might well reveal that this was the most frequent arrangement, followed closely by duos, consisting of a senior analyst and his assis-tant. This was and still is an efficient way of using personnel for practical and immediate operations research problems.

There is, however, a different use of personnel under rather different circumstances, which should not be confused with what has been above described as the " mixed team." Those groups previously mentioned, set up in the larger Air Force Operations Analysis sections to conduct field studies of bombing accuracy, flak damage, target analysis, and bomb and fuse selection, all presented their results separately to the military staff section sponsoring the particular study. If recommendations for improvement of bombing accuracy and for reduction of losses to flak or to fighters called for mutually exclusive measures, the staff officers or the Commander's Conference thrashed out the contradictions. The analyst in charge of bombing accuracy measurements reported his results to the Staff Bombardier or to the A-3 ; results of flak analysis were reported to the Staff Flak Officer ; target analyses went either to Intelligence or to someone in Ordnance.

It was possible under this arrangement for the Bombing Accuracy Subsection to report that the way to get more bombs on targets was to fly low and to fly slowly in combat formations, while the Flak Damage Subsection simultaneously reported that the way to reduce flak damage was to fly high and to fly fast in loose formations. The conclusions of each study team could have been correct within the assumptions made and the scope of their analyses; each team produced a sound study, but the sum of their recommendations was incapable of implementation. Each study was a component or suboptimization of one aspect of a complex operational problem involving many aspects, some of which were undoubtedly subjected to similar analysis, others of which were not. How were the differences resolved? During World War II, they were often resolved by a command decision from the cognizant operations officer, who acted on the basis of his experience and best judgment. In more recent operations research of a broader kind, it seems possible that much better means for decision-making are available, at least with respect to many aspects of such problems, through the use of a real mixed-team approach.

The real mixed-team approach is different from what was frequently labeled the "mixed-team approach" during World War II. It consists, first of all, of deliberately using specialists to work concurrently on each component part of a complex operational problem; these must be specialists and not merely operations analysts. The group is composed of people each of whom is competent in his special field and who simultaneously study the interrelationship among the various facets of the total operational or planning problem. Thus, to introduce the example of suboptimized research discussed previously, a real mixed-team approach would be to study the interrelationship among bombing accuracy, vulnerability to flak, vulnerability to other types of enemy action, optimum bomb load, type of fusing, vulnerability of targets, ability to fly certain types of formations, etc. The work would aim toward discovering a common denominator or means of evaluating the relative influence of conflicting component results, and to arrive at the optimum solution for the overall problem. In this case, the mixed-team would include specialists on physical vulnerability of targets, on electronics, on airplane vulnerability, and so on. They would be selected as specialists in these particular fields, and not merely to fill a quota of operations research people. They would be directed by a project leader within the group and their responsibility, as a team, would be to arrive at some common denominator which would produce an overall answer. This is the mixed-team approach in its real sense. While there were a few exceptional examples of this kind of activity in the last war, its extensive use is relatively new.

The hypothetical problem used to illustrate this point is more or less a conventional operations research problem, fixed in the sense of its limitations in respect to time and scope. WSEG, ORO, and RAND are now beginning to consider problems of much greater complexity, and these problems point up even more vividly the need for the real mixed-team approach. Entire weapons systems are now being studied, often with variations in the possible military objectives which they might be called upon to attain. A second source of complexity is the fact that such weapons systems are often not present but future systems. For example, a study might be made of what kind of tank the Army should buy or what kind of long-range bomber the Air Force should buy. The variables inherent in such problems are, obviously, legion. RAND, in one of its earlier jobs, did a simple analysis of this type and got 27,648 separate " best " answers, that is, answers which, for the particular case, were optimum. The *optimum optimorum* was next sought, and there appeared to be at least three, depending upon the relative importance attached to the particular measures of military effectiveness or efficiency used.

In this kind of operations research, the economist, who may appear to have been slighted in the earlier discussion of World War II " mixed-teams," plays an important part. This is because the preferred future weapons system must be selected according to some criterion; the problem is to select a weapons system, not to decide how to operate with an existing system. In selecting a weapons system, the aim is to get the " best " or " preferred " weapons system, whatever such terms may mean. Generally speaking, maximum performance from the technological point of view does not seem to be an adequate or proper measure. To use a civilian example, the sales manager of a large corporation engaged in door-to-door selling does not choose Cadillacs or Bentleys for his sales force even though they might give maximum automotive performance; the manager has limited resources to expend in buying cars, and wishes, quite naturally, to achieve maximum sales for his expenditure. This is essentially the problem which is facing the military. Consequently, the criteria normally chosen are economic, designed to answer such questions as how to get the maximum, in terms of some measure of military effectiveness, out of a whole system, for a given expenditure of resources, or how to get a particular job done for a minimum expenditure of resources. This is not to imply that the problem is focused mainly upon dollars as such; dollars are simply a way of measuring resources expended, and the economist can prove invaluable in selecting proper criteria for such measurements.

Political scientists and sociologists also have a contribution to make in the study of more complex problems by the real mixed team. In choosing the best future weapons system, the scope and variety of possible future military objectives must be considered, and this leads to consideration of strategy and of political objectives. What will the weapons systems have to do? This obviously will depend on where the war is to be fought, who the enemy will be, when it is to commence, and related issues. In these areas, operations research is reaching into the blue. But, even though the contributions of political scientists and sociologists may be difficult to obtain, and harder to use, since they are usually nonquantitative, it seems desirable and necessary to recognize the problems explicitly and to bring to bear the training and experience of specialists. Very few military men have training in such fields, and yet military power as an instrument of national policy, either in cold or hot war, has never been more important. Thus, in ORO, RAND, and WSEG, one finds economists and social scientists working together with specialists in electronics, areonautical engineering, and nuclear physics, operating as members of true mixed teams, each specialist bringing his specialty to bear on those parts of the problem which lie within his field and which are susceptible to analysis. This method has not entirely replaced and probably will never replace judgment and experience in the making of ultimate decisions by the operations research customer. It represents, however, a considerable extension of the basis of analysis and fact upon which decisions can be founded.

The organization geared to this broader type of operations research activity is likely to be different from the more conventional operations research agencies. Since the problems are of greater scope, the groups studying them are necessarily larger and more disciplines are represented; and, as groups grow in size and become heterogeneous, problems of internal communication are enhanced. Methods of coping with such problems are probably as numerous as are large operations research establishments. For administrative purposes, RAND has set up divisions by specialties: electronics, nuclear physics, aeronautical engineering, and so on. Within a particular division, information on the future capabilities of Air Force weapons systems and the state of the art is developed. The actual operations research, the analysis of such information in the solution of problems, is carried out by teams including personnel from various divisions, chosen as specialists, each team headed by a project leader. The structure is, of course, supported by the usual service agencies, such as the technical library and the computing center. ORO and WSEG have hit upon other workable patterns, similar in philosophy, for dealing with their mixed-team staff, which, once again, emphasizes the fact that flexibility and variety are necessary to the effectiveness of organization. Experience should be regarded not as a fund of rigid precedent but as a guide for shaping and adapting the organizational framework to fit the problems as they emerge, and as new methods are developed for their solution. Operations research organizations have established their right to freedom of action in this respect and have, in large measure, exercised it.

Management Consulting
and Operations Research

J. W. POCOCK

As the operations researcher looks to private industry for an opportunity to apply his talents, he finds himself contemplating a field of counsel to the executive in which the management consulting profession has been active for several decades. For this reason, those who are interested in becoming practitioners in the fledgling applied science of operations research should find it useful to consider the history and accomplishments of management consulting, encompassing as it does a wide variety of techniques proven useful in analysis and evaluation of business and industrial operations.

Although the term "management consulting" is now a familiar one and the place of the profession in our business community is well understood, it was only a bit more than fifty years ago that the activity was newly conceived, its objectives understood, and the first techniques practiced only by a small group of pioneers whose early work had been largely in the field of industrial engineering. These pioneers saw management consulting as a scientific endeavor which could provide a broader base and more penetrating, factual analyses upon which more intelligent executive decisions could be developed. Since industrial management problems are diverse, the diversity of techniques, skills, and training required by the management consulting profession have expanded greatly through the years. Problem areas susceptible to inquiry through operations research techniques today are also areas in which the management consultant has traditionally been active through many years. It is well, therefore, to identify the relationships of operations research to the general field of management consulting and so to foster interchange of experience and information to the benefit of both.

Growth of the Management Consulting Profession.

The genesis of management consulting is somewhat obscured in the mists of time. As one writer on the subject has observed, " If we define the management consultant as a man who helps business to do what it should do to become and stay efficient, then the idea probably goes back to the engineers who supervised the construction of the pyramids." The beginnings of its written history are more easily identified in the work of Frederick W. Taylor, Henry L. Gantt, Harrington Emerson, and other pioneers of scientific management who started their investigations about 1885. At that time, they formulated the doctrine that scientific methods of analysis and measurement could and should be used in industrial operations, and that, wherever possible, business decisions should be based on facts rather than on someone's intuition or emotion. The initial emphasis was on production operations.

Taylor's work on the shovel problem is almost legendary. The problem involved not the development of a new device, but the most efficient use of the old-fashioned shovel. Through a series of experiments, he determined the weight of a shovelful of material which the average laborer could handle regularly throughout the day so as to produce the maximum quantity of material moved without excessive fatigue. The solution, something in the neighborhood of twenty-one pounds per shovel load, was light when compared with contemporary practice; but it proved out over a full day. That experiment, plus others in the yard and shop, demonstrated the validity of Taylor's approach to a problem through observation, analysis, confirmation by experiment, and the follow-up and refinement of results in their ultimate application. This approach to problems, many of them more complex, was continued through the years by a long line of Taylor's students and their followers.

A recent evaluation of Taylor's work includes the following estimate:

In a very real sense the best of today's management is one form of expression, and a late form, of the growing impact of science upon society, for what Taylor did was to apply the *scientific method* to the problems of business management. Into this field he brought experimentation, the collection and classification of data, analysis of data, and the formulation of laws and principles based upon such analysis. Such matters as organization, the relationship of management to labor, of top management to management at the several lower levels, of the individual enterprise to the market, of business to government and to the whole economy, of the rights and powers of ownership, were long governed by tradition and custom and frequently found expression in, and were perpetuated by, law. However, the demonstrated results of the scientific method, slowly but persistently, have pressed upon these established relationships and traditional methods of thinking; they have brought about notable changes in some segments of business and left an expanding imprint upon all segments.[1]

Writing of his own work, Taylor made the following observation:

It will doubtless be claimed that in all that has been said no new fact has been brought to light that was not known to someone in the past. Very likely this is true. Scientific management does not necessarily involve any great invention, nor the discovery of new or startling facts. It does, however, involve a certain *combination* of elements which have not existed in the past, namely old knowledge so collected, analyzed, grouped and classified into laws and rules that it constitutes a science; . . .[2]

Taylor and his colleagues were working at comparatively elementary levels where, since little had been done, much could be done with relatively simple techniques of quantitative analysis. Operations research now brings to commerce and industry more powerful techniques of quantitative analysis and is an extension of Taylor's basic philosophy to possibilities probably beyond Taylor's vision, far-reaching as it was.

It was not long until the doctrine of scientific management had been expanded by Taylor and his followers beyond the production field into the area of general administration of enterprises. Holding fast

---

[1] George Filipetti, *Industrial Management in Transition* (revised ed.; Homewood, Illinois: Richard D. Irwin, 1953), p. 2.

[2] Frederick Winslow Taylor, "Principles of Scientific Management," in *Scientific Management* (3rd ed., New York: Harper and Brothers, 1947), pp. 139-40.

to the tenet that solutions should be based on objective analysis of fact rather than on personal intuition and experience, the management consulting profession achieved further success and growth.

During the twenties, the precise measurement of labor and production in the shop was carried to such a point that the human values inherent in a production operation became somewhat obscured. A wave of "efficiency experting" swept industry, along with the development of mass production operations and the assembly line. This submergence of the human values in the sea of purely mechanical analysis led to some discrediting of the efficiency expert's techniques. The experience pointed up the fact that quantitative measurement and the conclusions derived therefrom are not the only factors involved in executive decision, a point which should be everlastingly understood by those engaging in operations research.

By the time the depression was lifting, the management consulting profession had emerged from the wave of reaction to the over-exuberance of the efficiency experts and began to grow in stature as a balanced profession with a surer knowledge of how to use its tools with wisdom and mature judgment. During World War II, the profession was active in assisting the management of military administration and at times worked on problems similar to those military operational problems in which operations research scientists first gained their reputation. Since the war, American industry has turned increasingly to the use of professional management consultants. The profession may be regarded as firmly established today.

The main objective of today's management consulting profession is simply to assist the harassed executive in arriving at better administrative decisions and solutions to his operation problems, present and future. Its rapid development has been fostered by the growing pressures on executive and management personnel in business and industry, institutions, and government in this country over the past few decades. The executive's problems have become so large and so complex that it is no sign of weakness, but rather a demonstration of wisdom, for him to seek competent counsel. Major American companies now retain their management consultants along with their legal, financial, tax, public relations, and other consultants.

The profession today consists of numerous organizations and individuals with varying interests in the field of management and with varying competence in the field of their interests. Towards the end of the war, it was estimated that the total annual business was in excess of $65,000,000. Today, the total annual volume for professional business counsel in this country can be estimated to run well over $100,000,000.

Further identification of the profession insofar as its components are concerned is probably best done by reference to the Association of Consulting Management Engineers. This association, formed in 1929, includes some forty established management consulting organizations whose experiences in the field of management are substantial and whose solutions to the problems of the operating executive have withstood the test of time. Within this group, there are both those organizations which operate at broad, top policy levels and those which have made their way in special fields of interest, such as production, marketing, or personnel. Quite a few firms operate in both the top policy and technical or functional areas. The association is generally regarded as the backbone of the management consulting profession, in that it provides for the exchange of information among members, sets standards of professional ethics, and confines its conference of membership to established and reputable organizations in the field.

A Modern Management Consulting Firm.

A more specific picture of the management consulting profession can be provided through a brief description of the operating firm, Booz, Allen and Hamilton. The firm has been in existence for almost forty years and is one of several organizations with a similar long history of service to American management. The total organization includes 350 people. Offices are spread throughout the country. The firm renders counsel in the areas of top management, top policy creation and over-all programming, as well as in the various functional areas found in the normal business operation. The firm works for private industry, for institutions, and for government. Among its professional personnel are specialists in sales and marketing, personnel and labor relations, finance and control, manufacturing and production engineers, design and process engineers, men engaged in basic research activities, economists, procedures specialists and many other categories.

As one of the largest, fully integrated firms in the field, Booz, Allen and Hamilton carries a substantial responsibility to lead the way to better management methods. Thus the firm is continuously engaged in major research activity, the objective of which is to seek constantly for better tools and techniques for management's use and to insure that existing tools and techniques are exploited to the fullest advantage of all concerned. The application of operations research techniques to modern industry is high on the list for expanded development today.

The firm's approach, as with all reputable firms in the field, is to deal in the underlying fundamentals of problems, to seek out basic relationships, to analyze them with full and impartial objectivity, and then to attempt to relate these fundamental relationships to the better solution of the business or administrative problem at hand. The accusation that business problems are subjected to " the same old routine packaged solution " developed purely on the basis of experience cannot justly be leveled at any reputable management consulting firm, for impartiality and objectivity are the lifeblood of the profession. Previous experience is always helpful in orientation to a problem, but it is never permitted to obscure new and better solutions.

In view of the fact that objectivity is a prized characteristic of the reputable management consulting firm, it is not surprising that the firm employs many consultants drawn from the ranks of those who have had training or operating experience in the technical and scientific fields. Working side by side with men seasoned in such historical business functions as accounting, marketing, and industrial engineering, are aerodynamicists, thermodynamicists, structural designers, research chemists, and others whose immediate activity in management consulting work is not directly identified with their field of training. Their habitual pattern of searching for the basic relationships and of maintaining complete objectivity of analysis, however, are characteristics which are invaluable in dealing with the business problems with which they are presented.

Assume, momentarily, that the management consulting firm is about to embark on a new assignment. Before any final arrangement is reached, the firm and the client confer to outline the general objective to be sought or to identify the area to be analyzed for improvement. The reputable management consulting firm reserves the right to depart from a particular area of interest if it feels that the solution to problems in that area will be basically affected by factors elsewhere in the operation. The consultant will usually reject assignments if the client does not feel able to allow this freedom. For the management consulting firm and the client to arrive at a mutually acceptable

list of ground rules often takes considerable time, but it is better to
call off proceedings at this stage than to make compromises with principle which will later be sources of difficulty.

Once the problem is defined, the management consulting firm must
quickly swing into action. In business, time means money, and
businessmen are rightfully impatient. The management consultant
usually cannot engage in studies or analyses stretching over a year or
two if, through concentration of effort, a reliable answer can be
achieved in a shorter period of time.

Usually the nucleus of the working team is a full-time group
drawn, according to the talent required, from a general staff pool.
From time to time in the course of an assignment, specialists in one
or another pertinent function will probably join the study team.
But in all cases, the team is specifically tailored to suit the problem.

This, then, is a brief identification of a private, long established,
management consulting firm. Beyond such a brief picture, those outside the profession get very little specific information about the
projects and results of management consulting assignments, for this
is a profession which must resign itself to being a silent service. In
their dealings with the business community, operations research practitioners will find themselves similarly subject to competitive security.
This may prove baffling and frustrating to the traditionally open-
minded scientists, but business lives in a world of intense competition
in which only the fittest survive. The task of the management consultant is to assist executives to sharpen the competitive edge of their
operations; consequently, the results of management consulting work
normally retain a high security classification. Case examples, therefore, must paraphrase the real problems, thus making exchange of
experience across the profession somewhat complicated and tedious.

One interesting problem in which certain operations research techniques proved useful was a problem of airline traffic involving station
operations at an airport. There were three initial indicators of the
problem situation. First, there was a growing suspicion that there
were more people than necessary at work in stations, operating the
counters, ramp services, maintenance services, etc. Second, the passengers were complaining bitterly about the time consumed in getting
out baggage, readying planes, etc. Finally, it was clear that tight
schedules and earlier delays back along the line brought the planes

into a station behind schedule, thus invalidating the carefully developed work schedule at the station.

For several months, Booz, Allen and Hamilton had industrial engineers at work in representative stations along the airline, studying the actual operations, trying to select the best elements of each operation as it was practiced and to standardize a best common procedure for all stations. After such selection, it was possible to turn to industrial engineering standards developed in the traditional industrial engineering manner. Some of the standards developed were entirely different from industrial engineering standards previously used by airlines. For instance, it was learned that it takes three times as long to induce a passenger to board a plane as it takes him to go up the steps and pass through the door, that the problem of baggage handling is not related to weight but to the number of pieces handled, etc.

The next step was to apply these standards to operations, with all of the variables considered. The standards developed were combined into an ideal pattern for the day's work with the equipment then available. When this work load was plotted against the flight schedule, two defects in the work load pattern were immediately obvious. First, only about one-third of the man hours available in the day were worked. Second, the uneven work load required even more men during peaks if the schedules of the airline were to be met as advertised. Figure 1 shows a typical twenty-four hour work load. A slight alteration of flight schedules or certain expansions of ground time, involving lengths of time as short as a few minutes, would result in a substantial drop in the probable peak work load.

But if a beneficial arrival and departure schedule were developed, would the planes come in on schedule and, if not, how much leeway should be allowed? From the operating statistics (which airlines have in large quantities), probability factors were developed concerning schedule delays with variations for the time of year. It was found that, in well over 80 per cent of the delays, the planes arrived only a few minutes late. In other words, if the schedule through a station were opened up by only a few minutes, most of the late planes could be accommodated without overloading the ground crews and thereby exaggerating the schedule delay at the later stations.

Armed with standard times to measure the work on each plane through the station and a forecast of how much flights would vary from the existing printed schedule, the investigators forecast the

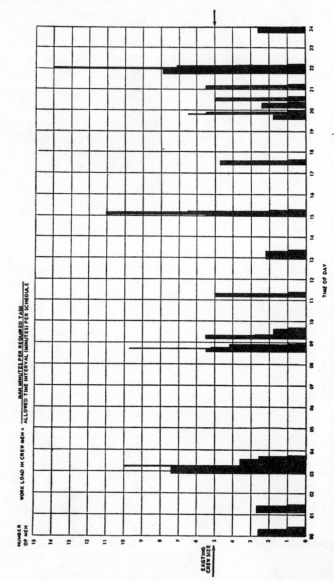

Fig. 1—Workload of an equipment service crew during a typical day at an airport.

$$\text{Number of men (work load)} = \frac{\text{man minutes per required task}}{\text{allowed time interval (minutes) per schedule}}$$

delays which would probably occur at a given station because of flight overlaps and resulting impossible work loads. One of the considerations accommodated by the forecast dealt with the increasing probability that stations on down the line would suffer delays because of trouble at earlier stops. The forecasts matched actual results well enough so that the analysis techniques were supported.

Through the use of these data, the planes could be rescheduled through the stations, the ground work force cut down, and time performance and customer service through the stations greatly improved. The major benefits were achieved by means of only minor schedule modifications, and all with existing equipment and procedures.

While other similar examples could be cited, this one points up an aspect in which management consulting goes beyond many operations researchers. Many of those engaged in operations research have stated that the operations researcher makes no recommendations as to decision, but merely offers organized facts as one basis for decision. Operations research people probably vary in this respect, but the management consultant cannot draw this line. He reviews all the facts, throws in the leaven of human judgment and experience which is necessary, and then " sticks his neck out " with a firm recommendation for action. He goes even farther and assists the executive in implementing the recommendation and observes the results. The management consultant is, therefore, vulnerable every step of the way to being criticized for unsatisfactory results of his work.

Operations Research as a Consulting Service.

With this review of management consulting as a background, one can now examine the new techniques of the operations researcher. The discussion can probably best proceed from the Morse and Kimball definition:

> Operations Research is a scientific method of providing executive departments with a quantitative basis for decisions regarding the operations under their control.[3]

While it can be stated that executive management over the past fifty years has used or been assisted by techniques which can be

[3] George E. Kimball and Philip M. Morse, *Methods of Operations Research* (New York: John Wiley and Sons, and Cambridge, Mass.: The Technology Press, M. I. T., 1951), p. 1.

included under this general definition, it must also be agreed that important and widespread usage of more sophisticated techniques of quantitative analysis of operations received its major emphasis in military operations during World War II.

The leadership of the British under the stimulus coming from Blackett and his group is well known. The effective use of the techniques in antisubmarine operations and air defense has received wide and well-deserved publicity and acclaim. Many of the less dramatic accomplishments during the war have remained relatively unknown, but, in the over-all, they perhaps contributed even more to the winning of the war.

By the end of the war, a fairly sizable and experienced group of scientists had been indoctrinated into the techniques of operations research in military operations, had demonstrated beyond the shadow of a doubt the powerful and effective contribution their techniques could make, and had found themselves in a position to consider the transfer of these techniques and skills to the peacetime world of commerce.

This is not to say that certain of these advanced mathematical techniques had not been used under different names in past years. Usually, however, where use had been made, it was on an isolated basis and centered about an individual who had had previous training in, or at least strong exposure to, the more sophisticated techniques of quantitative analysis, and who himself, by training or inherent mental characteristics, had the detached and objective curiosity which drove him on to see what made things tick.

The quantitative analyses generally used in the industrial engineering field are of a sound and fundamental nature. The tools of analysis, however, are simple compared with the more complex and sophisticated techniques which have proved such a useful lever in the field called operations research. In some respects it might be said that, so far as analysis technique is concerned, operations research begins where industrial engineering has stopped.

Perhaps the most direct way to speak of operations research in relation to other management consulting services is to point up what it has to offer which is new and, also, that which is not new. The failure of some of the early efforts at "selling" operations research to American business can partly be ascribed to a lack of clarity in pointing up these characteristics.

The " sales story " attached to operations research has usually been divided into two parts concerning, first, the conditions which must surround successful application of operations research techniques, and, second, the techniques themselves. In the description of the conditions under which operations research should be performed, considerable emphasis has been placed on the necessity of maintaining contact right at the top level of operations, on the necessity of maintaining a staff position, on the license for free inquiry into all elements of an operation, and on the requirement for extreme objectivity of analysis unswayed by emotional factors. All these are the conditions under which any successful consultant assisting top management must work; they are fundamental to the consulting relationship and have for years been accepted as the starting point for any major consulting effort. It is well and good for operations research to insist on these conditions, but to ask the business executive to accept them as new is only to credit him with extreme naïveté.

The second facet of the " sales story," which has been too often underplayed, concerns the specific techniques. These are truly new to business operations, for operations research recognizes and brings to bear on problems of business operations a more highly developed ability in precise quantitative analysis. Such analysis requires two things: first, the ability to sort out the various activities and factors of any operation and to represent them quantitatively; second, the ability to manipulate these quantities in abstract fashion—aiming at a maximum, minimum, or optimum condition—and then to translate the results back into terms of operating activities and factors once again.

These two skills are interdependent, since one must set up one's measurement of factors in terms which can be accommodated by the means of the analysis manipulation planned. The first requirement, the ability to translate, is far more infrequently found than the ability to manipulate. And this is at the heart of much of the operations research problem.

Unfortunately, competence in these analytical methods and the atmosphere of pure objectivity in which they must be applied is not casually developed as a side line by an individual whose major interests are elsewhere. Therefore, in speaking of these abilities, one must always consider the individuals who will apply the methods. The most valuable minds for operations research are those which, through long training and practice, automatically and almost unconsciously translate the activities in the world about them into curves, parameters, tables, and equations.

This ability parallels that of proficiency in a foreign language. There are many who possess a certain technical proficiency in foreign languages, who can converse or write in that language, working out their thoughts in English and then laboriously transposing them into the other tongue. But the truly competent linguist thinks in the other tongue and entirely abandons his native English as a tool for thought while working in the other medium.

In this same way, the true contribution of operations research to the solution of problems of commerce and industry must rest mainly with people whose minds are so trained and disciplined that they can immediately visualize these complex relationships in a quantitative fashion and then have the tools at their fingertips with which to manipulate and analyze them. Unfortunately, such mental dexterity, often based upon advanced mathematical and physical theory, is not common in the business community.

It is with this contribution of quantitative analysis operating on a higher plane of technical knowledge than is generally available in the mind of the businessman, whose specific training is necessarily in other areas, that operations research brings something vital and new to the American management scene. This is perhaps not a revolution in management technique, but it is certainly a new and powerful tool for analysis, which tool has its limitations and must be used intelligently by the executive. The executive must understand both the uses and limitations of the tool, even though he cannot master the entire technique of analysis.

Problems in Selling Operations Research to Management.

With the foregoing discussion as background, it is interesting to appraise briefly some of the fundamental obstacles confronting operations researchers as they strive to have their science accepted as a first-line analysis tool of management. First, there is the problem of explaining exactly what is done by the operations researcher. This is the primary difficulty of communicating to the businessman the nature of operations research and what it can accomplish. The operations research man who is trying to explain his field to the businessman is beset on either hand by opposite dangers of either not simplifying sufficiently or, conversely, of oversimplifying. The high technical level of quantitative analysis and manipulation inherent in the most advanced applications of operations research is simply not understood by the average American executive, and probably never should be. Therefore, in " selling " operations research, it is essential to translate the explanation of its procedures and its merits into the language of the executive. The immediate postwar heyday in which a scientist could sell his services simply because he was a scientist is happily gone. Today the executive wants to know what he is buying when he contracts for operations research work. While operations research has a perfectly sound story to tell, it is often difficult to make the explanation in terms other than those of mathematics and statistics, which explanations are usually lost upon men who have spent their lives in managerial rather than basic research fields.

A few years back, the writer had such an experience with the president of a large food processing concern. After several of the staff had worked over the company's basic distribution control problems, the suggestion was advanced that the application of what might be termed an hydraulic analogy would be a valid approach. This approach was presented with great clarity from the point of view of the consultants, but in their own idiom. It should not have been expected that the executive, for whose benefit the explanation was being presented, could immediately become educated in the major aspects of hydraulic theory. While he showed interest at the start, as the discussion wore on he became more and more frustrated, finding himself left behind at various turns in the road. Finally he asked why the problem could not be approached in a more normal manner. The entire presentation required a translation into the business tongue.

At the other extreme, in an effort to leap over this gulf between the language of the research man and that of the business executive, there has at times been a tendency to oversimplify the examples of operations research achievements. One such example, immediately identified as trivial by operations research authorities, is that of the dishwashing problem among soldiers on Guam. The story is simply told: first the delay as soldiers washed their mess kits after meals, in four tubs, two for washing and two for rinsing; then the passing operations research worker who noticed it took the average soldier only one-third as long to rinse his kit as to wash it; then, on the next day, the four tubs set up with three for washing and one for rinsing. The line of waiting soldiers disappeared. This was, of course, merely an elementary application of the principles of line flow and station work-loading long observed in industrial engineering, a point completely recognized by people telling the story. This story, however, has been repeated by businessmen with a chuckle, the implication always being that, if this was operations research, there was nothing new in it.

There is no simple solution to this problem. The matter of telling the story of a new technique is always a difficult one, and particularly so in view of the technical content inherent in operations research services. The management consultants have passed through the same problem. It was not solved by the development of a standard description which all professional consultants might use in describing their service. Rather, it was by a growing awareness on the part of both management consultants and businessmen of the areas in which the services were most useful and a broad acquaintance with some of the consulting techniques used. Such an awareness does not develop readily unless there is a consistency in the services being rendered, in the approach to problems, and in the professional standards employed. The establishment of the Operations Research Society is a sound step toward developing such consistency.

A second obstacle to the acceptance of operations research by industry is the presence of quacks and well-meaning incompetents in the field. The drama and glamor of operations research activities during the late war, plus the constructive publicity given these techniques insofar as their potential application to industry is concerned, have made the operations research field an attractive one to enter. Wherever an attractive field so emerges, it draws to it, along with the competent professional practitioner, both the carpetbagger, who looks only to exploiting the opportunity and making off with the spoils, and the half-trained, would-be practitioner whose competence and experience are so fragmentary as to be more dangerous than valuable.

Such people have hurt the operations research field in the immediate postwar years. A 'doctor's degree in some quantitative science, a passing affiliation with some project or organization which might be interpreted as operations research, a brief acquaintance with the terminology, and a certain degree of either courage or foolhardiness have been all that has been necessary to set oneself up as an operations research practitioner. Some of these people have done harm without ever actually undertaking an assignment, since their obvious lack of knowledge and experience has been sufficient basis for the businessman to decide that if these self-anointed consultants are operations research analysts, he wants none of operations research.

The management consulting profession knows well this annoyance. Constant vigil is required to keep the standards of the entire profession high, and it is a constant source of concern that fly-by-night operators are able to get away with as much as they do. There is little to be gained in taking direct action against the half-baked consultant. Rather, it is more effective simply to build up an increasing bank of highly successful assignments, which readily identifies the competent management consultant and winnows out the incompetents.

A third obstacle to the acceptance of operations research might be overcome by the better identification of those situations in which operations research can be helpful. The applications of operations research techniques are most easily made in businesses which operate in big numbers. It is the repetition of the operation, the event, the sale, which enables the operation to be reduced most readily via statistical techniques to quantitative form for analysis purposes. While there are many such possible applications to American industry, they are generally still identified with a minority of American business problems, such as those encountered in public utilities, large service organizations, retailing operations, marketing and distribution systems, and so forth. Unfortunately, some operations research people have not recognized that all business situations and problems are not surrounded by such large numbers. A concentration of effort in selling operations research to those areas where it will be most effective would do much to increase the faith of the business community in this method of approaching commercial problems. In contrast, the more general approach in which the operations research man confronts the executive with the promise, "I practice a new method of dealing with problems which I am certain can help you in your business," can only arouse mistrust.

This naturally leads into a fourth obstacle which operations research must hurdle, namely the lack of commercial and business knowledge on the part of the average operations research analyst. The analyst, in order to be successful in his dealings with industry, should develop enough of an affinity with management philosophy and methods to talk intelligently and freely with the business executive. The operations research man may ask himself what being able to analyze a balance sheet has to do with operations research; but the businessman may well wonder how an operations research man who can't even understand a balance sheet can expect to offer any help in business operations. The operations research analyst should, to be most effective, be able to speak both languages.

There are two good ways for the operations researcher to get this knowledge of business and industry worked into his portfolio. The first is to go out and work with the business community until he has absorbed the necessary experience and knowledge. The second is to identify himself with organizations, agencies or professions which already have a strong tie with the business community and are experienced in working with the businessman.

Conclusion.

With its advanced techniques of quantitative analysis, operations research has much to offer the business community as a member of the family of consulting services. Before full advantage can be derived from the new techniques, however, both operations research and business must learn more about each other. In this process of establishing acquaintance, the burden of effort will necessarily fall upon operations research as the newer party. Operations research can make this effort from firmer ground if it clearly evaluates itself as part of the grand design of industrial consulting. This balanced view should provide a double advantage. First, it serves to associate operations research with the group of accepted professional consultants with whom businessmen are already familiar. Second, within this consulting family, operations research can more clearly point up the advanced methods of quantitative analysis which distinguish it from the other management tools of American business and industry.

PART II

Methodology

Progress in
Operations Research

PHILIP M. MORSE

THE PRECEDING discussions, outlining the development and general provenance of operations research, bring us back again to the original question: What is operations research? The reader has now enough background to appreciate that a simple answer is not possible and, indeed, that a complete answer is also not possible, no matter how much detail is permitted. On the basis of the earlier chapters, however, a number of comments may be made here, which will perhaps serve as a partial answer and which will serve to introduce the next section of this volume.

Characteristics of Operations Research.

In the first place, operations research is a variety of *research*. Word usage of more than a half-century has distinguished between research and other technological activities, such as engineering, by implying that research is aimed more at *understanding* than toward immediate practical utility. Experience of several centuries also has made clear that such an understanding is necessary before large dividends in useful applications can be expected. Parenthetically it should be pointed out that the word "understanding" has rather specialized connotations when used in scientific discussion. Much has recently been written on the difference between the scientific use of the word "understanding" and its usual meaning, on the role of hypothesis and of mathematics in scientific understanding, and on the active, pragmatic point of view which is implied.

Operations research, then, is concerned with an attempt to understand something, in the scientific sense of the word understanding. It is an effort to discover regularities in some phenomenon and to link these regularities with other knowledge so that the phenomenon can be modified or controlled, just as other scientific research does. The difference comes in the phenomena which are studied, the subject matter. Instead of studying the behavior of electrons or metals or gasoline engines or insects or individual men, operations research looks at what goes on when some team of men and equipment goes about doing its assigned job. A battalion of soldiers, a squadron of planes, a factory, or a sales organization is more than a collection of men and machines; it is an activity, a pattern of operation. These operations can be studied; their regularities can be determined and related to other regularities; they can eventually be understood, and they then can be modified and improved.

Operations research is concerned not with matter or with individual machines or with men, but with the operation as a whole; with battle tactics, with strategic and logistic planning for future operations, with the interrelation between sales fluctuations, size of inventories and production scheduling, with the flow pattern of goods in a group of factories or of traffic in a city, to mention a few examples. We might use the word "level" to distinguish between the different subject material, if we can divorce the word from any connotation of relative importance or difficulty. Physics and chemistry would then correspond to research at the basic or material level, the study of bridges and television sets, to research at the engineering or applied level. Operations research would then be *research at the operational level*.

Although the name is relatively new, research at the operational level is not new, of course. Taylor and his followers, in their time-and-motion studies, have investigated a small part of the whole field; traffic engineers have been working on another part; systems engineers encroach on it, and so on. Perhaps the most useful service the new term "operations research" has performed is to emphasize the essential unity of the whole field, to force the recognition of similarities in behavior in areas hitherto separate, and to make apparent the broad usefulness of a number of research techniques and mathematical models.

As with any research, the development of understanding of the subject matter is intimately bound up in the *techniques* of investigation used. The understanding, of course, is the important thing; to obtain it one uses any technique of measurement or of calculation, any portion of a basic science which will produce results. We should expect that the techniques of the theory of probability and of statistics would be very useful tools; we should also expect that the techniques of the psychologist would be needed in other cases. This does not mean that operations research is applied statistics on the one hand or is a branch of social psychology on the other. It uses any and all of these disciplines to study *operations*, in order that they may be understood and thus controlled. Since a wide variety of basic science is involved, much of the research can best be carried on by a team of workers having a variety of background training, each contributing his specialized knowledge to the solution of the operational problem. The advantage of a mixed team for the study of many operational problems is obvious. In fact some persons have said that the use of mixed research teams is a characteristic of operations research. It certainly is important in many investigations; whether it is characteristic or necessary might be questioned.

Though the techniques are less important than the understanding, nevertheless it is worth while studying the techniques. In fact it is a sort of " hen or egg " argument as to which comes first, new technique or new understanding. New areas of understanding have always been opened up, in basic sciences, by the perfection of a new research technique, either observational or theoretical. In a new field, such as operations research, the development of research techniques may well appear to be more studied and discussed than is the basic accumulation of understanding; this is chiefly because the understanding is as yet scanty and fragmentary. It is not necessarily an unhealthy development, as long as most workers keep clearly in mind that methodology is but a means to the sought-for understanding.

At any rate, much of the rest of this volume will be devoted to discussions of techniques of operations research. Many of them will be mathematical techniques which have been found useful in some area of the field; sometimes they are called mathematical models. They represent the only scientifically fruitful type of *analogy*, the quantitative analogy. There is a close quantitative similarity, for example, between the behavior of bodies in a gravitational field and that of charges in an electric field, which is represented by the mathematical model called potential theory. Once the model is shown to hold in a new area, mathematical manipulation will suggest further possible characteristics to investigate and will thus rapidly increase our understanding of the new area. Mathematical models have been a powerful tool in the physical sciences.

A few such mathematical models, which have been found useful in operations research, will be sketched here in order to illustrate the general statements of the last several paragraphs, in spite of the fact that some of the examples are discussed in more detail, from a different point of view, in later chapters.

Queueing Theory.

For example, in many operations there is a lack of timing between the arrival, at some point in the operation, of a sequence of units, and the subsequent disposal of these units, so that a waiting line or queue is formed of newly arrived units awaiting disposal. Aircraft arrive at an airport and must circle in the air in what is often called a *stack*, to await their turn to land. Automobiles come to a traffic signal and must wait for the green light. Parts in a production line pile up in front of an inspector or a machine which is to do further work on them. People wait in line at a cafeteria and ships wait in harbor for a dock. This is a typical operational situation; the specialized methods for its analysis are coming to be called *waiting-line* or *queueing theory*.

In most of the cases encountered, the units arrive at a random rate in time; in many cases they are also serviced, or disposed of, randomly. If the mean arrival rate is greater than the mean service rate, it is obvious that the waiting line will increase indefinitely. But even if the mean service rate is larger than the mean arrival rate, the waiting line is not abolished unless both arrivals and service operations are regularized, not random. A central problem of waiting-line theory is the relationship between the mean length of waiting line and the degree of randomness of arrival and disposal. On it can be based estimates of the optimum capacity of the servicing facilities when one balances the cost of letting the unit wait in line against the cost of increasing the service rate.

A waiting line is characterized by the probabilities P_n that, at any given time, zero, one, two or n units will be waiting in the line. When another unit arrives, the line increases by one; when one is disposed of, taken from the line, it decreases by one. If service rate is larger than arrival rate, the line can reach an average equilibrium; when this has happened, these probabilities will be constant and equations can be set up to represent the balance of arrivals and disposals. For the very simplest waiting line, with one service exit, when both arrivals and service departures are purely random (according to the Poisson distribution) the values of these probabilities assume particularly simple forms. Thus it may be shown that the chance of having n units in the waiting line turns out to be $P_n = (A/S)^n[1-(A/S)]$ where A is the mean arrival rate and S the mean disposal or service rate (assumed larger than A). We see that, if S is twice as large as A, then P_n decreases rapidly with increasing n; the chance of finding a long line is quite small. But if A is nearly as large as S, then P_n diminishes very slowly with n. The mean length of line L is $A/(S-A)$, which goes to infinity as A approaches the value of S.

Having made these calculations, we can proceed to apply them to a specific operational problem by first determining whether arrival and service are, in fact, at random. For example, the arrivals and dockings of ships in harbor seem to be close enough to random to apply the theory, unless ships are routed in convoys; aircraft arriving at an airport come at random unless especial efforts are made to adjust their speeds during the half-hour preceding their arrival.

Next, one has to compare the cost of having n units waiting in line against the cost of increasing the service rate S. If the ratio of A to S is small, there is no great amount of time lost, but if the facility gets popular and A begins to approach S, the waiting line increases rapidly in length, and money must be spent to increase S or an effort must be made to reduce or to schedule arrivals. Administrators not familiar with waiting-line theory can make wrong decisions, with serious consequences, in such cases. Not so long ago, a shipping firm noticed that one port was somewhat more efficient than two others and decided to route all its ships to the one port. This had the effect of increasing the mean arrival rate up to 0.9 of the service rate for that port, and of increasing the mean waiting time threefold. Management misinterpreted the resulting considerable delay, attributing it to a sudden decrease in efficiency of the chosen port. When the theory was worked out, it was apparent that the increased delay was due to the increase in A, not to a decrease in S, and that the diversion of a few ships to the less efficient ports would reduce the waiting line considerably. In other words, a small use of the less efficient ports would produce the best overall results. Subsequent experience bore out the predictions.

In the case of aircraft stacking over airports, in bad weather when landings take time, it was hoped that careful scheduling of aircraft arrivals would materially reduce the line. Computing the effect on the waiting line of changes of randomness in arrivals and landings is a difficult mathematical problem. Preliminary analysis indicates that, if arrivals are completely regular, each a time $(1/A)$ after the next previous, but if servicing is still purely random, then the mean queue length is about half that previously mentioned for the case of both arrival and service random. The actual case of aircraft stacking, however, is still more difficult of analysis, for both arrivals and landings are " partially random " in the cases where scheduling of flights and landings is attempted. No matter how hard they try to stick to schedule, some randomness creeps in.

To solve this problem, a procedure known as the Monte Carlo technique was employed. By the use of a table of random numbers and of empirically determined probability distributions for scheduled and non-scheduled arrivals and for landings, a whole series of virtual arrivals and landings, which would have the same statistical properties as actual plane arrivals and landings, could be worked out on a high-speed computing machine. Instead of using planes and landing strips to get the figures, the electronic computer could be used to reproduce the essential elements of the problem and thousands of cases could be run off in a short time. The results do not have the elegance or generality of an analytic solution but they have the advantage of being numerical answers corresponding to the case of interest. They give, in an afternoon, data equivalent to several years of counting and timing at an actual airport.

Analyses of these Monte Carlo calculations indicate a small reduction of queue length with improvement in scheduling arrivals. Finally, it is then possible to find out whether any practicable procedure for tight scheduling of plane arrivals would or would not cost more than would be gained by the calculated reduction of delay time.

Perhaps by now the parallelism between the study of waiting lines and the study of some physical phenomenon is apparent. In both cases, one abstracts from the complexities of the specific case the typical aspects which are to be correlated with some mathematical model. From the model, the hypothesis which one fits to the data, one can learn the interdependence of these aspects and can begin to understand the phenomenon. At first the model is very crude, including only the few most outstanding aspects, but, as understanding grows, the model can be complicated to the extent needed to work out cases of practical interest. In neither physics nor operations research is the research a purely statistical hunt for correlations, by taking data and calculating cross-correlations or using the chi-squared rule. Observation and hypothetical model-making go hand in hand. As pointed out in many recent books on the scientific method, there is a very close relationship between the progression from tentative hypothesis to final theory and the growth of what we are calling scientific understanding.

But just as it is important to extend the scope of the raw data by the quantitative analogies of a mathematical model, so also it is necessary, for our increased understanding of an operation, to go back from theory to observation and, as soon as possible, to controlled experiment. On page 145 is discussed a mathematical model of a line of automobiles starting up when a traffic light turns green.[1] This model has been based on initial observation of actual behavior; by its means one is able to analyse some of the behavior of traffic at an intersection and thus to suggest improvements in the operation (such as modification of timing of red, yellow, and green lights, for example).

But this initial use of a mathematical model is but the first of a converging sequence in our steps toward understanding the operation of traffic flow. One must next observe, by changing light timing or other parameters, over how wide a range of these parameters the actual operation corresponds to the model. The next question will be why the model fails (if it does) beyond these ranges. To answer this will require more detailed operational experiments, perhaps involving teams of drivers working in a specially laid-out area, with timing equipment for each car and so on. The results of these true operational experiments will suggest further elaborations of the mathematical model, which, when checked against uncontrolled traffic behavior, will yield still deeper understanding of the nature of the interaction between cars, drivers and traffic controls, and so on. Each step in the sequence of observation-theory-experiment-theory will un-

---

[1] See also P. M. Morse, "Operations Research, What Is It?" *Journal of Applied Physics*, Vol. 23, No. 2 (February 1952).

doubtedly increase our ability to control the operation; the deeper the understanding, the greater the degree of control. As yet, we have only begun the sequence in a few simple operations. To say its continuation will help us make these and other operations more effective is a hope rather than a certainty; all we can say is that increased understanding has won analogous rewards in countless other cases.

Linear Programming.

Another sort of problem which turns up in a large number of operational studies has to do with the optimization of some function of a number of variables, subject to boundary conditions which limit the variables' range. For example, an oil company can produce various proportions of fuel oil, gasoline, and aviation fuel from their cracking plants, depending on the kind of crude oil they use, and can produce various proportions of these end products from a given crude, depending on the cracking process used. But crudes differ in price and cracking processes differ in cost. Suppose the company has orders for definite quantities of end products to be delivered in the next three months. What amounts of which crude shall it buy, and which processes shall it use in its cracking plants, to produce the required amounts of products at the least cost, subject to limitations of supply of crudes and of output of their plants?

The variables here are the various amounts of crudes to be bought and the degree of utilization of each plant. The function to be minimized is a linear function of these variables and the limits on each variable are accurately known. Such a problem is known as a *linear programming* problem. There are many such problems which turn up in operations research. Techniques of solution are not simple and many of them require high-speed computing machines; much further mathematical research is needed to simplify computing procedures in linear programming calculations. Further and more detailed discussion of some aspects are given on pages 217-37.

Parenthetically, the optimization of the crude-oil-cracking problem has been worked out by the research or the engineering departments of many large oil companies. The persons who worked out those solutions did not call what they were doing operations research; many of them had not heard of operations research. It is also true, however, that most of these workers were not aware that many other problems in the company's operations were also amenable to the same analysis. The value of the concept of operations research to these companies lies in making their research men aware that the techniques of theoretical analysis they have been using can be applied to a much wider range of operational problems than they had hitherto conceived, and in showing the company executives that they can use their own research departments to help solve production and sales and distribution problems, where they had not hitherto been used.

The linear programming problem can be visualized most simply in geometrical terms. The n variables define an n-dimensional space; a point of this space corresponds to a solution. Each limitation on the range of the variables corresponds to a hyperplane in this space, restricting the allowed solution points to one side of the hyperplane. By the time we have finished specifying all the restrictions (negative production not allowed, maximum limits on storage capacity, limits on production, and so on) we find we have surrounded the region of possible solution by hypersurfaces, so that the allowed region is the interior of a convex polyhedron in the hyperspace. If the function to be optimized is a linear function of the variables, then the requirement that this function have some constant value also corresponds to a hyperplane which may or may not cut through the polyhedron; if it does, it then corresponds to an operationally possible value of the function to be optimized. By changing the value of the constant, we can generate a family of hyperplanes parallel to each other, their distance from the origin being proportional to the value of the function to be optimized.

Some of the hyperplanes in this family cut through the polyhedron containing the region of solution; some do not. There are two limiting hyperplanes, one corresponding to the largest value of the function for which the hyperplane just touches the polyhedron, and one corresponding to the smallest value which just touches. Consideration of the geometry shows that for most orientations of the family of planes the two limiting planes just touch a vertex of the bounding polyhedron and thus contain just one possible solution compatible with all the boundary conditions. The outermost limiting point is the optimum solution if the function is to be maximized; the innermost point is optimum if the function is to be minimized. Once the geometry is clear in one's mind, it is easy to visualize the solution. But, at present, it is not easy actually to compute the optimum vertex when there are several dozen variables and about a hundred boundary faces of the polyhedron.

Important as linear programming techniques are, they need further generalization to be able to solve many problems in operations research. Production planning is an example. A factory can produce so many units of some product each month, but sales of the product are small during the summer and very large in December, so large that fall production cannot equal December sales. One solution is to run the factory overtime during the fall; but overtime production costs more than normal output. Another solution is to produce more during spring and summer and store it ready for the winter rush; but warehousing also costs money, in storage and handling charges and in interest on the money tied up. A third solution of course is to fail to meet orders in December, but this is a counsel of despair.

It should be evident by now that this is also a linear programming problem. The variables are the regular production each month and the overtime production each month. The excess of production over sales each month is warehoused. The boundary conditions are the limits on the production and overtime production each month and the additional requirement that the total production from the first of the year shall never be less than total sales from the first of the year. The quantity to be minimized is the total cost, including overtime charges and warehousing charges.

As stated, this is a straightforward linear programming problem, *if* we can predict exactly our sales throughout the coming year. If our sales forecast is exact, we can proceed to find the distribution of production and overtime production each month to minimize total costs and to satisfy all forecast sales. The trouble is that we never know exactly what the sales are going to be, and, if we have underestimated them, we shall not be able to meet orders; if we have overestimated them, we shall end the year with unsold products in our warehouse. All we really have is a probability distribution of expected sales; to put it pictorially, some of the sides of the bounding polygon are fuzzy, not sharp.

At present, our techniques of solution are not adequate for such problems, nor are they if the function to be optimized is not a linear function of the variables. Such more general problems might be called problems of *bounded optimization*. The problems are clear but a great deal of further analysis and devising of computational techniques is needed before solutions can be obtained with the requisite ease. Speed of solution is needed here, for in many cases we wish to find a whole sequence of solutions as we vary some of the limits: what happens if we build another factory, or if we close down our factory in August, for example? When solutions of problems of bounded optimization are easy to obtain, many tough problems of planning of production, of sales effort, of logistics, and so on will be easier to solve.

Game Theory.

Another field of investigation in operations research, of more interest so far in military applications than in industrial applications, is the study of the competition between two opponents. The mathematical model used here is the newly developed *game theory*, initiated less than twenty years ago by Von Neumann. It will be discussed in detail on pages 238 *et seq.* In this mathematical model the elements of competition, as evidenced in a game of cards, for example, are reduced to their simplest elements. The elementary concepts for the simplest, two-person game are that what one side gains the other side loses, that the opponents simultaneously choose a course of action (called a strategy), and that the outcome of the game (the payment of one side to the other) is determined by this dual choice of strategies. The outcome is not completely determined by either side alone; it is determined by the combined decisions of the two opposed players. This is, of course, the essence of actual games.

Analysis of the very simplest of games shows that there are two general kinds, which may be illustrated by two kinds of coin matching. In the first case the choice is between a penny or a nickel to match; if both coins are the same, it's a stand-off; if the coins differ, the penny takes the nickel. In this game it is always safest for either player to play a penny, for then he never loses, whereas if he plays a nickel, he may lose a nickel. Such games, where each opponent will find it safest always to stick to one strategy, are called *single-strategy* games. They are not very interesting as games and are not often played, though analogous situations sometimes occur in warfare.

The second general type of game may be illustrated by the usual penny matching, in which each player chooses heads or tails; if the coins match, the matcher wins; if they do not match, the matchee wins. In this case, if either player sticks to one strategy, he may consistently lose. If, for example, the matcher decides to play heads continuously, then the matchee, when he finds this out, can consistently play tails and win every time. As a matter of fact, any predetermined pattern of successive strategies (such as alternately playing heads and tails, for instance) could conceivably be foreseen by a clever opponent and countered, so that the losses would be continuous. The *only safe way* to play this game, therefore, is to play heads or tails in a completely random manner, as for instance by flipping the penny in the air just before one plays it. This is usually done in actual penny matching. It is interesting to see that it is *not* done to make the game fairer, but to protect each player from a too-clever opponent. Such games are called games of *mixed strategy*.

Of course, most games have more than two different choices of strategy for each player. The simple game called scissors-paper-stone has three choices; the game of tic-tac-toe has dozens of possible alternatives and checkers has thousands of possible strategies. In principle, once each player has chosen one of the sets of strategies available to him, it is possible to calculate the probable outcome of the game. The net pay-offs can thus be arranged in a two-dimensional schedule; two by two for penny matching, 80 by 70 (approximately) for tic-tac-toe and thousands on a side for checkers. From the schedule we can find whether the game is a single or a mixed strategy one and, if mixed, in what proportions to mix the playing to confuse the opponent most effectively.

As usual with mathematical models, most actual games are too complicated for the theory to analyze in detail as yet. Nevertheless, some of the crucial elements in many games may be clarified by studying simplified models. For example, in games of mixed strategy, bluff and counterbluff may enter. A simplified poker game can be analyzed in which it turns out to be advantageous to bluff occasionally on a poor hand and for the opponent occasionally to call a bet when he does not have a winning hand. From the pay-off charts, giving the amounts of losses or winnings for each choice of strategies of the players, it is possible to calculate the relative frequency with which bluff or counterbluff should be employed.

It should be obvious that game theory is basic to many situations in battle. In fact, game theory was used by operations research groups during the war to work out tactics, such as those to be used by a submarine in avoiding a searching aircraft (when to dive and when to surface and run for it) and also in the tactics to be used in an air engagement between a bomber and an opposing fighter.

In particular, the timing of the gunfire duel between fighter pilot and tail gunner of the bomber, as the fighter closes in for the kill, is a good example of what has been called *the duel problem*. If the fighter, for example, fires his rounds too early, he has a greater chance of missing, and he may be out of shells or rockets by the time he gets in close. If, on the other hand, he waits to fire till he gets in close, the tail gunner may shoot him down before he fires a round. Once the relative accuracy of the opposing guns, the vulnerability of the planes, and the number of available rounds are known, it is possible to use game theory to calculate the best range at which to commence firing and the probability that fighter or bomber will be shot down. These probabilities turned out to check fairly closely with the results of actual air duels in World War II, whereas the results computed without the use of game theory gave erroneous values and prescribed unsafe tactics. Both the submarine search and the duel problem are examples of games with a continuous range of possible strategies; these games are, in general, much more difficult to solve than those with only a small number of alternative strategies available for each opponent.

It should not be hard to see that game theory also has its applications in business. It has been used, to some extent, in deciding on the timing of an advertising campaign, when several companies are competing for the same market. Curiously enough, the solutions of game theory problems involving mixed strategies are closely related to solutions of linear programming problems; but there isn't space to go into these interesting interrelations here.

Optimum Distribution of Effort.

One more example of a field of investigation of current interest in operations research will have to suffice. It started, during the war, in connection with problems of naval operations, as a theory of search. Since the war its applications in a number of industrial cases led me to call it the theory of the *optimum distribution of effort*. Its naval aspect concerns the operation of search for an enemy vessel, or submarine or aircraft. The enemy is somewhere in a given area of the sea. How do you deploy your aircraft to find him? The connection between the mathematical model and the actual operation is the *rate of search.* A single plane can see the enemy vessel (by radar or sonar or visually as the case may be) R miles away, on the average. The plane can " sweep " out a band of width $2R$ as it moves along; the picture is analogous to a vacuum cleaner, of width $2R$, sweeping over the ocean at a rate equal to the speed of the plane and picking up whatever comes beneath it. An area equal to the speed of the plane times twice the mean range of detection will thus be swept in an hour. The sweep rates of planes vary from a few hundred square miles per hour to several thousand square miles per hour, depending on the plane, the radar equipment and the vessel searched for.

If the enemy is equally likely to be anywhere within a certain area, then the problem is a straightforward, geometrical one. The search effort is evenly laid out over as much of the area as one has planes available. The problem is a little complicated by the fact that detection is not certain at extreme ranges, so the probability of detection falls off near the edge of the swept band, and there should be a certain amount of overlap between bands to improve the chance of detection near the edges.

But if the chance that the enemy is present varies from area to area, the problem becomes quite difficult; non-mathematical intuition may lead to quite erroneous use of available effort. For example, if the enemy is twice as likely to be in one area as in another, then, if only a small amount of search effort is possible, all this effort should be spent in searching the more likely area; if more effort is available, some time can be spent on the less likely area and so on. A definite formula can be worked out in each specific case. Search plans for various contingencies were worked out by the operations research team attached to the Navy during the war; they materially aided the naval efforts in many cases.

It seems a far cry from planes and ships and submarines to industry and business activities. But the utility of the mathematical models is their wide range of applicability. One possible business application of search theory comes in the problem of assignment of sales effort. Suppose a business has a limited number of salesmen, who are to cover a wide variety of dealers. Some of these dealers are large stores, which will usually produce large orders when visited; some are small stores with correspondingly smaller sales return. If there are enough salesmen, every dealer can be visited every month and the optimum number of sales can be made, although the sales cost will be high. With fewer salesmen available, search theory indicates that the large stores should be visited more often than the small stores; with very few salesmen it may be that only the large stores should be visited. If the probable return per visit for each store is known, the optimum distribution of sales effort can then be calculated.

An interesting and typical variation on this problem comes when we consider the action of the individual salesmen, when we try to make his behavior conform to the best overall distribution for the company. For each individual salesman, with his limited effort, it may be best *for him* to visit only the large stores; if his visits are uncontrolled and if he is paid a flat commission, it may turn out that the large stores are visited too often, the small stores too seldom, for best returns *for the company as a whole*. It then becomes necessary to work out a system of incentive commissions designed to induce the salesmen to spread their efforts more evenly between large and small customers. If the general theory has been worked out, this additional complication can be added without too much difficulty.

This problem of balancing the tendencies of different parts of a large organization is one which is often encountered in industrial operations research. The sales force is out to increase sales of all items, though some items may return less profit than others; production resists change-over to making another product, though sales on the other product are increasing; and the financial department frowns on building up large inventories, though small inventories always put the production division at the mercy of sales fluctuations. It is often not too difficult to suboptimize each of these divisions separately, so each is running smoothly and effectively as far as its own part of the business is concerned. But to be sure that all these parts mesh together to make the company as a whole operate most efficiently requires much more subtle analysis and very careful quantitative balancing.

In the interest of reducing factory overtime and to keep down inventory, for example, it may be necessary to modify the salesman's incentive commissions, so he will be induced to push one line over another. It may be necessary for the production division to allow more overtime in one department than another, to make some part of its operation run at less than optimum in order that the overall operation be optimum; and one must take care not to penalize the production department, by reduced bonuses or the like, in reducing its efficiency so that the effectiveness of the whole is improved. Solutions of company-wide problems of this sort require all of the techniques of operations research and then some. They are not ones for a newly-formed operations research team to try at first; but they are problems to head toward. If the team can be of even the smallest help to the top executive in solving such company-wide problems, they will have paid their way many times over.

The Need for New Techniques.

These few examples will indicate the nature of the mathematical models which are being devised to help us understand operations, which bring out their underlying similarities and differences and which enable us to condense masses of observational data into compact equations. Other examples will be given in later chapters. More such models are being devised continually; one reads of the theory of value, of applications of communication theory and so on. Many of these models utilize branches of mathematics unfamiliar to physical scientists; this is not surprising, considering the difference in subject matter. Undoubtedly such fields as symbolic logic, other branches of modern algebra, and topology will be called on to help build models to fit various situations. As with game theory, new mathematical techniques will have to be devised.

There needs to be a similar development in experimental techniques before operations research can be said to have reached maturity. At present, we are engrossed in making the first step from crude observation to simple theory, and mathematical model-making has the center of attention. But soon we must refine these models, if deeper understanding is to be attained, and this can only be done by the thoroughgoing use of controlled operational experiments, set up to simulate the actual operation, with all its human and mechanical parts, but instrumented in detail and so controlled as to be reproducible in its major aspects. Here much remains to be done. Some of the techniques devised by modern experimental psychologists will be of value.

In some cases, where human reaction is a minor effect and where "random processes" control the operation, it may be possible to dispense with the actual men and machines and perform the operational experiment on specially-built analogue computers, as was indicated in the example of the plane landings, given on page 104. This use of analogue computers, particularly ones with random elements "built in," should be capable of a wide extension. Random input devices, utilizing radioactive sources or built-in random-number-generators, can be added to digital computers to duplicate waiting lines of any complexity, and many other operations.

"Simplified gaming" furnishes another means of operational experiment. Sometimes it is not sufficient to provide the random processes and then just compute the consequences; human judgment or human competition may also enter. In this case we may simplify the operation down to a specialized game (two-person or solitaire as the case may be) with the random events and other rules devised to provide a close analogue with the actual operation. By observing a reasonably intelligent person learning to play such a game we can often learn a great deal about an actual operation that is far too complicated to be analyzed by theoretical means.

During the war several antisubmarine air-search tactics were worked out by this means. The rules for the submarine player allowed him so many hours submergence, during which he could not be seen by the air player and during which he could see the plane only a short distance away; when he was on the surface he could be seen by the plane, of course, and was attacked unless he submerged in time; and so on. We worked up a gadget, with electrical contacts to conform to these rules of sighting, so that the submarine player and the air player could each chart his course unseen by the other. For several weeks the men in our group played dozens of games on this device. Within these few weeks we learned more about the more complicated problems of submarine search than six months of analytic work had taught us. Search theory could work out the simple cases well enough; the complex cases, when there were not enough planes, or when delays occurred in starting the search, had to be worked out by gaming.

Perhaps we can call this combination of Monte Carlo, analogue device, and human competition the "gaming technique" or the "simulated operational experiment." (This technique should not be confused with *game theory*, of course). It seems to me that a bit of ingenuity will often make it possible to use such a technique to analyze a complex operation, particularly if parts of the operation involve judgment on the part of the operators. In a sense the very interesting experiments of Bavelas [2] on communication patterns in

[2] Alex Bavelas, "Communication Patterns in Task-Oriented Groups," *Journal of the Acoustical Society of America*, Vol. 22, No. 6 (November 1950).

task-oriented groups are really operational experiments concerned with command structure of this simulated sort. I believe that various adaptations of the gaming technique will provide operations research with very powerful tools of investigation. Their range of use, and their techniques of application, should be intensively explored.

Operations Research and the Executive.

By this time you may have gotten the idea that operations research is going to make the executive obsolete, that the general manager or the general or the admiral is going to be replaced by a bespectacled operator of an oversized electronic computer. Far from it: I should remind you again that " research " is a part of the title and that research is concerned with understanding, not deciding. Having had some experience in management as well as in research, I can say that the process of management is inimical to the process of research. I don't mean that the two must be opposed in aims, but I do mean that when a person is bossing an outfit he can't be doing research, and vice versa. Consequently, I am convinced that the operations research team can never replace the executive and at the same time continue to do operations research. On the other hand, an executive and an operations research team can make a most potent combination, the team foreseeing the problems and providing the factual background for decision (which must usually leave out some aspects of politics or personalities or morale), the executive adding his experience and intuition to reach the necessary decision (which must always be to some extent arbitrary). Such close partnership between executive officers and their operations research teams is now the usual pattern in our military forces. It is being tried with success in a number of large industrial concerns; perhaps it will become the usual pattern here also.

Statistics in Operations Research
and Operations Research in Statistics

RUSSELL L. ACKOFF

I T IS scarcely necessary to urge those engaged in operations research to use mathematics and probability theory in their work.[1] These tools are already extensively employed, for the obvious reason that most practitioners of operations research have come from the fields of mathematics and the pure and applied physical sciences. The training of physical scientists almost invariably involves their extensive exposure to mathematics and probability theory, and both are constantly used in scientific work. But such training seldom involves any contact with mathematical statistics and the theory of statistical inference. As a result, although physical scientists are highly sophisticated in the construction of mathematical and probability models, that is, in providing a mathematical conceptualization of a problem area, they are usually naïve in their methods of gathering and analyzing data. In general, they still have recourse to statistical methods which were in use a century ago, despite the fact that the field of statistics has developed more since 1900 than in its entire previous history. Recently, W. Edwards Deming, one of the most eminent American statisticians, remarked that a scientist using the same statistical procedures that he was using *five* years ago was behind the times.

The reverse situation prevails in the human sciences. Those

---

[1] See the author's article "Some New Statistical Techniques Applicable to Operations Research," *Journal of the Operations Research Society of America*, Vol. I, No. 1 (November 1952), pp. 10-17.

working in the human science fields seldom are familiar with mathematics and probability theory; in general, however, they use, or are at least aware of, modern statistical methods. Consequently, the human sciences are less advanced than the physical sciences in their mathematical conceptualization of problem areas, but more advanced in the gathering and analysis of data.

Mathematical Statistics in Operations Research.

Committed as it is to the interdisciplinary approach to problems, operations research will be handicapped in its procedures and less comprehensive in its analyses if it has a deficiency either in mathematics and probability theory on the one hand or in mathematical statistics on the other. So long as the majority of operations research practitioners continue to come from mathematics and physical science backgrounds, there is little danger of the former deficiency. There is, however, a great danger of the latter, since mathematical statisticians have not become involved in operations research in such numbers as have mathematicians, and since operations research has drawn more heavily on representatives of the physical than of the human sciences. It is important for the future of operations research that its mathematical statistics be kept up to date and up to standard.

In most operations research problems, either a mathematical (certainty) model or a probability (uncertainty) model is constructed to represent the process, system, or set of operations under study. Such a model provides a quantitative conceptualization of the problem and a basis for an *abstract* or *ideal* solution. With the help of mathematical methods, it is frequently possible to find the value(s) of the manipulation or control variable(s) (i. e., the variables which can be controlled by manipulation) in the process that optimizes the outcome of the process. Such an optimization is abstract or ideal because it involves other (independent) variables, some of whose values are not known. The practical phase of the research consists, to a large extent, in obtaining estimates of these other independent variables, which represent a property of the components of the process, of their behavior, or of the process-environment. Research or experimentation is usually required before estimates of their values can be obtained.

For example, it is possible to define the number of parts of a machine which should be manufactured per unit of time as a function of the production costs, inventory costs, and demand. In one such instance, it was found that the total annual cost of producing parts of a machine was at a minimum where the number of runs scheduled, n, was defined as follows:

$$n = 12 \sqrt{\frac{C_2 LP}{C_1 (2 - P)}}$$

where $C_1 =$ set-up and take-down cost of a production run;

$C_2 =$ cost of material and of labor used in converting material;

$P =$ inventory rate per month as a function of dollars invested in parts;

$L =$ number of parts required per month.

The equation is an ideal solution; it provides a real solution only when the values of C_1, C_2, P, and L are known or can be estimated *with measurable error*. The values of these variables change over time. Therefore, one would want to use their average values. In most actual situations, it is impractical or impossible to determine, for example, the set-up cost for each past production run of the machine part. Therefore, a *sample* of past runs must be selected and an *estimate* of the average set-up cost derived.[2] It is at this stage that statistics is brought into play.

To state the problem more generally, whenever it is useful to determine a characteristic of a population of items or events where it is impossible or impracticable to determine the value of each member or instance of that class, the methods of mathematical statistics should be employed. The research design problems in such a situation are:

1. How should a subset of the total population be selected and how large a subset should be selected?

2. How should inferences be drawn from the characteristics of the subset to the characteristics of the population as a whole?

The first of these questions involves the theory and methods of sampling. The second involves the theory and methods of estimation or

---

[2] It is also necessary to determine whether the population whose characteristic is being estimated is in a state of statistical control, i. e., whether the parameters of the population have remained constant. If not, an average is meaningless, and more complex methods involving trend analysis may be necessary.

the theory and methods of testing hypotheses. There is available a considerable body of statistical methods and techniques which have been developed, but these are generally not part of the working knowledge of scientists who have not been trained in statistics. In operations research, of course, it is not necessary for any one person to know everything essential to the solution of problems, since the study team and its consultants should, among them, bring to bear the various kinds of knowledge needed for the development of a solution. Nevertheless, it is important that each member of the team have some conception of what tools are available and of the areas where each is useful.

For example, an operations research practitioner should at least be familiar with the following sampling methods: simple random sampling, systematic sampling, multistage random sampling, stratified sampling, cluster sampling, and multiple or sequential sampling. He should know, in a general way, what each of these methods is and how it can be used. Although it is not necessary that he be able, himself, to design the sample, he should know both where expert statistical advice can be helpful and how to communicate with statistical experts.

There is little point here in listing or describing the various methods of sampling and estimating. Consideration will, instead, be turned toward the basic problem of how to optimize the selection of a sampling and estimating procedure, that is, to the logic of statistical design. Statistical design will be subjected to an operations research type of analysis so that the effectiveness of statistical procedures can, in a meaningful way, be maximized.

Choosing a Sampling-Estimating Procedure.

Any estimate of a population characteristic which is based on a sample is subject to error; scientific sampling and estimating procedures make this error measurable. In general, errors decrease as the sample size increases. The cost of obtaining and analyzing the sample, however, increases as the sample size increases. Therefore, statistical theory has developed techniques both for minimizing the amount of error relative to a specified cost of performing the necessary operations and for minimizing the cost relative to an amount of error which is specified as tolerable. The procedures require that either permissible error or permissible cost be specified. In operations research, the approach to this problem is a more general one. There are two costs involved in any sampling-estimating procedure: the cost of carrying out the procedure; and the cost due to error. Instead of fixing one of the costs and minimizing the other relative to it, the sum of the two costs can be minimized. That sampling-estimating procedure which minimizes the total of the two costs can be said to be the " best."

The mathematics involved in such an optimizing procedure is complex, the concern of specialists alone. The logic of the approach, however, should be understood by all operations analysts, and can be disclosed through recourse to a simple illustration.

In a population of five elements having values of 2, 3, 6, 9, and 10, respectively, along some scale, the average value for the population is 6. Let it be assumed that this average value is not known, but that it is necessary to estimate it on the basis of data obtained from a sample drawn from the population. The possible samples would consist of one, two, three or four elements. How many should be selected? Table 1 delineates the processes involved in reaching a rational answer to the question.

Column A lists all possible alternative samples for selection, in terms of their size and composition. Let it be assumed that a simple random sampling procedure is used, one in which each sample in each group has the same chance of being chosen as has any other sample in the same group. Let it be further assumed that the average of the sample is taken as an estimate of the average of the population; these estimated averages appear in Column B. The inaccuracy or error of each estimate can then be determined simply by subtracting the true population average, 6, from each of the estimated averages. The results of this operation are listed in Column C.

Let it next be assumed that each error of overestimation will cost $3.00 per unit of error and each error of underestimation will cost $6.00 per unit. The cost associated with each possible error can then be computed, as in Column D. It is not known in advance which error will be made; the probability of making any particular error can, however, be calculated. For example, there are five possible samples containing only one element and, on the basis of the prestated assumption, each has an equal chance, $\frac{1}{5}$, of being selected. There-

TABLE 1

Sample Size	A Sample	B Estimate	C Error	D Cost of Error	E Expected Cost of Error
1	2	2	−4	$24.00	$ 4.80
	3	3	−3	18.00	3.60
	6	6	0		
	9	9	3	9.00	1.80
	10	10	4	12.00	2.40
					12.60
					3.00
					15.60 = TEC
2	2, 3	2.5	−3.5	$21.00	$ 2.10
	2, 6	4.0	−2.0	12.00	1.20
	2, 9	5.5	−0.5	3.00	.30
	2, 10	6.0	0		
	3, 6	4.5	−1.5	9.00	.90
	3, 9	6.0	0		
	3, 10	6.5	0.5	1.50	.15
	6, 9	7.5	1.5	4.50	.45
	6, 10	8.0	2.0	6.00	.60
	9, 10	9.5	3.5	10.50	1.05
					6.75
					6.00
					12.75 = TEC
3	2, 3, 6	3.67	−2.33	$14.00	$ 1.40
	2, 3, 9	4.67	−1.33	8.00	.80
	2, 3, 10	5.00	−1.00	6.00	.60
	2, 6, 9	5.67	−0.33	2.00	.20
	2, 6, 10	6.00	0		
	2, 9, 10	7.00	1.00	3.00	.30
	3, 6, 9	6.00	0		
	3, 6, 10	6.33	0.33	1.00	.10
	3, 9, 10	7.33	1.33	4.00	.40
	6, 9, 10	8.33	2.33	7.00	.70
					4.50
					9.00
					13.50 = TEC
4	2, 3, 6, 9	5.00	−1.00	$ 6.00	$ 1.20
	2, 3, 6, 10	5.25	−0.75	4.50	.90
	2, 3, 9, 10	6.00	0		
	2, 6, 9, 10	6.75	0.75	2.25	.45
	3, 6, 9, 10	7.00	1.00	3.00	.60
					3.15
					12.00
					15.15 = TEC

fore, the first error listed for samples of one element is –4, which will cost $24.00; in the long run, this particular error will occur $\frac{1}{5}$ of the time. In short, the *expected cost* of this error will be $\frac{1}{5} \times 24.00, or $4.80. The expected cost of each possible error in the group can be similarly computed, as shown in Column E. The total for each group in Column E is the *total expected cost of error* for that group. That is, in effect, the cost of error which will be incurred if the procedure is repeatedly used.

If $3.00 is the cost of making each observation, then the cost of observations for the various sample sizes are $3.00, $6.00, $9.00 and $12.00 respectively. If this is added, for each group, to its total expected cost of error, the resulting sum is the *total expected cost of the procedure (TEC)*. For the illustration given in Table 1, samples of two prove to be most economical. (The cost of a complete count would be $15.00.)

Through the use of this method, it would be possible to compare alternative estimating procedures for each possible sampling procedure. That combination of sampling and estimating procedures yielding the lowest minimum total expected cost is the one which should be selected. To make so complete a comparison would, obviously, be a lengthy and costly task. This is seldom necessary, however, since, in a majority of specific situations, the experienced sampler and statistician know which sampling and estimating procedures are the likeliest candidates. Very few analyses, therefore, are usually required.

In the illustration just described, it was possible to specify each possible error because the true value of the characteristic being estimated was actually known. In practice, of course, such knowledge would be lacking. This knowledge is not essential, however, since statistical methods permit the probability of any specified error to be estimated without a prior determination of the true value of the characteristic being estimated.

Interline Settlements—A Case Example.

Statistics has much more general applicability than the example just given can demonstrate. Part of an actual study conducted by the Operations Research Group at Case Institute of Technology will provide an additional example of the uses to which statistics can be put in operations research. In this particular problem, statistics played a very important role.

The study concerned the rail shipment of packages between cities. The whole process of intercity rail package shipments is initiated when a customer takes his package to the freight office of a local railroad. The clerk prepares a waybill and takes the package. If it is being sent prepaid, he collects the proper amount from the customer; otherwise the charges will be collected from the recipient. The railroad which takes in the package does not necessarily go to the city for which the package is destined. This means that, on part of its route, the package may be carried by at least one other railroad.

Let it be assumed that only two railroads are necessary to carry the package between the sender and its recipient. It will be necessary, at the end of the month, for these two railroads to divide the revenue collected both for the hypothetical package mentioned above and for all other packages which the two have jointly transported. Determining the share of the money received which goes to each of the carriers may be a very costly operation. It could involve consulting complicated I. C. C. regulations, memoranda, agreements, routing charts, etc. On the average, it costs approximately twenty-five cents to process each waybill so that such division of funds can be made. It is obvious that, if this process were undertaken for all packages shipped, some of which would involve even more than two carriers, the cost to the railroads would be enormous. Consequently, the railroads agreed, a number of years ago, on a procedure which considerably reduced the cost of such " interline settlements."

The method which was adopted involved having the carriers group the waybills by junctions; that is, by the point of transfer of packages from one line to another. Next, the apportionment of revenue for all less-than-carload (L. C. L.) shipments was computed through the processing of a large number of waybills. Certain percentages were observed to hold for the transfer between any two lines at each junction and these were set as guides for future apportionment without the processing of individual waybills. For example, it may have been observed that Carrier A received 40 per cent and Carrier B, 60 per cent of all revenue collected for L. C. L. shipments passing through Junction X over the year studied. The two lines agreed that, in the future, they would total their revenue received from L. C. L. shipments passing through Junction X and use the 40-60 per cent division. This solution was a reasonable one. It was recognized, however, that, over a period of time, the characteristics of the distribution of freight shipments through a particular junction would change. Therefore, an allowance was made for checks on the established percentages at the request of either of the lines which were party to the agreement, so that changes in apportionment could be made. The checks, however, proved to be a costly undertaking. As many as 5,000 shipments might pass through any junction in one month. Two lines might have several junctions, and each line might connect with several other lines.

One phase of the operations research problem, as it was formulated, was to develop a more efficient and less costly procedure for checking the established percentages. This was, fundamentally, a problem of sampling and estimating, involving two major questions: (1) What kind and how large a sample should be used? and (2) What type of estimate should be used?

The following procedure was undertaken in an effort to reach a solution to the problem. First, a large number of waybills for a number of junctions was studied in order to determine the distribution of the freight charges for shipments. This study indicated that, although most of the shipments were quite small, a significant portion of the total revenue came from a small number of large shipments. Table 2 lists a distribution which was typical for one junction during one month.

TABLE 2

Waybill Amount	Number	Per cent	Total Amount	Per cent
0—$ 4.99	3672	73	$ 9,658.51	37
$ 5.00— 9.99	818	16	5,663.40	21
10.00— 19.99	395	8	5,445.99	21
20.00— 39.99	119	2	3,148.32	12
40.00 and over	42	1	2,370.54	9
TOTAL	5046	100	$26,286.76	100

The problem of drawing an efficient sample and making an efficient estimate of a population of values distributed in this way was not new.

Methods for handling the problem were originally developed in connection with the sampling of human populations; therefore, the knowledge acquired in that field could be transferred to the interline-settlement problem. The method used was that of " stratified sampling with optimum allocation " combined with a ratio estimate.

The first step in the design involved discovery of the best way in which to break the population into groups or strata. Study indicated that the five classes listed in Table 2 were approximately the best; that is, 0–$4.99, $5.00–$9.99, $10.00–$19.99, $20.00–$39.99, and $40.00 and over. In stratified sampling, a sample is selected from each class or stratum; this procedure assures representativeness with respect to the property used as a basis of classification and, therefore, reduces error.

It was next essential to determine the proportion of the sample to be selected from each stratum, and the method of optimum allocation was used to achieve this. This method assures minimum error for a given sample size. In brief, the proportion of the sample selected from each stratum is made proportionate to the number of items in the stratum and to their standard deviation, i. e., the measure of the spread or dispersion of the values in the stratum. When this method was applied and modified in accordance with some practical considerations, the following allocations listed in Table 3 resulted:

TABLE 3

Strata	Per cent of Sample
0—$ 4.99	5
$ 5.00— 9.99	10
10.00— 19.99	20
20.00— 39.99	50
40.00 and over	100

This allocation puts the stress on the more costly shipments. The procedure yields, on the average, about a 10 per cent sample.

The next problem involved the method for selecting the sample from each stratum. Waybills are numbered uniquely and consecutively at each station in the order in which the corresponding shipments are brought in. Subsequently, an IBM card is prepared for each waybill. This type of set-up is eminently suited to a *systematic selection*. To select systematically a 5 per cent sample of waybills in the first stratum, the entire stratum was put through the sorter and all waybills with numbers ending in 02, 22, 42, 62, and 82 were selected. This selection yielded a sample of approximately 5 per cent. The question next arose as to whether another sequence, such as 03, 23, 43, etc., should be selected. The distribution of estimates based on the various possible systematic samples revealed that it made no practical difference which ending digit was used for the selection.

A systematic sampling plan for each sample was evolved as described in Table 4.

TABLE 4

Strata	Select Waybills Ending in
0—$ 4.99	02, 22, 42, 62, 82
$ 5.00— 9.99	2
10.00— 19.99	2 and 4
20.00— 39.99	01 to 50
40.00 and over	all

Next, there arose the problem of selecting a method of estimation. A ratio estimate was selected because, even though it is slightly biased, it yields minimum variation among estimates. The procedure consists in computing for each stratum: (1) the amount going to Carrier A in the sample; (2) the total amount in the sample; and (3) the total amount in the stratum. Once these three computations are made, the estimate for each stratum can be obtained by means of the following computation:

$$\frac{\text{Amount Going to Carrier A from Sample}}{\text{Total Amount in Sample}} \times \text{Total Amount in Stratum}.$$

To illustrate this computation more clearly, an hypothetical example will be used. Let it be assumed that the total amount of freight charges in the sample from a stratum is $2,000. A study of the waybills shows that $500 of this amount should go to Carrier A. Let it be further assumed that the total amount of freight charges in the stratum is $10,000. The estimate for this stratum, then, would be:

$$\frac{\$500}{\$2000} \times \$10,000 = \$2,500.$$

The estimates for each stratum are then added to obtain an overall estimate of the amount due to each company, and the overall percentages are determined.

The estimated percentages for two junctions as they were worked out are shown in Table 5. The variations in the percentage of the population (8.5 per cent and 10.25 per cent) falling into the sample is due to the way in which waybill numbers are assigned to freight offices and to variations in the distribution of freight amounts. In the two cases illustrated, complete counts were made so that the results could be compared with the results of the samples. In both cases, the estimate obtained was within 1 per cent of the true percentage. In fact, it can be shown that, when the method described is used, the estimates will fall within 1 per cent of the true percentage about 95 per cent of the time.

It might be well to make some assessment of the cost effectiveness of this method as a means for checking on the apportionment percentages. In the first example listed in Table 5, there were 5,046 waybills. Since it costs $.25 to process each one, the total cost of a complete count would have been $1,261.50. The cost of processing each item would run somewhat higher for the sample because of the cost involved in selecting the items. For convenience, it will be assumed that it costs twice as much, although this is somewhat excessive. Even so, the cost would be only $.50 × 483, or $241.50. In addition, the cost of error, $156.43, must be considered. Since this is an overestimate of the amount due to Carrier A, it would be a negative cost. Even if it were an underestimate, the total cost to Carrier A would be only $241.50 plus $156.43, or $397.93. He would save the difference between $1,261.50 and $397.93, or $863.57.

If this method were used to settle accounts for *four* junctions, the error would be no more than 0.5 per cent 95 per cent of the time. If, further, it were used by Carrier A with nine companies at four junctions each, the error would be no more than 0.167 per cent 95 per cent of the time. If settlements based on this procedure were

TABLE 5

Waybill Group	No. of Waybills		Total Freight		Share to Carrier A		
	Population	Sample	Population	Sample	Actual	Estimated	$ Deviation
0—$ 4.99	3672	186	$ 9,658.51	$ 488.84	$ 4,252.47	$ 4,306.85	$ 54.38
5.00— 9.99	818	72	5,663.40	497.99	2,537.82	2,575.19	37.37
10.00— 19.99	395	82	5,445.99	1,097.57	2,506.02	2,575.65	69.63
20.00— 39.99	119	51	3,148.32	1,382.82	1,426.66	1,421.71	−4.95
40.00 and over	42	42	2,370.54	2,370.54	1,070.22	1,070.22	—
TOTALS	5046	433	$26,286.76	$5,837.76	$11,793.19	$11,949.62	$156.43
% OF TOTAL		8.58%		22.21%	44.86%	45.46%	+0.60%

Waybill Group	No. of Waybills		Total Freight		Share to Carrier A		
	Population	Sample	Population	Sample	Actual	Estimated	$ Deviation
0—$ 4.99	880	40	$ 2,693.41	$ 122.87	$ 1,479.37	$ 1,546.95	$ 67.58
$ 5.00— 9.99	240	29	1,691.92	190.54	1,017.01	1,033.23	16.22
10.00— 19.99	106	20	1,462.87	284.31	886.74	859.89	−26.85
20.00— 39.99	35	16	961.55	459.71	603.39	597.39	− 6.00
40.00 and over	27	27	2,322.11	2,322.11	1,575.20	1,575.20	—
TOTALS	1288	132	$ 9,131.86	$ 3,397.54	$ 5,561.71	$ 5,612.66	$ 77.80
% OF TOTAL		10.25%		37.01%	60.90%	61.46%	+0.56%

made for several junctions and several lines, the errors would tend to cancel out and the cost of error would become negligible. This fact suggests that a smaller sample might have been selected. This is true. Initially, however, the factors determining the total sample size were psychological rather than statistical; the participating companies were unwilling to run the " larger risk " which they thought that a smaller sample might entail. Eventually, the sample size will be reduced, which procedure will in turn raise some interesting questions concerning the criterion which should be used, ideally, to set the optimum sample size. Although a complete discussion of this problem would be a digression here, it can be stated that the controlling factor will be one involving assurance that the nature of the population being sampled has not changed. If such change should have occurred, a different sampling procedure would be required.

It is generally assumed by the non-statistician that a complete count of a population yields a perfectly accurate determination of a population characteristic and, therefore, is preferable to a sample, provided time, money, and personnel permit. This is not the case. The United States Bureau of the Census, in fact, uses a sample survey as a check on its decennial census, which is a complete count. The better quality interviewer and the better, fuller questionnaire which are possible because of the smaller number of respondents achieve an accuracy for the sample which exceeds that for the total population.

In respect to the interline settlement problem, an interesting experiment was conducted to demonstrate this point. For one set of waybills a complete count was run off by means of IBM equipment. A similar second run was made and the results of the two did not agree. A third run was performed under highly controlled conditions and the results of this were accepted as correct. The difference between the first count and the last was $400.00. A 5 per cent sample conducted simultaneously, however, came within $7.00 of the correct amount. Such errors are common in complete counts, particularly where the operations are numerous and repetitive. The effects of fatigue and boredom, which may be far from insignificant, are substantially reduced when a small sample is used.

A New Technique for Social Surveys.

Statistics is in a state of rapid expansion and the rate at which new techniques are developed has been accelerating. Many of these techniques are inherently very useful to the solution of operations research problems. The description of one will, perhaps, serve as an illustration of the many.

A few years ago, a new technique was originated to be used in those surveys of human populations which are concerned with the preferences of consumers, public opinion and attitudes, the habits and off-the-job activities of workers, and other similar characteristics. The most persistent and harassing problem in social surveys has been one resulting from the fact that a large percentage of those designated for interview or observation are not available at the time of the survey. It is not unusual, in a survey of individuals, for 60 per cent of the designated respondents to be away from home when the interviewer first calls. Unfortunately, not-at-homes have been discovered to have characteristics different from those usually found at home. Estimates of population characteristics, therefore, which ignore the not-at-homes are apt to include serious biases. To prevent such bias, the usual procedure has been for the interviewer to repeat his call once, twice or more times if necessary on a sample of those who were absent at his first attempt. Even with this call-back procedure, which is very expensive and time-consuming, there usually remains a stubborn residue of non-response.

Recently, in order to combat this difficulty, Alfred Politz and Willard Simmons have developed a method consisting of the following steps.[3]

(1) Each person in the sample is called on only once.

(2) For each person contacted, a determination is made of the number of interview periods of the preceding week that he was at home. For example, if the interviews take place on six weekday evenings, the respondent is asked whether or not he was at home on the other nights of the week at the same time.

(3) Those respondents contacted are then grouped according to whether they were at home 6/6, 5/6, 4/6, 3/6, 2/6 or 1/6 of these evenings.

---

[3] "An Attempt to Get the 'Not-At-Homes' into the Sample without Call-backs," *Journal of the American Statistical Association*, Vol. 44, No. 9 (1949).

(4) Estimates of the characteristic being investigated are computed separately for each of these groups.

(5) Each estimate is weighted by a factor equal to the reciprocal of the proportion of the evenings that group was at home at the time of the interview.

(6) The total population estimate is obtained by combining these weighted estimates.

Let it be assumed, for example, that a survey is being conducted to determine what percentage of households have automatic home laundry equipment. A sample is designed, an interview procedure

TABLE 6

No. of Nights at Home	No. of Households Contacted	No. Having Equipment	Weights	Weighted No. of Those Contacted	Weighted Estimate of No. with Equipment
1	25	15	6/1 = 6.0	150	90
2	50	30	6/2 = 3.0	150	90
3	100	58	6/3 = 2.0	200	116
4	200	100	6/4 = 1.5	300	150
5	400	190	6/5 = 1.2	480	228
6	700	315	6/6 = 1.0	700	315
TOTAL	1475	708		1980	989

prepared and interviews planned for evening hours. One call is made at each designated household with the results shown in Table 6. The unadjusted estimate of families having equipment would be 708/1475, or 48 per cent. The adjusted estimate would be 989/1980, or 50 per cent.

This estimate does not take into account those who were not at home on any of the six nights. These can be included by determining the regression of *Weighted Number of those Contacted* on *Number of Nights at Home* and the regression of *Weighted Estimate of Number Having Equipment* on *Number of Nights at Home*. If these regression coefficients are not significant, the group away from home on all six nights can be disregarded without there being any introduction of bias. If, however, they are significant, estimates can be obtained for the corresponding *Weighted Number of Those Contacted* and the *Weighted Estimate of Number Having Equipment* by setting the number of nights at home equal to zero in the regression equations. The adjusted total population estimate can then take these figures into account.

Tests have indicated that the reliability of the data concerning number of nights at home is very high. It should be mentioned that this method assumes that the interview times are selected at random from the population of possible interview times.

Conclusion.

The preceding discussion has described a few of the ways in which statistics can be used in operations research. It is not an exaggeration to state that, without the application of modern statistical techniques, operations research cannot measure up to its full promise as a means to the solution of operational problems. The contribution works both ways, however. As the preceding examples demonstrate, the selection of the best sampling and estimating methods involves a kind of operations research within the field of statistics. The use of this approach in such selections substantially enhances the usefulness and timeliness of the statistical treatment of data.

Queueing Theory

BYRON O. MARSHALL, JR.

ALTHOUGH the term "queueing theory" and the definitions that comprise the rigor itself are relatively recent, actual work in the field began some forty-five years ago. The pioneer investigator was Erlang, who, in 1908, did work of a most fundamental nature on telephone switching for the Copenhagen Telephone Company;[1] this company has had the distinction of endorsing and supporting several important investigations in probability theory. Since that time, most of the work in queueing theory has been conducted by the British; one is tempted to explain this on the basis that there is no more stimulating time to speculate on queues than while one is standing in one. In the vernacular, one might speak of queueing theory as the theory of bottlenecks; frequently, the telephone system terminology of "holding time" or "waiting time" is used.

The Study of Queueing Problems.

The identifying and naming of the theory resulted from the discovery that miscellaneous problems have a common property that leads to a particular field of investigation, which, like so many others, draws not only on mathematics but also on many other branches of knowledge. Also, as the treatments of the problems will show, the mathematical techniques which are used vary widely; there is as yet no specific rigor nor set of theorems that can be identified as *the* theory. The work has only the common subject matter, namely the

---

[1] E. Brockmeyer, H. L. Halztrom and A. Jensen, *The Life and Works of A. K. Erlang* (Copenhagen: Copenhagen Telephone Company, 1948).

delays encountered at a service point. The mathematics required may sometimes be transferred entirely from one study to another but, whereas queues involving humans may necessitate certain studies in group behavior and communication theory, queues of items may require the consideration of weights of materials, the mechanical properties of conveyor belts, trucks, aircraft, etc. In short, the mathematical solution, when it exists, is not the whole answer. The qualification, " when it exists " must be interjected since, in many cases, the mathematics is extremely troublesome and does not always lead to an illuminating answer.

Most of the work in queueing theory falls into one of the following three categories:

     (1) Telephone switching problems
     (2) Traffic problems, and
     (3) Machine breakdown and feed problems

These three areas of investigation were the first to invite inquiry and still consume a majority of the effort devoted to the field.

In a queueing situation, one can assume that there are the following components:

     (1) Customers
     (2) A gate or service point
     (3) An input process
     (4) Some queue discipline, and
     (5) Some service mechanism

As this order implies, there are customers who desire service; as each moves to the service point, there is some time for service after which he leaves and is usually no longer a part of the problem. Any customers who arrive while he is being served must wait their turns; in other words, they form a queue. The elements of interest in an analysis of the situation are:

     (1) the waiting time of the customers,
     (2) the number of customers in the queue, and
     (3) the ratio of waiting time to service time.

Direct studies of these elements may be of interest to shops and stores. There are many cases, however, in which the queue is not a physical line of people or items, but rather a dispersed set of persons, such as those waiting for telephone service or those awaiting the service of a waitress in a restaurant. Customers in such situations may have the impression that the service they receive is random; to the waitress or the telephone company, however, these customers form a real physical queue.

The most rewarding studies of queues are those in which the "customers" of the queue are large and expensive physical items. In such studies, a small technological change, though it may allow for handling only a few more "customers" per unit time, will occasionally result in a surprising reduction in waiting times. In queue situations involving aircraft waiting to land or trains approaching a junction, lost time is often expensive in terms of dollars, equipment, and, in some instances, even lives.

One example may very vividly demonstrate the sort of situation demanding study, namely the conditions at airports where a state of saturation exists, such as at the air bases in wartime Britain after an all-out raid. Returning planes tended to arrive back at the home airport all at the same time, each with little excess fuel and eager to land. The situation was nearly one of oversaturation; planes were brought in for landings at the rate of one a minute or more. Such an accelerated landing schedule was tolerable so long as there were no accidents. Operation at the saturation point, however, is potentially very dangerous and costly. An aircraft which was actually running out of fuel would radio in for immediate clearance to land; the hasty rearranging of schedules to accommodate such an emergency might consume so much time that *two* other planes would run dangerously low on fuel. If planes were obliged to make "dead-stick" landings, there was always the possibility that they would ground-loop or otherwise obstruct the landing strip, thereby causing other emergency landings. In situations such as this, the waiting time is a vital point for consideration.

A variety of subjects has been studied from the waiting time point of view, as the following list indicates:

      (1) The landing of aircraft [2]
      (2) The loading and unloading of ore ships [2]

---

[2] See "Marshalling and Queueing," *Operational Research Quarterly*, Vol. 3, No. 1 (March 1952).

(3) The design of automobile parking areas [2]
(4) The design of taxi waiting areas [2]
(5) The scheduling of patients in clinics [2]
(6) The processing of X-ray films [2]
(7) The passage of travelers through customs [2]
(8) Telephone waiting times [3]
(9) Machine breakdowns [3]
(10) Pedestrian crossings [3]
(11) The timing of traffic lights [3]
(12) The movement of aircraft along taxiways, [3] and
(13) The servicing of knitting machines [3]

For economic reasons, the service-providing agency is usually principally concerned with servicing as many " customers " with as

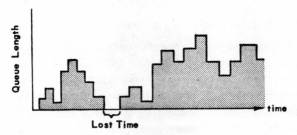

Figure 1.

few facilities as possible. The usual solution is to aim for a situation in which:

(The service rate) = (The average rate of arrival).

This is sometimes a very unsatisfactory answer. For example, if a service which can handle exactly 10 customers per hour has customers arriving randomly at an average rate of 10 per hour, one can show that, as time passes, *the probability of having to wait approaches 1, and the mean waiting time approaches infinity*. A partial explanation of this peculiar behavior is that, since the arrivals are random and average 10 per hour, there will eventually come a time when no customers are waiting. No service, therefore, will be made during such intervals and that time is lost forever. After such loss, the actual average number serviced becomes less than 10 per hour. Figure 1 illustrates this phenomenon.

[3] See David G. Kendall, " Some Problems in the Theory of Queues " and

In such cases, small changes in servicing produce large changes in the waiting time. If the rate of customer arrival is reduced to 8 per hour, only three customers in five will be obliged to wait; the *mean* waiting time will then be 4.8 minutes vs. the infinite value of the previous case. As soon as the mean arrival rate approaches the service rate, both waiting time and line length change disastrously. It is in this delicate region that most queueing problems are generated.

Such problems are certainly susceptible to the operations research approach. The variety of contexts in which queue-like phenomena arise, their susceptibility to some form of analysis, mathematical or otherwise, and the benefits to be gained from studying the queue in relation to the entire operation which encompasses it make queueing problems apt areas for the work of the operations research team.

Analysis of the Single-Queue Problem.

Most examples of published work concern single queues at a single service point. Lindley [4] and Kendall,[5] both of whom have published in the field, state that the multiple-queueing problem seems, except under simplified assumptions, to be one of considerable difficulty; indeed the single-queue problem is, in itself, remarkably complex. In respect to the single-queue case, it is useful to investigate the waiting times of customers to determine whether stationary states exist, in which the queue approaches neither infinity nor zero, and whether any remedy can be applied to difficult cases of customer waiting.

Following Mr. Lindley's analysis, one can first assume that there is some starting time from which the customers can be labeled 1, 2, 3, . . . in the order of their arrival. Certain assumptions can be made about the times at which customers might arrive and about their service time, which here will be allowed to vary.

To begin with, the analysis is based upon: (1) how much later a customer arrives after his predecessor, and (2) the time used for

discussion, *Journal of the Royal Statistical Society*, Series B, Vol. XIII, No. 2 (1951), pp. 151-85.

[4] D. V. Lindley, "The Theory of Queues with a Single Server," *Proceedings of the Cambridge Philosophical Society*, Vol. 48, Part 2 (April 1952), pp. 277-89.

[5] "Some Problems in the Theory of Queues."

servicing a customer. Neither of these quantities is determined beforehand; they may, in fact, assume any value whatsoever. What must be specified is the distribution of each, or the probability that the service will take so long, or that an arrival interval will be of such and such a length. Realistic assumptions are made that the average service time and interval are not infinite and that each customer's arrival and service are independent of all the others. In other words, a curve such as in Figure 2 is specified and a similar one for the service time.

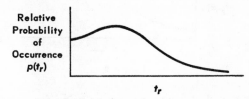

Figure 2.

This all may be formally stated as follows:

(1) Let t_r be the time interval between the arrival of the rth and $(r+1)$st customers.

(2) Let s_r be the service time of the rth customer.

(3) The t_r are independent random variables with identical probability distributions and the mean, $E(t_r)$, is finite.

(4) The s_r are independent random variables with identical probability distributions, each mean, $E(s_r)$, being finite and s_r being independent of t_r.

Although a customer's arrival and service times are independent of the others, his waiting time is not. It is, in fact, equal to:

(the waiting time of his predecessor)
plus (the service time of his predecessor)
minus (the difference in their arrival times)

or zero, if this sum is negative. This may be formally stated as:

$$w_{r+1} = w_r + s_r - t_r \qquad \text{if } (w_r + s_r - t_r) > 0$$
$$= 0 \qquad\qquad \text{if } (w_r + s_r - t_r) \leqq 0,$$

where w_r is the waiting time of the rth customer. Let a new function $F_r(x)$ be defined as follows:

$$F_r(x) = (\text{probability that } w_r \leqq x) = p(w_r \leqq x),$$

where $p(\ )$ means "the probability of $(\ )$." This function will be of the sort shown in Figure 3. It increases monotonically towards 1;

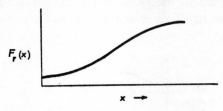

$F_r(x)$

$x \rightarrow$

Figure 3.

it is zero for $x < 0$ and may have some value for $x = 0$:

$$F_r(0) = (\text{probability that } w_r \leqq 0),$$

which is the probability that the rth customer will not be obliged to wait. In general, there is a different F for each r, but each F depends upon the previous one and the distribution $F_{r+1}(x)$ can be found if $F_r(x)$ is known:

$$F_{r+1}(x) = p(w_{r+1} \leqq x),$$

but:

$$w_{r+1} = \begin{cases} w_r + s_r - t_r \\ 0 \end{cases},$$

therefore:

$$F_{r+1}(x) = p(w_r + s_r - t_r \leqq x).$$

For convenience, the following substitution may be made:

$$u_r = s_r - t_r,$$

which has some probability distribution, $G(u_r)$, so that:

$$F_{r+1}(x) = p(w_r + u_r \leqq x)$$
$$= \sum_{u_r} (\text{probability that } w_r \leqq x - u_r) \cdot (\text{probability of that } u_r)$$
$$= \int_{u_r \leqq x} F_r(x - u_r) dG(u_r).$$

In this case, one can pass to the limit for infinite r, so that the limiting case is:

$$F(x) = \int_{u \leq x} F(x-u)dG(u).$$

The quantity $F(x)$ contains all the information about the behavior of the waiting line. It should be noted that the significant quantity is u, the difference between s and t, and its distribution. It remains to study the behavior of $F(x)$ for the following three cases:

(1)   the expected value of $u_r = s_r - t_r > 0$, i. e. $E(u) > 0$,

(2) $E(u) < 0$,

(3) $E(u) = 0$.

For the first case, where $E(u) > 0$, the service time is generally greater than the interval between the arrivals; oversaturation, hence large queues, results. $F(x)$ does not rise rapidly, but remains far from 1, as in Figure 4.

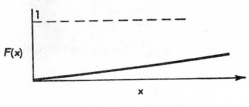

Figure 4.

The second case constitutes one of undersaturation and $F(x)$ approaches 1 rapidly, as in Figure 5.

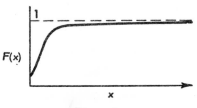

Figure 5.

The third case, $E(u) = 0$, is one of exact balance. With a distribution in s_r the process can be considered to have a new starting point each time the queue disappears. The following conclusions can then be reached: it is certain that some customer will not be obliged to wait, but the time for this event to occur may be infinite; the probability of a particular customer's having to wait, however, approaches 1 and the mean waiting time approaches infinity.

The cases which can most easily be handled are those in which the service time and arrival periods have a Poisson distribution.[6] In other words, it is assumed that the probability of an arrival interval exceeding length t is given by:

$$D(t) \sim e^{-At},$$

in which the mean value is $1/A$. Similarly, for the service times, the probability of the service time's exceeding length s is given by:

$$D(s) \sim e^{-Bs},$$

with a mean of $1/B$. Fortunately, many real cases appear to follow a distribution of this sort. One can then speak of a " traffic density," ρ:

$$\rho = \frac{A}{B}$$

the ratio of the means. Kendall[7] has demonstrated that:

$$\frac{E(w)}{E(s)} = \frac{\rho}{s(1-\rho)} \left[1 + Var(sB)\right],$$

where:

    $E(w)$ is the mean waiting time,
    $E(s)$ is the mean service time, $1/B$, and
    $Var(sB)$ is a measure of the spread of s.

This result points up some of the effects previously found:

(1) as the mean arrival rate approaches the mean service rate, $\rho \to 1$, then $\dfrac{E(w)}{E(s)} \to \infty$, or the mean waiting time is many times the mean service time;

(2) infinite queues and waiting times occur if $\rho > 1$; or

---

[6] William Feller, *An Introduction to Probability Theory and Its Applications* (2nd printing; New York: John Wiley and Sons, Inc.), pp. 364-66.
[7] " Some Problems in the Theory of Queues."

(3) If ρ is determined, then the best condition occurs when $Var(sB)$ is smallest, i. e., when the service time is nearly constant. Regular arrivals can be shown to have a similar effect.

The term, $\dfrac{E(w)}{E(s)}$, may be called a " figure of demerit " and is a good measure of the behavior from the *customers'* viewpoint . The server, however, wishes to minimize the time that the counter is free. This proportion of free time may be shown to be:

$$\frac{\text{Free time}}{\text{Total time}} = (1 - \rho)$$

which, when it is zero, leads to infinite queues. The disparity in aims between the customer and the server is tempered somewhat by second-order effects. For example, sometimes the server should not minimize $(1 - \rho)$, because:

(1) customers may depart prematurely if their waiting time is too long;

(2) there is the discouraging effect of a long queue to new customers; and

(3) a natural tendency is to serve more rapidly with a long queue.

These, together with other effects, may seriously influence the proper choice of service facilities and must certainly be considered in all practical cases.

An interesting view of the situation may be obtained by considering the first person to reach an empty counter as the originator of a " generation " consisting of all those people who arrive while he is being served. The second then becomes the ancestor of those who arrive during his service time, and so on until the counter is empty again. The problem resembles that of the extinction of surnames which Galton studied in the last century.

Only a restricted number of cases, of course, can be handled by those analytical methods just described. Fortunately, there are techniques for finding numerical answers when the arrival and service distributions are not conveniently susceptible to mathematical description. Explanations of such techniques are found in the literature under the following variety of titles:

(1) Monte Carlo techniques
(2) Gambling methods
(3) Throwdown problems
(4) Stochastic processes in general, and
(5) Theory of games

In order to amplify the method somewhat further, a simple example may be used. Let it be assumed that a particle is free to move along a line. It starts at the origin and makes one jump for each customer; the size of this jump is u_r, to the right if u_r is positive, to the left if it is negative. The distance covered by the jump u_r is found by consulting two tables of random numbers with the proper distributions for s_r and t_r. The particle performs a " random walk " along the line, behaving rather like a confused but expert drunk on a tightrope.

A restriction is placed on this particle at the origin, in the form of an impenetrable barrier; when the particle reaches the origin, it remains there until the next positive step. It is not difficult to see that the waiting times, being the non-negative accumulation of the u_r, are represented by the position of the particle on the line:

$$w_{r+1} = x \text{ (after } r^{\text{th}} \text{ step)}.$$

In an actual computation, one would keep track of the values of w_r and, after sufficient runs, find the distribution in queue size and waiting times. Variations of the s and t distributions, with runs at different sets of these, permit the study of their effects.

This sort of approach may seem tedious; it is, however, ideally suited to the use of large-scale computing machinery. On newer machines, about one thousand steps can be made each second. A few hours' running, therefore, can provide very satisfactory indications of the effects of various parameters. This kind of indication is regarded by many as a temporary stopgap until analysis can be made. There seem to be many problems, however, which are very difficult to describe in closed terms and for which solutions would add very little to the general theory. This is, in fact, the case with most experimental data on service and arrival times, which are handled in the same manner as the others, by machine. If numerical results are required, automatic computation, because of its flexibility and economy in professional man-hours, is recommended for all but the simplest problems.

Delays at Traffic Lights.

The brief presentation of a few case studies may put queueing theory into more concrete terms. One simple study, conducted by the author, concerns the delay in automobile traffic at traffic signal lights. There is probably no driver who has failed to observe that vehicles far from a traffic light do not begin to move until a considerable time after the light has changed from red to green. For purposes of investigating the effect of this delay upon the number of vehicles which can pass the light, one can proceed from the assumption that the vehicles have a uniform acceleration from zero to some maximum velocity, V. This can be approximated by a delay period, t_o, followed by uniform motion at velocity V (since the acceleration time is rather short). Hence the time, t, to go a distance, S, is

$$t = t_0 + \frac{S}{V}.$$

Next, let it be assumed that there is a uniform delay period, t_d, between the starting of a vehicle and the one after it. Then, the total time for the kth vehicle to reach the light is:

$$T = kt_d + t,$$
$$= kt_d + t_0 + \frac{kL}{V},$$

where L is the length of a vehicle. Therefore, for a certain green light period, T, the number of cars which will be able to get through will be:

$$k = \frac{T - t_0}{t_d + \dfrac{L}{V}}.$$

To ascertain the relative importance of the different variables, one can assume some typical values. For vehicles following speed regulations, V might be taken as 30 mph, or 44 ft/sec. For the sake of round numbers, L could be taken as 11 ft., so that:

$$\frac{L}{V} = \tfrac{1}{4} \text{ sec.}$$

Timing observations have indicated that t_d is usually greater than 1 second, and t_d is thus about four times as large as L/V. In other words, the final velocity and spacing of the cars have very little relationship with how many get through the traffic signal while it is green; the important factor is the *delay in starting*, or the communication from one car to the succeeding one. This is not to imply that there are not many more first and second order effects in real traffic light problems, the study of which might yield useful results.

Congestion at Airports.

Another example of a solution to a queueing theory problem is described in "The Flow of Scheduled Air Traffic" by Adler and Fricker.[8] These two reports cover a study of the congestion that occurs at airports when scheduled aircraft arrive off schedule. They analyze several methods of reducing congestion so as to meet the following aims:

(1) Assuring safety,
(2) Using the landing strip more effectively, and
(3) Reducing the total-trip times.

In the case of scheduled air traffic, the same aims are shared by both the customer and server, a relatively rare situation.

The study proceeded with the assumption that the deviation from the scheduled arrival times had three types of distribution: rectangular, triangular, and parabolic. These had a certain spread, S, outside which the distribution function was assumed to be zero; that is to say, delays or advances greater than $S/2$ were not considered. The value of S was given in units of t_o, the minimum safe landing interval. Without loss of generality, it was also assumed that all variations were delays.

The actual study was performed numerically with the use of IBM equipment. A group of 1,000 hypothetical planes was used; each was represented by a card and each was "flown" into the airport with a delay selected from a table of random numbers of the proper distri-

---

[8] R. B. Adler and S. J. Fricker, "The Flow of Scheduled Air Traffic," Massachusetts Institute of Technology RLE *Technical Reports* Nos. 198 (2 May 1951) and 199 (13 August 1951).

bution. This was done for several values of traffic density parameter, E, which is here defined as:

$$E = \frac{(\text{mean scheduled arrival interval})}{t_0}.$$

As one might expect, the results varied with E. For E with values near 1 (near saturation), the delays proved to be largest, having a mean near $S/2$. The delays for $E = 0.9$ were approximately $S/6$; and, for $E = 0.5$, the delays were quite small. No great amount of dependence on the delay distribution curve was found. The mean value of the delay for $E = 1$ was considerably smaller than that found by other analyses. This is indicative of one limitation in the study; the probability of delays greater than any value, such as S, is small, but it is not zero, as the study assumed. In real cases, these few large delays cause a considerable piling-up of traffic, and may make these results somewhat overoptimistic.

The solution for a typical case illustrates the type of results which were obtained. If an average flight time of two hours is assumed, delays or advances of more than one-half hour are unlikely, so that one may take S as equalling 12, the t_0 or minimum safe landing arrival being 5 minutes. With $E = 0.95$ and a landing time of 5 minutes, the average stack delay would be 2 t_0 or 10 minutes and the probability of having to remain in the stack for ½ hour would be about 1 in 200. These results would provide reasonably satisfactory service, both from the customers' and server's point of view.

Two methods were studied for the rescheduling of aircraft for the purpose of relieving congestion. These were: (1) "one point rescheduling control," in which the aircraft are rescheduled at an intermediate point so as to arrive at the terminal one unit apart; and (2) "one point on time control," in which the aircraft are put on their original schedules at an intermediate point. The point at which rescheduling occurs is not necessarily a physical point somewhere between two airports, but may be a zone near one terminal and under its control. Neither method yielded a startling improvement; both, however, allowed some relief of congestion during critical situations.

A type of block scheduling was also studied, in which the aircraft were scheduled so that a certain allowable number would arrive within a given block of time. This too failed to yield significant improvements. The method of all three studies was that mentioned above, namely the use of a card for each aircraft with changes in actual arrival time selected randomly according to the three distribution functions.

" The Flow of Scheduled Air Traffic " studies provide significant results for the steady-state conditions, namely those time periods during which the scheduled rate of arrival and of landing are static. (A small portion of the investigation also deals with the transient condition of airport shutdown.) Actual operations at an airport, however, are rarely static, and the critical periods are those of widely-spread bad flying conditions. Even with normal weather, the airport load and aircraft landing rate are not constant. There is, therefore, a clear need for further and more extensive studies in which queueing theory is applied to airport operations.

The traffic light study and the airport operation studies described above offer, very briefly, two examples in which practical problems have been approached. The body of problems susceptible to operations research obviously contains many instances in which the flow of items or persons through various points or stages is an important part of the total operation. In these cases, queueing theory becomes part of the body of methods which should be employed in efforts to achieve a solution.

Information Theory

DAVID SLEPIAN

THE SUBJECT treated in this chapter is relatively new. In fact, a scant five years ago, the title "Information Theory" would not have been meaningful. Despite its youth, however, information theory is a science of considerable scope. Unfortunately for the expositor, it is not a particularly easy science. It is highly mathematical in nature, and a complete understanding of it requires the use of a brand of mathematics somewhat foreign to the usual working tools of the average engineer.

It is impossible, therefore, within the limits of a single chapter to give a thorough treatment of this new field. To discuss some small aspect of the theory in detail without a presentation of the overall picture would, on the other hand, scarcely be profitable from the reader's point of view. By way of compromise, the material which follows will be divided into two parts: the first will briefly sketch a general picture of the theory, pointing out its central ideas and principal applications; the second will treat in more detail one of the basic building blocks of the theory, namely the intriguing idea of attaching a numerical measure to the information content of messages.

A General Description of Information Theory.

Information theory had its formal birth in two papers published in 1948 by Claude Shannon in the *Bell System Technical Journal*. These were entitled "A Mathematical Theory of Communication," a title which describes the subject most accurately. The popular name, "information theory," was soon attached to this new field because the notion of a quantitative measure of information was a central theme in Shannon's papers.

Essentially, Shannon's theory differed from previous work in communications in two aspects. First, he introduced statistical notions which, prior to that time, had not been used extensively in communication work. Second, his theory differed from earlier treatments in being macroscopic rather than microscopic. It is not concerned with the small-scale details and circuitry of particular communication systems, but instead focuses attention on the large-scale or gross aspects of communication devices.

These two new avenues of attack have proved to be most fruitful. They have indicated that many of the varied problems and limitations

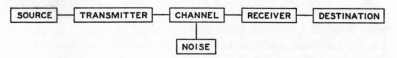

Fig. 1. Diagram of a typical communication system.

observed in specific communication systems are not peculiar to the special structure of those systems, but are limitations inherent in all communication processes. For example, it is well known that one cannot transmit information at an arbitrarily great rate over a given communication means. As more dots and dashes are transmitted per second over the telegraph channel, the incidence of errors in the decoded message increases. A similar situation obtains in all other real communication systems. Information theory has shown how the maximum rate for transmitting error-free information over any system can be computed. This is, clearly, of considerable theoretical importance. It has, furthermore, indicated the general procedures which should be followed in order to approach these ideal rates. Unfortunately, many of the improvements in communication systems which the theory suggests are too complicated and too expensive of realization to have practical importance at this time. Nevertheless, as technology progresses, cheaper means of performing the complicated operations suggested by the theory will undoubtedly be found; information theory can, therefore, be expected to play a more important role in practical communication systems of the future.

The system treated by information theory is shown in Figure 1.

It consists of six components: source, transmitter, channel, receiver. destination, and noise.

The block labeled " source " is to be regarded as that person, thing, or process which produces the messages to be transmitted over the system. An important observation concerning the source is that its exact output is not known beforehand to the engineer designing the communication system. If it were, there would be no point in building the system. A machine could, instead, be provided locally to supply the destination with the source output. What *is* known about the source is that it will produce sequences of messages drawn from some fixed (and usually very large) list of possible messages. For example, if one considers telephone systems, the output of the source is human speech. The source produces messages drawn from the list of all possible human utterances. This is an extremely large list, but it is important conceptually to realize that such a list exists. It does not contain, for example, sounds with a frequency of 20,000 cycles per second, nor sounds with pressures corresponding to the shock wave of a nearby cannon's fire.

Usually, more is known about the source than just the list of possible messages which it might produce. Something is generally known of the relative probability that the source will produce certain messages from the list of possibilities. For example, if the source is the sequence of messages written in English and passed over the counter of a Western Union office, one knows beforehand that the symbol e will occur much more frequently than k, and that the combination th will be more common than tp. In most systems now in use, this knowledge of the statistics of the source is ignored. Information theory points to the utilization of this knowledge of the source statistics as an important means for making more efficient communication systems.

The destination is the ultimate recipient of the message. It may be either a person or a thing.

In most communication systems, there is a certain portion of the system devoted merely to the transportation of some form of message between physically remote points. This part of the system will be referred to as the " channel." In telephony, for example, the channel consists of the wire path leading from one subscriber's handset to another subscriber's handset. In radio communication, the channel consists of the " free space " through which the message is propagated.

All the equipment which links the source with the channel can be labeled the "transmitter." This is a more general use of the term than is normally made. In respect to radio communication, it would include the microphone, antenna, and all the equipment between the two.

Similarly, all the equipment between the channel and destination can be designated as the "receiver." Again, this represents a generalization of the word's usual meaning.

In every real communication system, there is always present a certain amount of unwanted interference which tends to corrupt and alter the transmitted messages in an unpredictable manner. Such disturbances are here called "noise." In real systems, of course, noise would be present in all the components of the block diagram in Figure 1. Practically, however, noise is only significant in those parts of the system where the "message power" is low; that is, in the channel, and possibly in the first parts of the receiver.

In order to make the diagram of Figure 1 correspond more closely to real systems, the definition of "channel" will be slightly altered. Here the word will be enlarged to mean not only the link between the physically separated terminal equipment, but also those parts of the terminal equipment which are subject to significant noise disturbance. In radio communication, therefore, the channel would include the receiving antenna and first stage of the terminal equipment as well as the "free space" through which the electromagnetic signal is propagated.

It is important to understand that noise refers only to those disturbances the exact effect of which cannot be predicted in advance. For example, distortion of signals due to the transmission characteristics of the channel medium is not to be regarded as noise insofar as these characteristics are known in advance. Ideally, the effects of such distortion can be completely compensated for by proper equipment at the receiver. Examples of noise are static, interference from power lines, crosstalk, thermal "noise," etc.

It is obvious that the system just described is exceedingly general and that an amazing number of communication systems can be made to fit this picture. Radio, telephony, and telegraphy have already been mentioned. A few more bizarre examples may serve to illustrate the generality of the system.

Automatic Door:

    Source—Stream of people interrupting light beam;
    Transmitter—Photocell and attendant circuitry;
    Channel—Wires leading to door-activating solenoid;
    Receiver—Solenoid mechanism;
    Destination—Door.

Royal Proclamation:

    Source—Speaking king;
    Transmitter—Scribe;
    Channel—Equestrian messenger;
    Receiver—Town crier;
    Destination—Populace at large.

The noise on the channel in the latter example can be taken as all the unpredictable hazards of journey, such as the messenger's temptation to stop for an ale at a roadside inn.

Although the actual equipment in the diagrammatic boxes of Figure 1 varies from one system to another (horse and man in one case—a pair of wires in another), it should be noted that the equipment in a given box serves the same overall function in every case. In all systems, the source serves to provide sequences of messages drawn from some list of possible messages. The transmitter, in every case, operates on the messages provided by the source, changing them into a form suitable for the channel. The channel transmits the new form of the message to a remote location. The noise disturbs the message on the channel. The receiver, in any system, tries to decide which message was impressed on the channel and revamps this guessed message into a form appropriate for the destination. It is to this simple observation, namely, the macroscopic function of the parts is the same for all systems, that information theory owes its great generality.

What the theory does is to replace each box of the diagram by a mathematical model intended to duplicate the large-scale behavior of the corresponding box. It then studies the interplay of these mathematical models and, by analyzing their interdependence, arrives at general theorems applicable to all those communication systems which can be represented by a block diagram of the sort pictured in Figure 1. The mathematical models themselves, apart from their interplay, are quite interesting.

The manner in which information theory draws conclusions about a wide class of communication systems through study of abstract mathematical models is analogous to similar procedures in many other sciences. In thermodynamics, for example, it is observed that a wide assortment of different physical systems exhibit the same sort of large-scale behavior in respect to their heat relations. In thermodynamics, therefore, the actual physical equipment is replaced by abstract mathematical models which have the same macroscopic behavior. Infinite heat reservoirs, perfectly insulating containers, ideal gases, etc., are invented and their interplay studied. These ideal components are described by certain parameters, such as temperature, energy, entropy, etc., and the study of the interplay of these ideal components results in relationships that must hold between the parameters. Such relationships are the well-known laws of thermodynamics. The parameters have real physical significance, and, in the laboratory, their values can be measured for any given piece of equipment. The laws of thermodynamics then permit one to make useful statements about that particular piece of equipment. It should be noted that the measurement of parameters in the laboratory usually requires a departure from the macroscopic point of view and an examination of the apparatus in detail.

Information theory is analogous to thermodynamics in this respect. With the mathematical models of information theory two parameters of real physical significance are associated. These are a parameter, H, associated with the source and called the "information rate" or "entropy" of the source, and a parameter, C, associated with the noisy channel and called the "channel capacity." The formal definitions of these two quantities in terms of the models of the theory are quite complicated and will not be given here. Their significance will become clearer in later pages of this chapter. It is important to note here, however, that these quantities are defined in such a way that, for any real communication system, the values of H and C can be determined by a sufficiently detailed examination of the system.

Study of the interplay of the mathematical models of the theory has led to a most important relationship connecting H and C. This relationship is known as the fundamental theorem of information theory and can be stated as follows:

Given a source producing information at the rate H and a noisy channel having a capacity C: if $H \leqq C$, then there exists a transmitter and receiver such that the messages produced by the *source can be delivered over the channel to a destination with arbitrarily small error rate; if $H > C$, then there is no possible way of transmitting the messages from the source over the channel to a destination without a certain fixed finite rate of errors.*

It is apparent from this theorem that C is a bound on the rate at which information can be sent over the noisy channel with the error rate kept arbitrarily small. The theorem does not explicitly indicate how to construct a transmitter and receiver which will make the error rate arbitrarily small when $H \leqq C$; it merely asserts that such a transmitter and receiver do exist. The proof of this fundamental theorem does indicate, however, the *general nature* of the transmitter and receiver needed. As might be expected, the closer H is to C, the more complicated are the operations performed by the transmitter and receiver in order to maintain a fixed small error rate in the messages delivered to the destination.

The following simple example may help to clarify this fundamental theorem and to indicate intuitively how it is that noisy channels do have a maximum rate for the transmission of information with arbitrarily small error. The example is, admittedly, completely artificial and of no practical consequence. It serves, however, to illustrate many of the principal features of communication systems in a rather clear and undisguised manner.

The source in the example will be a man reading letters of the English alphabet at some fixed rate. The transmitter will be a writer armed with a fountain pen. The channel consists of a large supply of one-inch square pieces of blotting paper which the transmitter can pass on to the receiver at the rate of one per second. The receiver is a reader who observes each piece of blotting paper which he receives and then pronounces a letter of the English alphabet. The destination is another man located near the receiver. The channel is clearly noisy, for the symbols made by the transmitter on the blotting paper tend to spread out, and it will not always be clear to the receiver what symbol was written by the transmitter. The assumption will be made that every letter read by the source has the same information content, so that the information rate of the source is proportional to the rate at which letters are produced. It will further be supposed that the writer can make instantaneously any symbol he may desire on the blotting paper and that the receiver can likewise read any symbol instantaneously.

For this system to transmit from the source to the destination, it is necessary that the transmitter and receiver arrange a code between themselves beforehand. For example, if the source is reading letters at the rate of one per second, the code could well be chosen to be the usual written form of English letters, namely $A, B, C, \ldots Z$. As the source pronounces a letter, the transmitter writes it on a blotting paper slip and passes it on to the receiver. The latter reads the letter to the destination. Since the source produces letters at the rate of one per second and since the transmitter can pass blotting paper slips at just this rate, all goes well. The probability of error at the destination is exceedingly small, for it is easy to distinguish among the twenty-six letters of the English alphabet when each is written in ink on a one-inch square of blotting paper.

Suppose, however, that the source doubles his rate, so that two English letters are produced each second. Since the transmitter can only pass the blotting paper slips at the rate of one per second, each slip must contain the information content of two English letters. The transmitter could do this by writing pairs of English letters produced by the source on each card. In this case, each letter on the card would occupy half as much space as formerly, and it would become somewhat more difficult for the receiver to interpret the letters properly. The transmitter and receiver could do better in combatting the noise-like property of the blotting paper by changing from English letters to some other scheme of notation. They could, for example, agree upon $26^2 = 676$ new symbols, one to represent each of the 26^2 possible pairs of English letters, $AA, AB \ldots ZY, ZZ$. These 676 new symbols should be chosen, of course, for maximum distinguishability when written in ink on blotting paper squares. By choosing the symbols with sufficient care, the transmitter and receiver can succeed in presenting the English letters to the destination with as small an error as desired.

If the source next increases his rate to three English letters per second, the transmitter and receiver must adopt a new code, containing 26^3 symbols, one to correspond to each triple of English letters from AAA to ZZZ. These 26^3 symbols must be chosen with considerable care, for to devise 17,576 different symbols capable of being distinguished with arbitrary accuracy, even when each is written in ink on a one-inch square of blotting paper, is not a simple problem. It will be assumed that such a set of symbols can be found.

As the source rate is continuously increased, however, the transmitter and receiver must devise codes with more and more symbols to be distinguished from each other with arbitrary accuracy. It is apparent that this situation cannot continue indefinitely. For some sufficiently great source rate, the transmitter and receiver will be called upon to invent a code with so many different symbols that, no matter how inventive or imaginative they may be, they will be unable to make the frequency of error at the receiver arbitrarily small. The very best code that they can devise with the necessary number of symbols will give a finite probability that certain of the letters will be confused and mistaken for each other. Nothing that they can do will reduce the frequency of errors at the destination below this value, for they are attempting to transmit information at a rate which exceeds the channel capacity.

Some obvious factors which determine the capacity of this blotting paper channel are the rate at which the squares of paper can be passed, the viscosity or stickiness of the ink, and the porosity of the blotting paper. The channel capacity is proportional to the rate at which the transmitter can pass the slips of blotting paper. If the stickiness of the ink is increased, symbols tend to spread less and the channel capacity is increased. If the paper is made more porous, written symbols tend to spread more, fewer different symbols can be accurately distinguished, and the channel capacity is decreased.

These three factors have their counterparts in the important band-limited electrical channel. The band-width corresponds to the rate at which blotting paper slips can be passed. The maximum frequency that the channel can accommodate indicates the number of independent pieces of information which can be sent per second. The signal power used on the channel corresponds to the viscosity of the ink. An increase in signal power enables the noise to be combatted more effectively. The noise power in the channel clearly corresponds to the porosity of the blotting paper.

In order to transmit information over the blotting paper channel at a rate less than the channel capacity with very small error rate, it is necessary to use an elaborate set of symbols, or, in language now becoming common, to " encode " the messages produced by the source. A similar situation holds true for the electrical channel. In order to signal with a small error rate, the voltage waves to be impressed on the channel must be most carefully chosen. This is the job of the transmitter, or, rather, of the man who designs the transmitter. Information theory provides some general hints about how to choose the best voltage waves in order to keep the error rate small. Unfortunately, the " encodings " suggested are complicated. The fact remains, however, that, through the use of these complicated encodings, communication systems can be made more error proof, or, alternatively, can be made to handle information at a greater rate without an increase in the occurrence of errors. The practical realization of these complicated encodings is a challenge to the communication engineers of the future.

Information Rate of a Message Source.

With the above brief sketch of the general structure of information theory as background, it now becomes possible to discuss in some detail the method whereby a numerical measure is attached to the information content of messages produced by a source. Such a discussion, however, requires a prior digression about the sources themselves.

Attention here will be restricted to the discrete source as opposed to the continuous source. A discrete source produces messages which are sequences of symbols, the symbols being drawn from some finite list. The most familiar example of such messages is printed English text, and the reader will find it helpful to keep English in mind during the following discussion. The sequence of telegrams passed to the telegrapher for transmission can be regarded as such a source of English text. Other examples of discrete sources are the input tape to a large computer, the string of symbols printed on a stock exchange ticker-tape, or the sequence of numbers representing the position of an aircraft at millisecond intervals presented by a radar to a gun computer.

In order to provide an analogy with English, the different symbols of the message will be called " letters," and the finite list of letters from which messages are composed will be called the " alphabet." The number of letters in the source alphabet will be called the " size " of the alphabet. For the sake of simplicity, all punctuation will be ignored in the discussion of printed English, and the alphabet will be considered as being of size 27, the usual twenty-six letters plus the space symbol. One further definition will prove useful. The occurrence of a letter in a message will be called a " character " regardless of which letter it is. For example, the word " Mississippi " contains eleven characters but only four different letters.

The first step in describing a given source is to list its alphabet. This is far from a complete description of the source, however, for the messages produced by most sources have an elaborate statistical structure. The character now being printed is not independent of characters just produced by the source, but depends upon them in a complicated way. One can rarely predict with certainty what the next character produced by a source will be; a best guess as to this next character, however, strongly depends upon how much of the past message one is permitted to see. If the source is a telegrapher and one sees the message " President Eisenho," he can be quite certain of what letter the next character will be. If, however, one is permitted to see only the last letter of the message, namely " o," his best guess concerning what will follow is not so clearly indicated.

The statistical structure of the messages produced by a given source can be described mathematically by associating with the source a long list of probabilities. The first probabilities on this list are p_i, the probability that the source will produce the ith letter of the source alphabet. These quantities reflect the best guess as to what letter the source will produce when none of the text already produced is seen.

The next set of characterizing numbers for the source are quantities p_{ij}, the conditional probability that the source will next produce the jth letter of the alphabet when it is known to have just produced the ith letter. Next, one can list quantities p_{ijk}, the probability that the source will next produce the kth letter of the alphabet when it is known that the source has just produced the ith letter followed by the jth letter. Clearly, it is possible to go on in this manner, listing probabilities which give information about the increasingly long-range structure of the messages. In the mathematical model of a message source used in information theory, this list of probabilities along with the source alphabet characterizes a particular source.

In actual sources, the infinitely remote past of a message certainly exerts no influence on characters being printed now. In fact, for many sources, correlation between characters does not extend at all far into the past. Sources can be classified, then, according to the number of past characters that exert an influence upon the character being produced by the source at the present moment. A source in which the past characters exert no influence on the present character is called a " monogram " source; one in which only the last character produced influences the choice is called a " digram " source, etc.

Consideration of some concrete examples of sources of various classes may serve to clarify these ideas. In every example, the alphabet will be the twenty-six letters A to Z, plus the space symbol. The simplest monogram source using this alphabet is one in which every letter is chosen independently with equal probability. A typical message for such a source is:

XFOML RXKHRJFFJUJ ZLPWCFWKCYJ FFJEYVKCQSGXYD.

This message was generated by putting 27 chips bearing letters A through the space symbol in an urn and by making drawings (with replacement) from the urn. A slightly more complicated monogram source would assign unequal probabilities to the various letters. The following message was produced by such a source:

OCRO HLI RGWR NMIELWIS EU IL NBNESEBYA TH.

The " urn " used in this case contained 1305 chips labeled E, 781 labeled A, 129 labeled G, 9 marked Z, etc. The numbers chosen are proportional to the actual letter frequencies in English text. The message is what English would look like if there were no correlation between letters.

To demonstrate a digram source, twenty-seven urns are required, each of which is labeled with one of the twenty-seven letters, and each of which contains varying numbers of chips bearing letters of the alphabet. Thus, when the letter R is produced in the message, a drawing is then made from the urn labeled R in order to determine the next letter of the message. If that next letter proves to be an E, the following drawing is made from the urn labeled E, and so forth. A typical message is:

ON IE ANTSOUTINYS ARE T INCTORE ST BE
S DEAMY ACHIN D ILONASIVE TUCDOWE AT
TEASONARE FUSO.

In the actual experiment as performed, the urn labeled T contained 315 chips marked H, 128 marked I, 16 marked W, 4 marked V, etc. That is, the urns were populated according to the probabilities p_{ij} for actual English text. These latter quantities were established experimentally by means of frequency counts of pairs of letters in books, newspapers, and other printed matter. The message shown is what English would look like if correlation between letters existed only for adjacent characters. It is interesting to note that so many of the words are pronounceable.

For the trigram source, a sample message is:

> IN NO IST LAT WHEY CRATICT FROURE BIRS GROCID
> PONDENOME OF DEMONSTURES OF THE REPTAGIN IS
> REGOACTIONA.

Once again, the urns used to generate this message were populated so as to provide messages with the same trigram structure as in English. For example, the urn labelled *IS* contained *A*'s *B*'s, *C*'s, etc., in numbers proportional to the probabilities that *IS* would be followed by *A*, *B*, *C*, etc., in actual English. With just this small amount of structure, the result is surprisingly similar to English.

One could, of course, go on in this manner to construct " urn " sources with outputs more and more closely resembling English. The task of determining the higher order probabilities, p_{ijkl}, p_{ijklm}, etc., for English becomes, however, prohibitive. There is, though, a simple way of circumventing all this data gathering and, since it results in a process which can be amusing, it will be described here.

The process requires several experimenters, who, for convenience, will be called *A*, *B*, *C*, etc. Experimenter *A* has a sentence in mind. He writes down one word of that sentence and passes the word to *B*, requesting *B* to add a word. In adding his word, *B* must have in mind a sentence in which *A*'s word occurs followed by *B*'s word. *B* then folds *A*'s word under so that only the word he has added is visible, and passes the paper on to *C*. *C*, in turn, adds a word, folds the paper and passes it on to *D*, and so forth. Those who speak English have unconsciously acquired an enormous knowledge of the statistics of English. It is this knowledge that enables one to complete a half-finished cliché or to understand the speech of others in noisy surroundings. The word which *B* writes, therefore, will be chosen by him according to actual probabilities in English for words following *A*'s word. This is, in fact, a digram source in which the basic units are words rather than letters.

The following are samples of quatrigram word English constructed in a similar manner. Each experimenter saw three words and added one word. The samples represent English as it would appear if correlation between letters extended for only twenty or so characters.

In each case, the experimenters were previously advised of the subject matter.

Salaries. Money isn't everything. However, we need considerably more incentive to produce efficiently. On the other hand, too little and too late to suggest a raise without a reason for remuneration obviously less than they need although they really are extremely meager.

Murder Story. When I killed her I stabbed Claude between his powerful jaws clamped cruelly together. Screaming loudly despite fatal consequences in the struggle for life began ebbing as he coughed hollowly spitting blood from his ears. Burial seemed unnecessary since further division was necessary.

Sources, then, are characterized mathematically by an alphabet and a list of probabilities. The probabilities to be associated with a given real physical source can be found through examination of long messages produced by the source and a count of their letter frequencies, letter-pair frequencies, etc. Consideration can now be given to the method for numerically measuring the information content of messages produced by a given source.

The following situation will serve as an example. A customer wishes to order a certain lawn mower from a large mail order house. He can inform the company of his wish in many ways. He can write, " I would like one lawn mower, 16″ cutting blades, rubber wheels, etc.," or he might use the catalogue number and write, " I want one item #13574." In either case, the customer's letter succeeds in telling the mail order house what it is that he wants; intuitively, one feels that both messages have the same information content insofar as the company is concerned. How can this content be measured numerically? The only obvious number involved here is the number N of different items carried by the mail order house. From the company's point of view, both of the customer's letters succeed in specifying one object out of N. Tentatively, the information content of either message can be set equal to $f(N)$. Intuitively, one would like f to be an increasing function of N. A message which succeeds in specifying one object out of a million objects contains more information than a message specifying one object out of two.

Now let it be assumed that, in addition to ordering a lawn mower, the customer also writes to a seed supplier for a bag of a certain type of grass seed. The seed supplier can, say, furnish its customers with any one of M different items. With a letter requesting seed, therefore, the information content $f(M)$ must be associated. Now the mail order house and the seed supplier taken together can supply their customers with NM pairs of items. With the two letters written by the customer, therefore, $f(NM)$ units of information must be associated. Taken separately, the letters had $f(N)$ and $f(M)$ units of information, respectively. It is natural, then, to require that:

$$f(N) + f(M) = f(NM).$$

That is to say, it is required that the sum of the information contents of the two letters taken separately be equal to the information content of the two letters considered as one long message.

A solution to the functional equation just written is $f(N) = \log N$, which permits the formal definition: The information content of a message that specifies one object from a list of N a priori equally likely objects is $H = \log_2 N$ bits.

The choice of the base for the logarithm corresponds to a choice of units for measuring information. The base 2 is most commonly used, for then a message specifying one object out of two equally likely objects has one unit of information. The situation whereby one is to choose one object from a list of two is, of course, the simplest non-trivial case. Only when base 2 is used are the units of information called " bits," an abbreviated form of " binary digits."

The above definition indicates the method for measuring the information content of messages produced by the simplest type of source mentioned earlier, namely the monogram source with an N letter alphabet in which every letter is produced with the same probability, $1/N$. A single character produced by such a source is a message. Since, a priori, any one of N letters was equally likely, with this one character produced by the source there must be associated $\log_2 N$ bits of information. In a message produced by this source which is x characters long, conceivably the source might have produced any one of N^x different messages with equal probability. With the actual message produced, then, there must be associated $H_x = \log_2 N^x = x \log_2 N$ bits of information. The information content *per character* of this message is $H_x/x = \log_2 N$ bits, as before. Since the probability that the source will produce the ith letter of the source alphabet is

$p_i = 1/N$ for this simple source, the information content per character of messages produced by this source can be written as:

$$H = - \log_2 p_i \text{ bits/character.}$$

These notions can be extended so as to assign an information content per character to the messages produced by the more complicated sources previously mentioned. For the monogram source in which letters are not all equally likely, one obtains the formula:

$$H = - \sum_i p_i \log_2 p_i \text{ bits/character.}$$

for the average information content per character of messages. Here the sum is over all letters of the source alphabet. For the digram source, one obtains the formula:

$$H = - \sum_{ij} p_i p_{ij} \log_2 p_{ij} \text{ bits/character.}$$

Similar formulae can be written down for sources with longer range statistics. These formulae are, in form, similar to expressions found in statistical mechanics for the entropy of a system. For this reason, the quantity called " the information content per character " of messages produced by a source has also come to be known as the " entropy " of the source.

Starting from very simple intuitive notions of information, one is able to develop rather elaborate formulae which indicate the method for computing the information content per character of messages produced by complicated sources. This information content is measured in bits per character. One bit is the amount of information to be associated with the choice of one object out of two a priori equally likely objects. Such a choice may be called a simple " alternative." The number H associated with the messages produced by a source would seem, then, to indicate, on the average, to how many simple alternatives the message is equivalent on a per character basis.

This interpretation is indeed borne out by the following theorem:

Given a source producing message with information content H bits per character, it is possible to encode these messages into a form containing only two letters, say 0 and 1, in such a way that a message of N characters length produced by the source will be represented on the average by a string of 0's and 1's NH characters long.

The theorem, as just stated, lacks some mathematical refinements, but it conveys the general idea and is a strong justification for the measure of the information that has been adopted above.

A simple example will serve to illustrate this theorem. Let it be assumed that there is a monogram source producing the letters A, B, C, D with probabilities 1/2, 1/4, 1/8, 1/8, respectively. A typical message produced by the source might read:

BCBBADABAADACDABBAACAABACABC.

If one uses the formula $H = -\sum p_i \log_2 p_i$, one finds that the information content per character of messages produced by this source is 7/4 bits per character.

Next, the message produced by this source can be encoded into 0's and 1's with the following correspondence:

$$A \to 0$$
$$B \to 10$$
$$C \to 110$$
$$D \to 111.$$

The above message then becomes:

1011010100111010001110110. . . . .

It is not difficult to see that this string of 0's and 1's can be decoded in a unique manner to yield the original A-B-C-D message.

One can now compute the average number of characters in the 0-1 message per character of the A-B-C-D message. For every A, there corresponds one character in the 0-1 message. For every B, there are two characters, and for every C or D there are three characters. Now A occurs 1/2 of the time, B, 1/4 of the time, etc. Therefore, the average number of 0's and 1's per character of the A-B-C-D message is:

$$1/2 \times 1 + 1/4 \times 2 + 1/8 \times 3 + 1/8 \times 3 = 7/4$$

which is just the number of bits per character already computed for this source.

The entropy of English text has been computed by Shannon and others through a variety of techniques. It turns out to be quite low. Best estimates seem to place its value at about one bit per character. In view of the above theorem, this means that a typical book in English could be rewritten so as to contain only 0's and 1's without alteration in the length of the book. The complicated rules of English spelling and grammar cause the alphabet of twenty-seven letters to be used most inefficiently. A two-letter alphabet could be used to convey the same messages without increasing their length on the average.

This inefficiency of English can be expressed in another way. It can be shown that the maximum entropy obtainable from a source using twenty-seven letters is 4.75 bits per character. This entropy is obtained from the monogram source in which twenty-seven letters are equally likely. Since the entropy of English is only one bit per character, we say that English has an efficiency of 1/4.75, or that English is only 21 per cent efficient. This statement has the following meaning. It is possible to encode English into messages using twenty-seven letters in such a way that the new form of the message will be, on the average, only 21 per cent as long as the original English text. This fact can also be expressed by saying that English is 79 per cent redundant.

The ability to measure redundancy and to eliminate it by proper encoding clearly has important implications for the communications engineer. Most of the messages with which he deals are highly redundant. The redundancy of television signals, for example, is, in all likelihood, greater than 99 per cent. Space does not permit a detailed description of the attempts which have so far been made to remove this redundancy prior to transmission.

The notion of information content can be applied to problems outside the strict domain of communications engineering, as a few simple examples may illustrate. A magician places three columns of cards face up on the table. Each column contains ten cards. A "victim" is asked mentally to choose one card and to indicate the column in which it lies. The magician then picks up the cards, rearranges them, and again lays them out in three columns of ten. The "victim" again indicates the column in which his card lies. This process is repeated once more. After the "victim" indicates the column for the third time, the magician announces the card. Is this trick possible?

The magician must select one card from thirty equally likely cards. He must, therefore, be supplied with $H_M = \log_2 30 = 4.90$ bits. Each time the "victim" specifies a column, he potentially supplies the magician with $\log_2 3$ bits of information, since he designates one column out of three. He does this three times and, therefore, supplies the magician with, at most, $3 \log_2 3 = \log_2 27 = 4.75$ bits of information. This is less than the amount needed by the magician so that the trick, as stated, is impossible.

Had the magician used twenty-seven cards placed in three columns of nine cards each, the computation would have been $H_M = \log_2 27$ bits needed by the magician, $\log_2 27$ bits potentially supplied by the "victim." In that case, one cannot draw any definite conclusion as to whether or not the trick is possible. Potentially, the magician is given sufficient information to determine the card. Whether or not he can devise a means of rearranging the cards so as to make full use of this potential information is another matter. As it happens, he can in this case. The essential point is for the magician to pick the cards up by columns, always picking up the designated column second. He must then lay the cards out by rows. The reader can now easily work out the details.

A simple application of the measure of information can be made to many guessing games. In a common form of guessing game, one must determine an object from a list of N objects by asking questions. Usually, the questions are restricted to those requiring a "yes" or "no" answer. The questioner, therefore, receives one bit of information per question. Ideally, $\log_2 N$ bits are needed to specify the object, so that a clever questioner should, on the average, require $\log_2 N$ questions to identify the object. Sometimes the list of objects to be determined is not very well defined, as in that form of the game of Twenty Questions where the object to be determined is described typically by a four-word English phrase. That is, if the average word is taken as containing five letters, the usual object to be identified is a twenty-character English test message. Now the entropy of English text is one bit per character, so that about twenty bits of information are needed, on the average, to determine the object. Since twenty bits is just what the questioner is allowed, a skillful player should frequently be able to determine the object. As the reader is well aware, such is the case; hence the game's interest.

Suboptimization in
Operations Problems

CHARLES HITCH
and ROLAND McKEAN

IN OPERATIONS research, scientific knowledge and method assist in the choice among alternative means (including newly devised means) of achieving objectives.[1] The "means" may be alternative motions, factory layouts, operational procedures, objects of expenditure, allocations of a budget, or other kinds of alternatives. It is readily apparent that no intelligent evaluation of the means can be made without reference to the "ends" or "objectives." When one refers to the efficiency of a steam engine, one means its *useful* output in relation to input.[2] If the word "useful" is omitted, "efficiency" loses its significance; the law of the conservation of energy requires that all inputs become outputs in some form; without the notion of useful output, therefore, efficiency is always 100 per cent. Furthermore, some care must be taken to define useful output. A steam engine may be relatively inefficient in getting usable energy from fuel, yet relatively efficient in making profits for a particular establishment.

In brief, the real objectives must be kept constantly in mind. Of

[1] See also Charles Hitch, "Suboptimization in Operations Problems," *Journal of the Operations Research Society of America*, Vol. 1, No. 3 (May 1953), pp. 87-99.

[2] F. H. Knight, *The Economic Organization* (The University of Chicago, 1933), p. 8.

course, the concept of ends or objectives is not a mere listing of several desirable goods or events, but may be visualized as a preference surface relating a firm's profits (or a group's well-being, or an individual's utility) to various combinations of goods and events. Such a surface reflects the function that one would actually want to maximize.

In operations research, criteria are the practical counterparts of, or substitutes for, the functions which one would like to maximize in choosing among alternative courses of action. If it were possible, one would like to compare alternative policies or operations by projecting the streams of utility, profits, or well-being under each of the various alternatives; then one could choose the policy which yielded the "largest" stream. In real problems, however, it is necessary to examine some proximate criterion that serves to represent what is happening to utility, profits, or well-being. Criteria that can be used in actual problems are usually not the functions whose maximization is desired; rather, they are *proximate* indicators.

This point can be illustrated with a simple example. An industrial-machinery firm might wish to compare alternative methods of delivering parts to customers. Ideally, the firm's criterion in this as in other choices would be the maximization of profits.[3] The firm's analysts, however, would probably approach the problem through the use of some proximate criterion. They might adopt any of a number of possibilities: maximum expected profits, if they could be projected; maximum revenues for a given cost, or minimum cost of generating a given volume of revenue; maximum volume of deliveries within a specified time period for a given cost, or minimum cost of achieving a specified type and number of deliveries.

[3] Under uncertainty, the maximization of profits (or of utility, etc.) has to mean the maximization of some *function* of the profits expected in various periods and with various "probabilities." At best, management can make only the following sort of projections: Under Policy 1, expected profits will be X_1 in the first period, X_2 in the next period, etc.; under Policy 2, expected profits will be Y_1 (less than X_1) in the first period, Y_2 (greater than X_2) in the second period, etc.; under Policy 3, expected profits will be greater than under alternative policies in every period, but there is a greater risk, on the other hand, of suffering huge losses. For a discussion of this point, see A. Alchian, "Uncertainty, Evolution, and Economic Theory," *The Journal of Political Economy*, Vol. 18, No. 3 (June, 1950), pp. 211-21, or S. Enke, "On Maximizing Profits," *American Economic Review*, Vol. 41, No. 4 (September, 1951), pp. 566-78.

Now the validity and, therefore, the usefulness of operations research depend to a great extent upon the shrewdness with which such criteria are selected. Too often, the criterion problem has been " solved " by the acceptance of the first plausible objectives function which occurs to the researchers; if several such functions spring to mind, all are tried and the research people compromise (or allow the business executive or military commander to compromise) among the results of alternative computations. The problem is much too important for such casual treatment. The calculation of quantitative solutions based on the wrong criteria is equivalent to providing answers to the wrong questions. Moreover, while the customer can help the research group by describing his general objectives, the researchers must and should select the proximate criterion. It is an inescapable part of their task. No one is going to hand *appropriate* criteria to them on a platter. Unless operations research develops methods of evaluating criteria and choosing good ones, its quantitative methods may prove worse than useless to clients.

Difficulties of Criteria Selection in Suboptimization.

One of the main reasons that criteria selection is difficult is the fact that one always deals with incomplete optimization and suboptimization. It may be helpful to distinguish between the two. Full optimization would require: (1) simultaneous consideration of all possible allocations of one's resources, that is, all possible alternatives and all possible allocations among those alternatives; (2) consideration of the probable impacts of all exogenous events (i. e., those not under the optimizer's control); and (3) the maximization, subject to certain initial constraints, of the utility function of the optimizer (who would be an individual, the managers of a firm, or the decision-makers in a government).

Any piece of operations research falls short in all three respects. First, operations research considers only a few of the possible alternatives and, usually, only a few allocations of resources among those alternatives in the attempt to select an optimum policy. The hypothetical industrial-machinery firm comparing methods of delivering parts will serve as an example. The company may compare the results of using railway shipments with the consequences of operating its own fleet of trucks. In this process, they may ignore air freight, or some other method, and thus risk missing the best answer. It may not be enough to consider all alternatives which are "close substitutes." The difficulty is that relevant alternatives are not always obvious substitutes; they are often dissimilar in physical appearance or even in their specific functions. Indeed, in the extreme, *all* the things which a firm buys are alternative objects of expenditure which can contribute to the general objective, even though their specific functions are widely different. Bookkeepers and overhead cranes, telephones and typewriter ribbons are all alternatives, substitutable in varying degrees, and competing for the purchasing agent's check. It is obviously impossible to consider the entire range of alternatives. Furthermore, it is remarkably easy to overlook a crucial course of action which, if considered explicitly, might drastically change the preferred allocation of funds among the various alternatives.

A second reason that operations research deals with incomplete optimization is that it is possible to make only a few assumptions about events other than those which are controlled. To return to the example of the industrial-machinery firm, some event not explicitly considered might affect revenues or costs with railroad shipments differently from the way it would affect revenues or costs with the firm's own fleet of trucks or with air freight. Operations might suddenly expand on the west coast; the price of gasoline might rise; competition might emerge from a different quarter. Even if the optimizer were able to quantify expectations about such occurrences, he could not conceivably take into account all possible contingencies.

Finally, incomplete optimization is almost inevitable because one must nearly always use an imperfect criterion. Presumably, the industrial-machinery firm would really want to "maximize profits." But the firm's analysts might be unable to translate the use of various delivery systems into effects of expected sales, expected costs, and, ultimately, expected profits. They might settle for a more manageable, though less appropriate, criterion, and, for example, choose the delivery system which minimized the cost of achieving a 48-hour delivery service, or the system which minimized the cost of delivering parts regardless of the by-product effects on the cost of delivering other items. As mentioned earlier, the criterion is likely to be a proximate one—and an imperfect one that fails to reflect the full range of effects on revenues, costs, and profits.

Incomplete optimization, then, is unavoidably the task of operations research. And incomplete optimizations will not automatically reveal optimal choices; they may give worse results than the flipping of coins. It is incumbent upon the researcher to use care and judgment to select those partial optimizations which look promising and to establish appropriate criteria in terms of which to judge the alternative courses of action.

Actually, the operations researcher always encounters a special variety of incomplete optimization which has been called "suboptimization." In governmental or business operations, different administrative levels allocate the resources at their disposal among the uses under their supervision. For example, at relatively high levels, the federal budget is allocated among Departments (Interior, Defense, Agriculture, etc.), the independent agencies, and broad programs. The allocations of funds among different projects and operations within programs are accomplished by lower-level administrators who face narrower problems. The same is true in large business corporations; broad decisions are made at the top level; divisions or departments choose among narrower ranges of alternatives; and the shop foremen choose among alternative work schedules or shop operational procedures. Even the individual may find that he optimizes at different "levels." He may allocate his income among such broad categories as food, clothing, and housing, then select the individual cuts of meat and suits of clothes which fall under these larger headings. Suboptimization is this process of choosing among a relatively small number of alternatives by an administrative level other than the highest.

The difficulties of selecting proximate criteria are aggravated by the necessity of suboptimizing. Unless criteria are selected with great skill, operations analysis may improve a department's efficiency in terms of some plausible test, yet actually decrease the firm's efficiency in terms of its ability to make profits. As the organization grows and the number of levels increases, the chances for adopting inferior criteria multiply. If the sales department of a firm fights to maximize the ratio of sales per dollar of selling expense or the shop strives to minimize "seconds" or "rejects" per month, it may cause the firm as a whole to sacrifice profits. In government, it is usually impossible to measure the counterpart of a firm's profits, and suboptimization criteria can get still further out of hand. The criterion of an office's efficiency may be the number of licenses granted per dollar spent, or the number of letters written per typist. Such criteria, particularly ratios, may not lead to increased efficiency in terms of what the government really wants to do.

Even where downright errors about the nature of appropriate criteria are avoided, suboptimization poses obstacles to other aspects of criteria selection. In general terms, the appropriate criterion for the firm, government, or individual seems to be maximization of gains minus costs (*not* the ratio of gains to costs). For purposes of operational analysis, this still leaves large, unanswered questions. Precisely what should be counted as the costs of the alternative operations or policies? The costs of one alternative ought to measure the gains that might have been obtained through other uses of the same resources. The costs of a firm's operating its own fleet of trucks are whatever must be given up in order to do this. If the trucks must be purchased, the cost is the dollar outlay over the relevant period, minus salvage value at the end of the period. If the trucks are already on hand, the cost is not their original cost but rather their current value in alternative uses. This may be merely their resale, or even scrap, value. If, however, the trucks could be used to advantage in another department or operation, their value in that alternative use—if greater than the amount for which they could be sold—would be their cost to this operation. In suboptimizations, particularly for government or military operations, it is easy to overlook the worth of equipment and various resources in other departments.

Suboptimization aggravates another aspect of deciding what costs should be included. In operational analysis pertaining to one department's operations, it is easy to neglect the indirect effect on the costs of other operations. For example, the use of trucks in one department may increase transportation costs in other departments by making less-than-carload shipments necessary.

In addition to costs of each alternative, the gains to be derived from each must be considered. Again, there are many problems. Precisely what should be included in the calculation of gains? In operations analysis, the researchers often " set " the gains; that is, they specify a fixed objective and attempt to determine the cheapest way of achieving these gains. This is not the *ideal* criterion, but it is often satisfactory, and it serves to bring out the problems of suboptimization.

If the gains are "set," the difficulty is the selection of a reasonable fixed objective. It is hazardous to narrow the objective to a single variable (unless profit-streams can be estimated under each of the policies). In the case of the industrial-machinery firm, the operations researcher comparing alternative methods of delivering machine parts could not restrict himself to such a goal as 48-hour service to all customers; in addition, he would be concerned with the reliability of delivery and the condition of parts on arrival. Also he ought to take into account the possible gains to other operations. For instance, if this hypothetical machinery company delivered parts with its own fleet of trucks rather than via air freight, it could presumably use the sides of the trucks for advertising. These gains, which might conceivably be substantial, would occur in a different department. In short, it is not always a simple matter to measure gains, or to fix a reasonable objective, from the firm's, rather than the suboptimizing department's, point of view.

From this standpoint—the difficulties of measuring the gains, or of specifying an appropriate fixed objective—there are three kinds of suboptimizations. First, there is the "one-dimensional" objectives function in which there is only one important objective or, if there are several, all can be reduced, in practice, to a single measure. For example, if a family, in suballocating its travel budget, wants to go to New York by the cheapest means of transportation and cares nothing about other transportation variables, the objectives function is one-dimensional and the operations researcher can make a definite recommendation. Second, there is the kind of multi-dimensional objectives function in which all *important* objectives are subject to quantitative analysis. The same family, for example, may be interested in both cheapness and safety in travel, but will be unable to place a money value on safety. Operations research can analyze both factors and present the facts to the family, which must exercise judgment in reaching a decision. A third type is the partial suboptimization in which objectives which are known to be important are omitted because they are not subject to quantitative analysis. Thus, if the family thinks it attaches importance to the thrill of a first airplane trip, an experienced operations researcher might help in putting the "thrill" factor in proper perspective, but he would use no computing equipment to accomplish this.

There are, of course, problems in which no relevant quantitative calculations are possible. Suppose that our family cannot decide whether to spend its vacation in New York, Boston, or Washington, and the operations researcher discovers, through preliminary reconnaissance, that its members have two primary vacation objectives, namely, visiting historical monuments and eating good food. Background studies on the culinary and historical merits of the alternatives would be of assistance to the family in making its choice, but such studies would be essentially nonquantitative.

Examples of Criterion Problems.

The criterion problem is simplest in industrial operations research; there the measuring rod of money, which is appropriate for both gains and costs, sometimes permits the use of a one-dimensional objectives function—the profits of the operations or (at a higher level) of the firm. There are, however, complications associated with uncertainty and time as well as temptations to maximize or minimize physical quantities whose measurement is easy but whose relationship to profits is obscure. As indicated earlier, straight, hard thinking about criteria is, therefore, necessary even in industrial applications. In military operations research, more difficulty is encountered, since the problem is usually a suboptimization with a multidimensional objectives function as well as some important nonquantifiable factors. This requires that a great deal of judgment be exercised in the interpretation of results, either by the operations researcher in making recommendations or by the commander in deciding whether and how to implement them.

Occasionally, an obviously appropriate one-dimensional objectives function permits a neat, simple, and completely persuasive solution to be presented, even in military applications. But criteria which appear plausible or even obvious at first glance are quite likely to turn out to be traps for the unwary.

The operations research solution to the convoy problem in World War II provides an excellent example. This case, described by Morse and Kimball,[4] perfectly illustrates the dangers of suboptimizing with

[4] Philip M. Morse and George E. Kimball, *Methods of Operations Research* (Cambridge, Massachusetts: The Technology Press of the Massachusetts Institute of Technology; New York: John Wiley and Sons, Inc.; and London: Chapman and Hall, Ltd., 1951), pp. 46-48.

a partial objectives function; yet action based on this study happened to be right, undoubtedly because of the good sense and judgment of both the operations researchers and the commanders involved.

The data which were collected revealed that, over a wide range, the number of merchant vessels sunk in a U-boat attack on a convoy was proportional to the number of U-boats in the attacking pack and inversely proportional to the number of destroyer escorts, but independent of the size of the convoy. They also revealed that the number of U-boats sunk per attack was directly proportional both to the number of attacking U-boats and the number of defending escorts. The objectives function was taken, quite plausibly, to be the "exchange rate" or ratio of enemy losses, measured in U-boats, to Allied losses, measured in merchant ships.

The conclusion was as follows: "The important facts to be deduced from this set of equations seem to be: (1) the number of ships lost per attack is independent of the size of the convoy, and (2) the exchange rate seems to be proportional to the square of the number of escort vessels per convoy. This squared effect comes about due to the fact that the number of merchant vessels lost is *reduced*,[5] and at the same time the number of U-boats lost per attack is *increased*,[5] when the escorts are increased, the effect coming in twice in the exchange rate. The effect of pack size cancels out in the exchange rate. *From any point of view, therefore, the case for large convoys is a persuasive one.*[6]

"When the figures quoted here were presented to the appropriate authorities, action was taken to increase the average size of convoys, thereby also increasing the average number of escort vessels per convoy. As often occurs in cases of this sort, the eventual gain was much *greater*[5] than that predicted by the above reasoning, because by increasing convoy and escort size the exchange rate $(U/B$ sunk$)/(M/V$ sunk$)$ was increased to a point where it became unprofitable for the Germans to attack North Atlantic convoys, and the U-boats went elsewhere. This defeat in the North Atlantic contributed to the turning point in the 'Battle of the Atlantic.' "[7]

This happy outcome depended on the intuition and good sense

[5] Italics the authors'.
[6] Italics ours.
[7] *Op. Cit.*, p. 48.

of the participants rather than upon a sophisticated choice of criterion. The criterion actually chosen is subject to criticism from many points of view. For example, while enemy losses and our losses would clearly both be important elements in the ideal objectives function, there is no reason (and none is suggested by the authors) why one should be divided by the other. Prima facie, it would appear that the absolute magnitude of either loss is too important to be ignored.

What is far more important in this case is the complete neglect of another dimension of the objectives function which appears to be as important as those considered, namely, the reduced operating efficiency of ships in large convoys, and hence the inverse relation between the size of convoy and the capacity of any given number of merchant ships to transport men and materiel across the Atlantic. It does not seem that the case for large convoys is a persuasive one " from any point of view." Collecting a large convoy takes time. The arrival of a large convoy swamps port facilities, which means longer turn-around time. Because the speed of a convoy cannot exceed that of the slowest ship, there is an inverse average relationship between its size and speed. It might well be worth a few additional sinkings to insure the delivery in time of the forces required for the Normandy invasion. The complete omission of this objectives dimension is curious because it is so admirably adapted to analysis by quantitative methods. Presumably the explanation is that a quantitative analysis had already been made, perhaps by others, of the effect of convoy size on the carrying capacity of the merchant fleet, and the commander was therefore able to weigh the gain *and the cost* of marginal increments in convoy size.

That something was wrong with their plausible criterion should have been immediately evident to the authors; it proves far, far too much. It shows that it would be desirable to increase the size of convoys without limit—until the whole merchant fleet and all the destroyers are assembled in a single convoy. Morse and Kimball warn the reader that the equation cannot be expected to be valid for " very small " and " very large " values; this, however, is the conventional admonition against extrapolating functions far beyond the range of the data from which they are derived. The point is that, long before the whole Atlantic Fleet became a single convoy, the significant reductions in losses would have been achieved and the reduction in the efficiency of utilizing shipping would have become unacceptable. Of course, regardless of the criterion used, it will always be necessary to use judgment and good sense in applying the results of operations research; the researcher, however, should try to find criteria which place a less overwhelming burden on these qualities.

A further word about the convoy case seems appropriate. Morse and Kimball, in writing it up, emphasized the fact that the results of the recommended action were even more successful than the equations had predicted, because the U-boat fleet was withdrawn and sent elsewhere on other missions. This is really a case of taking one's suboptimization criterion too seriously. By the criterion, results were better than predicted, but if one considers a higher-level criterion— say, the effect on the probability of Allied victory—the presumption is that Allied operations other than in the Atlantic were adversely affected by the diversion of the U-boat fleet. Moreover, if one assumes that the Germans reached a rational decision, their U-boats, or the resources going into them, made a more significant contribution to German prospects of victory in the war elsewhere, after enlargement of the convoys, than they could have made by continuing to operate in the North Atlantic. In terms of the higher criterion, the effect of implementing the recommendation on the probability of winning the war was *less* than one would infer from the calculation of results in the North Atlantic, which was based on the assumption that enemy U-boat tactics and deployment would remain unchanged. As operations are changed, different tactics and deployment become optimal for the enemy; by adopting them, he can reduce his loss, as he did on this occasion.

The point is an important one—in many cases more important than it probably was in this instance, for the North Atlantic, while not the only shipping area, was by far the most vital one within easy reach of German U-boats. Suppose, for example, a railway net were to be defended against air attack. The researchers might decide that the net was most vulnerable to attack on its bridges and then carry out operations analysis to determine tactics and deployment for minimizing damage to bridges. If such tactics were then put into effect, the results in terms of damaged bridges might well be "even better" than predicted. The enemy would probably direct his attack not at the defended bridges, but at the undefended tunnels or rolling stock or open lines.

The moral in this type of case is that the low level suboptimization criterion is not good enough. Effects must be assessed at least at the next higher level, in terms of the *operation* or function which is being defended against enemy attack. Furthermore, some capacity for rational adjustment to our tactics must be attributed to the enemy—using, if not the analytic methods of game theory, at least some of its concepts and spirit.

Suboptimization in Economic Theory.

Economic theory is unusual and perhaps unique among disciplines in having attempted to explore the characteristics of operations criteria, and the closely associated question of the relationship between lower and higher-level suboptimization. This has been done in a very different terminology, and has largely been confined to a particular context, that of the economy. Some of the conclusions and insights achieved, however, have wide applicability to operations research in other contexts; indeed they constitute the modest beginnings of scientific analysis of the problem of selecting operations criteria.

The relevant portions of economic theory attempt to analyse the effect of maximizing or optimizing behavior by individuals and firms in the economy upon the production of the economy. The theory therefore constitutes an analysis of the relations between suboptimizing at two levels—a lower and a higher—and specifically of the consequences, in terms of a higher-level criterion, of actions dictated by alternative lower-level criteria.

An important conclusion of this branch of economics is that, on certain assumptions which will not be examined here, profit maximizing behavior on the part of individuals and firms results, for any given level of employment of resources, in an " efficient " organization of production in the economy—in the precisely defined sense that it is impossible to produce more of any single good or service without producing less of some other.[8] There are a number of ways in which this economic theory can be generally useful in dealing with certain operations research problems.

1. For the firm's suboptimizing, the test of profit maximization as a criterion is the effect on production in the economy. *Similarly, in operations research, the test for " good " criteria is always consistency*

[8] Leisure is counted, rightly, as an economic good.

with a " good" criterion at a higher level. Thus, in the convoy example, the test of the exchange rate as a suboptimization criterion was consistency with the higher-level criterion of probability of victory; there proved to be, in the general case, no necessary connection. This appeal to higher levels involves no circular chasing of mirages, but acceptance, at some level of optimization, of an authoritative or self-evident statement of objective.

2. *Where, for practical convenience, a suboptimization criterion must be used which is known to be inconsistent with a higher-level criterion, allowance must be made for gains and losses imposed on other operations related to the higher-level criterion.*

The profit-maximization criterion in economics results in maximum production in the economy only if " social " product equals " private " product, and " social " cost equals " private " cost. If a farmer, in draining his field, also drains his neighbor's, social product exceeds private. If the smog generated by an oilman's refining operations imposes costs on the city of Los Angeles, social costs exceed private. Divergences of this kind in *either* direction lead to uneconomic use of resources from the point of view of the economy as a whole.

Examples in all types of operations research are plentiful. It would apparently have been easy to win the Battle of the Atlantic against the U-boats in such a way as to have imperiled Operation Overlord. Certain methods of carrying out Air Force missions impose special burdens on Army, Navy or other air operations, or, alternatively, relieve them of burdens previously assumed. In industrial operations research related to a single process, product, or plant of a company, it is almost inevitable that solutions will affect, favorably or adversely, other operations of the company.

Occasionally it is possible to take divergences between private and social (or, in operations research, lower and higher) criteria explicitly into account in the analysis.[9] Optimizing production and inventory policy for a single product will almost certainly affect the costs of other products produced by the firm, possibly in ways which can be readily estimated and, once estimated, included in the criterion, since all costs have a common monetary dimension. More frequently, as

[9] See, for example, Herbert Solow, " Operations Research," *Fortune*, Vol. 43, No. 4 (April 1951), pp. 105-107.

in the convoy example, there will be divergences between low-level and high-level effects about which only the direction or, at most, the magnitude along some dimension not commensurable with those in the local criterion can be determined. Good decisions cannot ignore such divergences, but must take them into account intuitively.

3. In the economy, production is maximized (in the sense previously defined) if firms maximize their profits in an absolute sense, i. e., gross receipts *minus* costs. It might appear as plausible, or more so, that the economy would be most efficiently organized if each firm minimized cost per unit of output, or maximized profits per unit of output. It can be demonstrated, however, that both these suboptimization criteria will result in inefficient utilization of resources by the economy. *Ratios are particularly treacherous as operations criteria, whether they are exchange rates (enemy losses divided by Allied losses) or, more generally, ratios of objectives achieved to costs incurred.*

There are two interacting reasons why this is so. Ratios, first of all, ignore the absolute magnitudes of both numerator and denominator. Secondly, solutions with ratio criteria tend, in many operations problems, to rush to corners—in the convoy case, for example, to the corner in which all vessels are assembled in a single convoy. This may be because the ratios are *really* maximized or minimized in corners, or because, for simplicity, linear functional forms are assumed. But it is precisely in rushing to a corner that absolute magnitudes cannot be ignored.

If the *scale* of the operation is given either in terms of resources or budget available, or in terms of a precise objective to be accomplished, then it does no harm to maximize the ratio of objectives to costs. This is mathematically equivalent to maximizing the objectives function subject to resource constraints, or to minimizing the costs of achieving a given objective. If, however, the scale of the operation is not given—that is, if both costs and objectives are permitted to vary freely—the calculation of an optimum ratio between them will suggest a scale for the operation which bears only an accidental relation to any higher-level criterion.

4. *A common and fatal mistake in selecting suboptimization criteria is to concentrate on a single input—to maximize some objectives function for a given quantity of the input or minimize requirements for the input to achieve some given objective.* For example,

maximum output *per head* (or per man-hour) seems so obviously
desirable that most non-economists would never question it as a
suitable criterion for organizing production within the economy. In
point of fact, as a suboptimizing criterion for any firm or industry,
it is quite wrong by our only test, namely, the next higher level
criterion. Its use would result in an inefficient organization of production in the economy. The reason is obvious on reflection. There are
scarce, valuable resources needed in production other than man-hours.

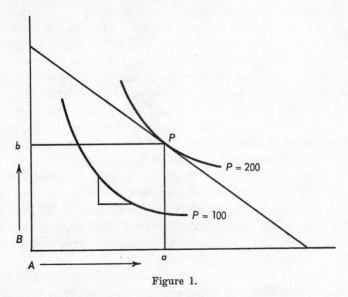

Figure 1.

A method of production chosen to minimize man-hours is likely
to be wasteful of capital, land, management, and labor with special
skills or training. A bombing system designed to minimize requirements for bombs will be unnecessarily and inefficiently (from the
point of view of the higher-level criterion) wasteful of aircraft and
crews. Conversely, if it is designed to save aircraft and crews, it will
waste bombs. "Hemibel thinking," as described by Morse and
Kimball,[10] does not come to the rescue here. Systems which minimize
input A frequently emerge as utterly different from systems which
minimize input B, as in the case illustrated in Figure 1.

[10] *Methods of Operations Research*, p. 38.

5. In economic theory, the " Golden Rule " for allocating scarce resources is to make each resource equally scarce in all uses. This is a theorem of "welfare economics," with precisely and operationally defined terms, which enables operations researchers to give practical advice on allocation problems *even where the values of the alternative uses are incommensurable* in the higher-level objectives function.

An objective can usually be achieved by various combinations of resources. Motor cars can be made with much capital and little labor, as in Detroit, or with more labor and less capital, as in Coventry. An air defense of a specified effectiveness may be achieved with very different mixes of interceptors and anti-aircraft artillery. Some substitutions are direct and obvious; many others are indirect and subtle. The operations researcher typically discovers that the possibilities of substitution in carrying out any operation are much greater than are at first apparent.

This theorem can be illustrated geometrically as in Figure 1. It is assumed that there are only two scarce and valuable resources, A and B, which are combined to produce a single product, P. A might be land, B, labor, and P, wheat; alternatively, A might be bombers, B, bombs, and P, targets destroyed. If A is measured along one axis and B along the other, production possibilities can be represented by a series of curves which will usually be convex to the origin. Any given curve, or production " isoquant," shows the minimum combinations of resources A and B which are needed to produce a given quantity of P. The slope of the curve at any point measures the amount of B one must substitute per unit of A to maintain the output of P, and is called the " marginal rate of substitution " of B for A. Its numerical value in the normal convex case diminishes as A is substituted for B, i. e., as one moves along the isoquant from left to right.

For some simple types of suboptimizations, such an array of possibilities provides sufficient information for a solution. Thus, if the quantities of A and B have been fixed (e. g. for a field commander) at a and b by a higher authority, the optimal operation is the one represented by point p, where all of both resources are optimally utilized to produce a P of 200. Alternatively, if what is given is the *scale* of the operation (e. g., $P = 200$) and the relative costs of the two resources (represented by the slope of the diagonal through p), the optimal (i. e., the "least cost") operation is p, at which the relative cost diagonal is tangent to the production isoquant—or, in other words, where the relative costs of the resources are equal to the marginal rate of substitution between them.

The problem, however, can be more complex. There might be several objectives, either industrial products or military missions, requiring the same scarce resources. In some such cases, there is a common measure for the various objectives, as in industry, where the products of a firm can be measured in a common monetary unit. This sort of case is trivial, for it reduces to the simple case already considered.

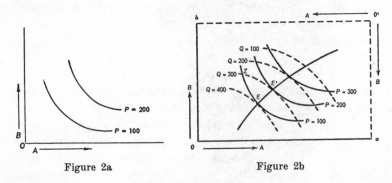

Figure 2a   Figure 2b

It is in the case where no common measure can be found [11] that the Golden Rule for allocating becomes a helpful device for operations researchers who might otherwise be frustrated. Equal scarcity of each resource in each use means equal marginal rates of substitution among resources in each use. To illustrate, let it be assumed that there are only two resources, A and B, and two objectives, P and Q. A could be Robinson Crusoe's time, B, the arable land on his island, and P and Q, beans and squash, respectively. Alternatively, A and B could be merchant ships and destroyers, and P and Q, tons of material moved across the Atlantic and Pacific.

First the production possibilities for P are shown in Figure 2a, and b measured, as before, from the origin, O.

[11] That is to say, where no common measure can be found which is practicable to use; knowing that a common measure exists in principle (e. g., contribution to the probability of victory) is not enough.

Next Oa and Ob are drawn to represent the total quantities of A and B available for both uses, P and Q; and the rectangle is completed, as in Figure 2b. Then, from the origin O', the production possibilities of Q are represented, with B measured south and A west. The isoquants will (normally) be convex to the origin O'. In the usual case, therefore, each P isoquant will be tangent to one and only one Q isoquant.

Each point in the rectangle represents a particular allocation of the resources A and B between the objectives P and Q. The isoquants passing through that point " score " the allocation in two dimensions, P and Q. Because there is no common measure for P and Q, one cannot say what is the " most preferred " of the points or the optimal allocation. But the Golden Rule permits one to make some practically useful statements about bad allocations and better allocations.

Point Z is assumed to be the actual allocation or the currently programmed allocation. Is it a good one? It will produce 100 P and 300 Q; it is perfectly apparent that something better can be recommended. In moving along the $P = 100$ isoquant, one finds a point of tangency, E, where $Q = 400$. No common measure for P and Q is needed to see that ($P = 100$, $Q = 400$) is better than ($P = 100$, $Q = 300$).[12] This superior point can be reached simply by transferring some A from Q to P and some B from P to Q. Point Z is an " inefficient " point, when the marginal rates of substitution of the resources (represented by the slopes of the isoquants) are different in different uses. It is therefore possible, by reallocating, to get more of at least one product without having less of any other. Point E is an " efficient " point, where marginal rates of substitution are the same in all uses. It is very easy to get allocations represented by very inefficient points, especially where command responsibility is divided and there is no system of prices to indicate relative scarcities.

Point E', of course, is also an efficient point and demonstrably better than Z. So are all points of tangency between E and E', where more of *both* objectives is produced than at Z. It is impossible, therefore, to recommend a unique optimum. The philosophy of operations research, however, is that it is far more important to be able to demonstrate that some courses of action, E, are better than proposed

---

[12] Of course, one must know *something* about the character of the higher-level criterion to be sure of even this, but he need not know much.

courses of action, Z, than to spend one's life seeking the *optimum optimorum*.

These considerations have been presented to suggest that economic theory contains the beginnings of a scientific and practically rewarding approach to the problems of choosing criteria. That approach involves the analysis of relations between suboptimizations at lower and higher levels. The analysis of these relations can be helpful even where the full optimization at the higher level cannot be calculated. There is some doubt as to whether operations researchers can contribute in an important way to high-level problems directly; the researchers, however, must understand the general characteristics of the higher level optimization if they are to exercise good judgment in the selection of criteria at the lower levels—that is, if the suboptimizations are to contribute even indirectly to the high-level objectives.

Symbolic Logic in
Operations Research

WALTER E. CUSHEN

O PERATIONS RESEARCH, in its concern with complex processes, must have at its disposal a large set of powerful analytic and synthesizing techniques. Perhaps the most frequently used methods are those in the mathematical nexus. But the mathematical nexus is a close blood relative of a further theoretical method which has as yet received little attention—that of symbolic logic.

The attempt to analyze an operation or a process derives its justification from a faith in the rationality of the process. Frequently, however, the interconnections between the entities in an operation are so numerous and complex that the expectation of being able to perform a complete analysis is remote. Nevertheless, the multitude of available facts makes the attempt attractive. It is in just such a situation that symbolic logic will offer its greatest assistance.

If the rationality of an operation be posited, the search for the logical structure of that operation begins. The human mind seems to experience a natural desire to know " the form in the facts." The facts in any process seem to be the expression and exemplification of general principles. If, therefore, the general principles could be delineated, it would be possible to predict the behavior of the remotest parts of the system. The truth of this assertion is as much a matter of faith with the operations analyst as it is with the metaphysician or with the creator of systems describing the physical world.

Logic provides the techniques for investigating the anatomy of any particular formal framework. Symbolic logic might be known as "the algebra of logic." In place of word-propositions, or classes of things, or functional statements, it substitutes symbols. Relations between propositions, classes, and functions are, furthermore, concisely and unambiguously expressed in symbols. The rules of a formal system, given in symbolic form, then define permissible transformations from one statement to another. By using such transformations, one is enabled to operate upon complex logical statements in much the same manner as one does upon algebraic expressions.

Although the primary interests of its advocates have been theoretical, some faltering attempts have been made toward the practical use of symbolic logic. Perhaps the most conspicuous application of this new discipline has been in the logical design of the components of computing machinery. For the logical designer in this field, symbolic logic is the staff of life. Aside from this application, symbolic logic is still clad in its academic gown. This chapter will explore some other possibilities for applying symbolic logic to practical problems.

The Calculus of Propositions.

One of the major interests in symbolic logic is the calculus of propositions. For the sake of brevity, we shall define a proposition as a sentence which says something of a subject. The calculus of propositions, accordingly, examines the implications of several statements when considered concurrently.

One might elect, for example, to symbolize a statement by a letter. Thus, the statement, "Aluminum may be used for the framework of an airplane," may be symbolized by the letter "a." Whenever, then, the symbol "a" appears, it is understood to be an assertion that the statement is correct. The denial of a proposition might be accomplished by qualifying the symbol negatively; in that case, "$\sim a$" would mean "It is false that aluminum may be used for the framework of an airplane." Certain synonymous phrasings would also be valid; for example, "One cannot use aluminum for the framework of an airplane." Generally, however, it is safest to prefix the statement by "Is it false that. . . ."

The calculus of propositions is known as two-valued if any proposition considered can exist in only one of two states—true or false. Thus, one might define a two-valued logic as one wherein it is false that a statement is both true and false at the same time, and wherein the statement must be in one or the other of these two states.

If several propositions are true at the same time, they are connected by a dot, which is usually interpreted as " and." Thus

$a \cdot b$ means " a is true and b is true ";

$\sim a \cdot b$ means " a is false and b is true ";

$\sim(a \cdot b)$ means " it is false that a and b are both true."

It is possible similarly to combine large numbers of propositions:

$\sim[a \cdot b \cdot \sim(c \cdot \sim d)]$ means " it is false that [a and b are true and it is false that (c is true and d is false)]."

This example may be more clearly demonstrated if some meaningful statement is assigned to each proposition, as, for example:

$a =$ There is only one set of fingerprints on the gun.

$b =$ The gun is the murder weapon.

$c =$ John's fingerprints are on the gun.

$d =$ John is guilty of murder.

$\sim(c \cdot \sim d)$ then reads, " It cannot be that John's fingerprints are on the gun and that he is not guilty of murder." $a \cdot b \cdot \sim(c \cdot \sim d)$ extends the former situation by adding that the gun is the murder weapon, and that there is only one set of fingerprints on the gun.

If this were a legal situation, the prosecution would be asserting that $a \cdot b \cdot \sim(c \cdot \sim d)$; the defense would attempt to show that $\sim[a \cdot b \cdot \sim(c \cdot \sim d)]$ and any of the short statements below would suffice to prove the case for the defense. $\sim[a \cdot b \cdot \sim(c \cdot \sim d)]$ proclaims that these statements are not all true at the same time. Any one or combination of the following situations would serve to negate the conjunction $[a \cdot b \cdot \sim(c \cdot \sim d)]$:

(1) $\sim a$
(2) $\sim b$
(3) $c \cdot \sim d$

Further connectives are defined for use in symbolic logic. One in common use is the implication: " If ' a ' is true, then ' b ' is true."

The symbol for this meaning is " $a \supset b$." Groups of statements can be connected by this implication horseshoe, for example:

$\sim a \supset b =$ If " a " is false, then " b " is true.
$\sim(a \supset b) =$ It is false that " a " implies " b."
$(a \cdot \sim b) \supset c =$ If " a " is true and " b " is false, then " c " is true.

It is interesting to note that " $a \supset b$ " is equivalent to " $\sim(a \cdot \sim b)$." In other words, " If ' a ' is true, then ' b ' is true " is the same as saying, " It is false that ' a ' is true and ' b ' is false at the same time." To pass from the form " $a \supset b$ " to the form " $\sim(a \cdot \sim b)$ " is known as " dissolving " the implication; the reverse procedure is known as " resolving " the implication. This is one of the transformations defined to be a part of the system of logic.

Statements are frequently connected by the relating term, " or." There are, however, two kinds of " or " to be distinguished. One, which is known as the inclusive " or," allows the interpretation, " Either ' a ' or ' b ,' or both, is true." It is the equivalent of the " and/or " expression frequently encountered in ordinary prose. The second, which is known as the disjunctive or exclusive " or," means " Either ' a ' or ' b ,' but not both, is true." The everyday language use of " or " is somewhat equivocal on this score and frequently requires long, qualifying statements. Perhaps one of the best discourses on the translation from ordinary discourse to formal logic is contained in P. F. Strawson's *Introduction to Logical Theory*.[1]

In symbolic logic, the two " or's " can be distinguished by a difference in notation, as:

$a \lor b$ for the inclusive " or."
$a \veebar b$ for the exclusive " or."

" $a \lor b$ " is equivalent to saying " $\sim(\sim a \cdot \sim b)$ " or " It is false that ' a ' and ' b ' are both false." " $a \veebar b$ " is equivalent to saying " $\sim(\sim a \cdot \sim b) \cdot \sim(a \cdot b)$ " or " It is false that ' a ' and ' b ' are both false, and, furthermore, it is false that ' a ' and ' b ' are both true." Again, these transformations can legitimately be made without alteration in the value of the statement.

[1] *Introduction to Logical Theory* (New York: John Wiley and Sons, Inc., 1952).

An implication can be transformed into an "either . . . or" type of statement, as:

$$(a \supset b) \equiv \sim(a \cdot \sim b) \equiv (\sim a \vee b)$$

It then becomes possible to express the conditions for a two-valued logic. A logic is two-valued if

$$a \vee \sim a.$$

Thus, a statement must be either true or false, but not both. There is no in-between state.

It is of interest to note that a simplified propositional statement whose major operations are the connectives "and" and "not" is known as the conjunctive normal form. A simplified statement whose major operations consist only of "or" and "not" is known as the disjunctive normal form. It is possible to pass from a statement involving any of the connectives to either of the two normal forms. Thus, $a \supset [(b \cdot \sim c) \vee d]$ can be reduced to

Conjunctive Normal Form

$$a \supset [(b \vee d) \cdot (\sim c \vee d)]$$
$$\sim a \vee [(b \vee d) \cdot (\sim c \vee d)]$$
$$(\sim a \vee b \vee d) \cdot (\sim a \vee \sim c \vee d)$$

Disjunctive Normal Form

$$\sim a \vee [(b \cdot \sim c) \vee d]$$
$$\sim a \vee (b \cdot \sim c) \vee d$$

An Example of Symbolic Logic in Production Engineering.

To illustrate the manner in which symbolic logic might be used in an actual problem, an example from the field of production engineering will be described. A certain manufacturer produces an article which has three major components. Recent engineering research indicates that materials other than those now being used might effect an improvement in the product.

On the basis of engineering decisions, it is determined that there are five substances which might be used in Component #1 of the product, six substances which might be used in Component #2, and three which might be used in Component #3. It is known, furthermore, that if a certain substance is used in one component, certain other substances cannot be used in the other components. These combinations may be impossible because of the mechanical, electrical, or chemical characteristics of the substances. It is further known that certain operating characteristics will follow from the use of certain substances in each of the components.

There are, then, ninety (5 x 6 x 3) possible new combinations of components. It might be observed that the propositions, (1) that one and only one substance may be used in Component #1, (2) that one and only one substance may be used in Component #2, and (3) that one and only one substance may be used in Component #3, represent a set of implicitly accepted propositions which immediately narrows the field of possible combinations of the fourteen variables from 2^{14} to 90. Because of the prohibitions involved in using each of the substances, certain further combinations can be immediately eliminated. In the particular example being described, it will be found that physical prohibitions rule out all but nineteen of the possibilities.

In addition to the restrictions imposed by the nature of the physical situations involved, there may be certain policy decisions which must be followed. For example, it may be that $80,000 is the maximum which can be expended in the change-over of equipment. It may also be desirable that the cost of the new materials rise no more than 10 per cent if operation of the necessary new machinery will cost the company an additional 5 per cent. Furthermore, certain performance standards must be maintained.

These restrictions and relationships may be summarized as in Tables 1 and 2.

The restrictions and freedoms in the use of the components will be expressed as propositions in symbolic form.

The cost of materials will be considered a true proposition for figures of 110 per cent or less. The conversion cost proposition will be considered true for figures of $80,000 or less. The operating cost proposition will be considered true for figures of 105 per cent or less. The Y's in the performance characteristics will be considered true. With the lower case letters used for the propositional components, the following propositions express the total situation:

(1) $a \supset (\sim i \cdot \sim j \cdot \sim k \cdot \sim l \cdot p \cdot q \cdot \sim r \cdot s \cdot t \cdot u)$

(2) $b \supset (\sim j \cdot \sim k \cdot \sim n \cdot p \cdot q \cdot \sim r \cdot s \cdot t \cdot \sim u)$

(3) $c \supset (\sim f \cdot \sim j \cdot \sim m \cdot p \cdot \sim q \cdot r \cdot s \cdot t \cdot \sim u)$

(4) $d \supset (\sim f \cdot \sim h \cdot \sim m \cdot \sim p \cdot q \cdot \sim r \cdot s \cdot t \cdot u)$

(5) $e \supset (\sim f \cdot \sim g \cdot \sim i \cdot \sim j \cdot \sim k \cdot \sim l \cdot \sim m \cdot \sim p \cdot \sim q \cdot r \cdot s \cdot \sim t \cdot u)$

TABLE 1

Proposition	I	II	III	A / a	B / b	C / c	D / d	E / e	E / f	F / g	G / h	H / i	I / j	J / k	A / l	F / m	G / n
a	A										No	No	No		No		
b	B											No	No				No
c	C								No		No					No	
d	D								No		No					No	
e	E								No	No		No	No	No	No	No	
f		E				No	No	No									No
g		F					No									No	No
h		G					No										
i		H		No				No							No	No	
j		I		No	No	No		No									
k		J		No	No			No								No	
l			A	No				No									
m			F	No	No	No	No	No		No		No					
n			G			No			No	No		No					

TABLE 2

Proposition	I	II	III	Cost of Materials % (p)	Conversion Cost $1000 (q)	Operating Cost % (r)	L s	M t	N u
a	A			110	75	130	Y	Y	Y
b	B			95	80	150	Y	Y	N
c	C			80	105	95	Y	Y	N
d	D			120	60	110	Y	Y	Y
e	E			170	150	60	Y	N	Y
f		E		170	20	60	Y	Y	Y
g		F		95	30	85	Y	N	Y
h		G		80	15	100	Y	N	N
i		H		95	35	90	Y	Y	N
j		I		110	10	90	Y	Y	N
k		J		105	40	75	Y	N	Y
l			A	110	90	130	Y	Y	N
m			F	95	80	85	Y	Y	Y
n			G	80	90	100	N	Y	N

(6) $f \supset (\sim c \cdot \sim d \cdot \sim e \cdot \sim n \cdot \sim p \cdot q \cdot r \cdot s \cdot t \cdot u)$

(7) $g \supset (\sim e \cdot \sim m \cdot \sim n \cdot p \cdot q \cdot r \cdot s \cdot \sim t \cdot u)$

(8) $h \supset (\sim d \cdot p \cdot q \cdot r \cdot s \cdot \sim t \cdot \sim u)$

(9) $i \supset (\sim a \cdot \sim e \cdot \sim l \cdot \sim m \cdot p \cdot q \cdot r \cdot s \cdot t \cdot \sim u)$

(10) $j \supset (\sim a \cdot \sim b \cdot \sim c \cdot \sim e \cdot p \cdot q \cdot r \cdot s \cdot t \cdot \sim u)$

(11) $k \supset (\sim a \cdot \sim b \cdot \sim e \cdot \sim m \cdot p \cdot q \cdot r \cdot s \cdot \sim t \cdot u)$

(12) $l \supset (\sim a \cdot \sim e \cdot \sim h \cdot p \cdot \sim q \cdot \sim r \cdot s \cdot t \cdot \sim u)$

(13) $m \supset (\sim c \cdot \sim d \cdot \sim e \cdot \sim g \cdot \sim i \cdot \sim k \cdot p \cdot q \cdot r \cdot s \cdot t \cdot u)$

(14) $n \supset (\sim b \cdot \sim f \cdot \sim g \cdot p \cdot \sim q \cdot r \cdot \sim s \cdot t \cdot \sim u)$

(15) s

(16) q

(17) $p \vee r$

(18) $t \vee u$

To tabulate the results for obtaining a final result, in other words, to discover which one or ones of the ninety possible cases are consistent with the demands placed upon the new development of the product, all ninety cases can be listed so that the inconsistent ones are immediately obvious. This has been done in Table 3.

The preparation of such a table can be done by hand, or mechanized for solution by a computing machine. The results appear, showing that only two new developments may be considered. This is in marked contrast to the impression of wholesale ambiguity conveyed by the original statement of the problem.

It is readily apparent that there is a transition in the application of logical methods to problems which involve administrative decisions and production control. It is also apparent that, in cases where legal decisions are clear-cut, or when it can be assumed that certain judicial precedents will prevail, certain consequences can be predicted. In the case of a contract, the logic will indicate which conditions will break the contract and will further indicate which clause of the contract has been violated and by whom.

In the design of experiments, it is possible to state certain propositions which will define the relationships between entities to be observed. It is further possible to assert certain truth-values. For example, let it be required to explore the case where p, q and r are all true, and s and t are false. The results of the computation will indicate what variations may be introduced into each of the components in order to permit the desired conclusions.

TABLE 3

Case		Inconsistent with Proposition
(1)	a.f.l	(1) (12) (16)
(2)	a.f.m	(16)
(3)	a.f.n	(6) (14) (15) (16)
(4)	a.g.l	(1) (12) (16)
(5)	a.g.m	(7) (13) (15) (16) (18)
(6)	a.g.n	(7) (14) (16) (18)
(7)	a.h.l	(1) (8) (15) (16)
(8)	a.h.m	(8) (18) (16)
(9)	a.h.n	(8) (14) (16) (18)
(10)	a.i.l	(1) (9) (12) (13) (16)
(11)	a.i.m	(9) (13) (16)
(12)	a.i.n	(9) (14) (15) (16)
(13)	a.j.l	(1) (10) (12) (16)
(14)	a.j.m	(10) (13) (15) (16)
(15)	a.j.n	(10) (14) (15) (16)
(16)	a.k.l	(1) (11) (13) (16)
(17)	a.k.m	(11) (13) (16)
(18)	a.k.n	(1) (11) (14) (15)
(19)	b.f.l	(12) (16)
(20)	b.f.m	(2) (6) (14) (15) (16) (18)
(21)	b.f.n	(2) (16)
(22)	b.g.l	(12) (13) (16)
(23)	b.g.m	(2) (7) (14) (15) (16)
(24)	b.g.n	(2) (7) (16)
(25)	b.h.l	(8) (12) (14) (15) (16)
(26)	b.h.m	(8) (18) (16) (18)
(27)	b.h.n	(2) (8) (14) (16)
(28)	b.i.l	(9) (12) (16)
(29)	b.i.m	(2) (9) (13) (15) (16)
(30)	b.i.n	(2) (14) (16)
(31)	b.j.l	(10) (12) (16)
(32)	b.j.m	(2) (10) (13) (15) (16)
(33)	b.j.n	(2) (11) (14) (16)
(34)	b.k.l	(11) (14) (15) (16)
(35)	b.k.m	(2) (11) (12) (16)
(36)	b.k.n	(2) (11) (14) (15)
(37)	c.f.l	(3) (13) (16)
(38)	c.f.m	(6) (12) (16)
(39)	c.f.n	(3) (6) (14) (15)
(40)	c.g.l	(12) (16) (16)
(41)	c.g.m	(3) (7) (13) (15) (16)
(42)	c.g.n	(7) (14) (15) (16)
(43)	c.h.l	(3) (8) (12) (16) (18)
(44)	c.h.m	(3) (8) (13) (16) (18)
(45)	c.h.n	(3) (8) (14) (15) (16)

Case		*	Inconsistent with Proposition
(46)	c.i.l	(9)	(12) (16) (16)
(47)	c.i.m	(3)	(9) (13) (16)
(48)	c.i.n	(14)	(15) (16)
(49)	c.j.l	(3)	(10) (12) (16)
(50)	c.j.m	(3)	(10) (13) (15) (16)
(51)	c.j.n	(12)	(10) (14) (15)
(52)	c.k.l	(3)	(11) (13) (16)
(53)	c.k.m	(3)	(11) (16) (16)
(54)	c.k.n	(4)	(6) (12) (16) (17)
(55)	d.f.l	(4)	(6) (13) (16) (16)
(56)	d.f.m	(4)	(8) (14) (17) (17)
(57)	d.f.n	(4)	(6) (15) (16) (16)
(58)	d.g.l	(12)	(7) (17) (17) (17)
(59)	d.g.m	(4)	(13) (16) (18) (18)
(60)	d.g.n	(7)	(14) (15) (17) (17)
(61)	d.h.l	(4)	(8) (12) (16) (18) (18)
(62)	d.h.m	(4)	(8) (13) (17) (16)
(63)	d.h.n	(4)	(8) (14) (15) (16)
(64)	d.i.l	(9)	(12) (16)
(65)	d.i.m	(4)	(9) (13) (16)
(66)	d.i.n	(14)	(15) (16)
(67)	d.j.l	(4)	(10) (13) (17)
(68)	d.j.m	(4)	(13) (16)
(69)	d.j.n	(4)	(15) (16) (17)
(70)	d.k.l	(12)	(16) (16)
(71)	d.k.m	(4)	(11) (13) (17)
(72)	d.k.n	(14)	(16) (17)
(73)	e.f.l	(5)	(6) (13) (16)
(74)	e.f.m	(5)	(8) (14) (16)
(75)	e.f.n	(5)	(6) (15) (16)
(76)	e.g.l	(5)	(7) (13) (16) (16)
(77)	e.g.n	(5)	(7) (14) (16) (18)
(78)	e.g.n	(5)	(8) (12) (15) (18)
(79)	e.h.l	(8)	(14) (16) (18)
(80)	e.h.m	(5)	(8) (12) (16) (16)
(81)	e.h.n	(5)	(8) (13) (16) (16)
(82)	e.i.l	(5)	(9) (12) (16)
(83)	e.i.m	(5)	(13) (16)
(84)	e.i.n	(5)	(14) (15) (16)
(85)	e.j.l	(5)	(10) (12) (16)
(86)	e.j.m	(10)	(13) (16)
(87)	e.j.n	(5)	(14) (15) (16)
(88)	e.k.l	(5)	(11) (12) (16)
(89)	e.k.m	(5)	(13) (16)
(90)	e.k.n	(5)	(11) (14) (16)

The situation as stated thus far concerns certain frequently recurring problem types in the calculus of propositions. It suffers from the restriction that the logic is two-valued. The scope of treatment is further restricted by the fact that consideration of the problem of quantification is absent. There is no reason why these obstacles cannot be readily surmounted.

The advantages of the method just described are primarily those of rapid and thorough analysis, combined with an output which designates inconsistencies. It would seem that it would be more laborious to instruct the computer or the analyst to generate a table of 2^n values and indicate whether each is consistent or inconsistent than to interpret the results of a selected set of combinations of interest. All such tables are known as truth tables.[2]

It should be further observed that, although the propositions here investigated are limited in the number of variables, a process of nesting will accomplish the required results should more variables be present. For example, a proposition such as $(a \supset b) \supset (c \supset d)$, when subjected to the nesting technique, could be treated as three simple propositions:

(1) $a \supset b$

(2) $c \supset d$

(3) $e \supset f$ $(e = (1))$ $(f = (2))$

The case inconsistent with (1) is $(a \cdot \sim b)$; the case inconsistent with (2) is $(c \cdot \sim d)$; with (3), $(e \cdot \sim f)$. When these computed results are used,

$$(4) \quad \sim(e \cdot \sim f) = \sim \{[\sim(a \cdot \sim b)] \cdot \sim [\sim(c \cdot \sim d)]\}.$$

Since $\sim \sim a = a$,

$$(5) \quad \sim(e \cdot \sim f) = \sim \{[\sim(a \cdot \sim b)] \cdot (c \cdot \sim d)\}.$$

But $\sim(a \cdot \sim b)$ can be expressed as $\sim a \vee b$. Therefore,

$$(6) \quad \sim(e \cdot \sim f) = \sim [(\sim a \vee b) \cdot (c \cdot \sim d)].$$

[2] A computer method for generating a truth table is outlined in Wilton R. Abbot, "Computing Logical Truth with the California Digital Computer," *Mathematical Tables and Other Aids to Computation*, Vol. 5, No. 35, (July, 1951), pp. 115-84.

The case inconsistent with $(e \supset f)$ is $(\sim a \vee b) \cdot (c \cdot \sim d)$, which is reducible to the disjunctive normal form $(\sim a \cdot c \cdot \sim d) \vee (b \cdot c \cdot \sim d)$; this is the same result which would be delivered from an analysis of the original proposition. Similar analysis can be performed on more complex propositions.

Symbolic Logic in a Game Situation.

To illustrate another possible application, one might consider a conflict or *game* situation. Before proceeding, it should be mentioned that, in this example, several ready extrapolations are possible. The game need not have a particular application; it may be regarded as describing actions and reactions in an advertising campaign; it may describe the moves allowed in a game which simulates warfare; it may represent the alternatives open to an executive as he makes a policy decision; or it may represent the clauses of a contract.

With the use of the symbolic notations introduced earlier in the chapter, one can express the rules of the game in a deterministic form—if a, then b. It should be noted that there may be a "feedback" in this game; if one player does a particular thing affecting his opponent, the opponent may be forced into a retaliatory position. The original player, therefore, may find himself in an embarrassing position as a result of his own actions.

Let p_i be the use of move (or advertising technique, or weapon, or policy choice, or action dictated by a contract) i by the blue player. Let q_i be the effect on the ith counterpart of player red.

The following rules are arbitrarily constructed. In practice they should be consequent upon the empirical relationships.

$$p_1 \supset [q_1 \vee q_2 \vee (q_3 \cdot q_4)]$$
$$p_2 \supset [\sim q_2 \vee (q_4 \cdot q_5)]$$
$$p_3 \supset [q_5 \supset (q_3 \cdot q_1)]$$
$$p_4 \supset [q_2 \cdot (q_3 \vee q_5) \cdot q_4]$$
$$p_5 \supset [q_3 \cdot (q_4 \vee q_5)]$$
$$\sim p_1 \supset (\sim q_1 \cdot \sim q_4 \cdot \sim q_2)$$
$$\sim p_2 \supset (q_2 \cdot \sim q_5)$$
$$\sim p_3 \supset \sim (q_3 \cdot q_5)$$
$$\sim p_4 \supset (\sim q_1 \cdot \sim q_3)$$
$$\sim p_5 \supset [(q_3 \cdot \sim q_4) \vee \sim q_5]$$

Let P_i be the use by red of his i^{th} choice.

$$q_1 \supset [\sim P_1 \vee P_2 \vee (P_3 \cdot \sim P_4)]$$
$$q_2 \supset \sim P_3$$
$$q_3 \supset (P_5 \supset P_3)$$
$$q_4 \supset [P_4 \cdot \sim P_2 \cdot \sim P_5]$$
$$q_5 \supset (\sim P_1 \vee P_3)$$
$$\sim q_1 \supset [P_4 \supset (\sim P_1 \cdot P_2 \cdot P_3)]$$
$$\sim q_2 \supset [(P_5 \vee P_3) \cdot \sim P_4]$$
$$\sim q_3 \supset \sim (P_5 \cdot \sim P_3)$$
$$\sim q_4 \supset (P_1 \vee P_4)$$
$$\sim q_5 \supset [(\sim P_2 \cdot \sim P_4) \vee P_4]$$

Let Q_i be the effect on blue's i^{th} choice.

$$P_1 \supset (Q_1 \cdot \sim Q_2 \cdot Q_3)$$
$$P_2 \supset [Q_4 \supset (Q_5 \cdot \sim Q_1)]$$
$$P_3 \supset \sim (Q_1 \cdot Q_3 \cdot Q_5)$$
$$P_4 \supset (\sim Q_2 \vee Q_4)$$
$$P_5 \supset \sim [(Q_3 \cdot \sim Q_4) \vee Q_5]$$
$$\sim P_1 \supset [(\sim Q_2 \vee Q_4) \cdot \sim Q_3]$$
$$\sim P_2 \supset (\sim Q_4 \cdot Q_1 \cdot \sim Q_5)$$
$$\sim P_3 \supset [\sim Q_1 \vee (Q_5 \cdot Q_3) \vee (\sim Q_2 \cdot \sim Q_4)]$$
$$\sim P_4 \supset (Q_1 \cdot \sim Q_2)$$
$$\sim P_5 \supset \sim (Q_1 \cdot Q_3 \cdot Q_5)$$
$$Q_1 \supset (p_1 \vee p_2)$$
$$Q_2 \supset [\sim (p_3 \cdot p_4) \cdot \sim p_5]$$
$$Q_3 \supset \sim (p_2 \cdot p_5)$$
$$Q_4 \supset (p_1 \supset p_3)$$
$$Q_5 \supset (p_2 \cdot p_4)$$
$$\sim Q_1 \supset [(p_1 \cdot p_2) \vee (p_3 \cdot \sim p_4)]$$
$$\sim Q_2 \supset (p_3 \cdot \sim p_5)$$
$$\sim Q_3 \supset (\sim p_5 \vee p_2)$$
$$\sim Q_4 \supset (p_4 \vee p_2)$$
$$\sim Q_5 \supset [(\sim p_1 \cdot \sim p_3 \cdot \sim p_4) \vee p_2]$$

The truth table shows the following conditions to be the only ones consistent with the propositions as stated.

	p_1	p_2	p_3	p_4	p_5	q_1	q_2	q_3	q_4	q_5	P_1	P_2	P_3	P_4	P_5	Q_1	Q_2	Q_3	Q_4	Q_5
(1)	F	T	T	F	F	F	F	F	F	F	T	F	T	F	T	T	F	T	F	F
(2)	F	T	T	F	F	F	F	F	F	F	T	F	T	F	F	T	F	T	F	F
(3)	F	T	T	F	F	F	F	F	F	F	T	F	F	F	F	T	F	T	F	F
(4)	F	T	T	F	F	F	F	F	F	F	F	T	T	T	T	T	F	F	F	F
(5)	F	T	T	F	F	F	F	F	F	F	F	T	T	T	T	F	F	F	F	F
(6)	F	T	T	F	F	F	F	F	F	F	F	F	T	T	T	T	F	F	F	F

Thus, only six combinations from a possible 2^{20} are consistent solutions. There are only six histories of the interaction. This conclusion stands out again in strong contrast with the initial impression of overwhelming complexity and the feeling that there may well be many solutions. The reduction of all forty propositions, taken conjunctively, to its disjunctive normal form would give the same result.

It is apparent that, under the rules, Blue is obliged to adopt only one employment of his resources—namely, to use p_2 and p_3 positively, and to use the negative of p_1, p_4, and p_5. Red, on the other hand, has a choice among five alternative uses of his resources. He can, furthermore, select his choices from the point of view of the effects he elects to obtain. The Red player would then undoubtedly hire an operations analyst to make a cost-effectiveness evaluation of the courses of action open to him.

Blue, on the other hand, has the choice of submitting to the operational system described by the formulae, or of rejecting it. The use of the truth table technique from symbolic logic has given him the raw data for his executive decision, dependent on his appraisal of the value to him of the effects of which he can be assured.

The example under discussion, although arbitrarily constructed, serves to indicate the strengths and limitations of the method of logical analysis.

The Advantages and Limitations of Symbolic Logic.

Advantages

(1) A complex situation, when analyzed into its logical components, can frequently be simplified into a clear and simple picture in a short period of time. The possibilities are drawn into sharp contrast with the impossible or unwanted situations. In general, the greater the number of statements about the known variables which can

be symbolically formulated, the greater the reduction of permissible combinations.

(2) The operation is expressed concisely and without equivocation. There is no doubt about the intent of any statement. This benefit is derivative from rigidly defined relational expressions.

(3) Algebraic transformations of the symbolic statements are not too difficult. Results can be cross-checked for accuracy. As a member of the logico-mathematical nexus of analytic techniques, symbolic logic will be a tool which analysts can readily add to their repertoire.

(4) Redundancies are quickly disclosed; unnecessary elements can be isolated and removed.

Limitations.

(1) Symbolic logic, in the application here envisaged, is employed in a strictly empirical situation. The difficulty in expressing actual situations in analytic-type statements extends not only to the accuracy obtained, but also to the completeness. Everything which can be said should be expressed. Logicians have discoursed at great length on " the logic of ordinary language," and the summation of these thoughts underlines the difficulty of making analytic statements about empirical relationships. (See P. F. Strawson's *Introduction to Logical Theory*). For the purposes for which symbolic logic has been used here, however, the practical benefits seem to warrant a bold attempt to include this methodology in the repertoire of the operations analyst. No attempt has been made to indicate the immense area of thought explored by symbolic logicians; attention has been restricted purely to elementary notions in one branch of symbolic logic.

(2) Acknowledgment of the difficulty in the translation of empirical relationships into symbolic expressions has been made. Related to this limitation, but more basic, is the perpetual difficulty associated with all models. In using a symbolic expression of the empirical situation, the analyst is no longer dealing with the operation, but with an analogy. Results obtained from inspecting a formal model of a complex operation must therefore be reappraised in the light of all the simplifying assumptions which have been made. Models are not an unmixed blessing. For instance, the analogy of mechanisms has become so ingrained in human thinking that it is difficult to imagine anything which does not work like a machine. The notion

of mathematical models is at least as old as the *Timaeus* and the Pythagoreans; its latest major recurrence seems to favor matrix notations as an expression of the "state of the system." But the difficulty with all models seems to be that, when some analytic complex is substituted for the observed operational components, it is not obvious that the analogy is fully adequate. An observation made by Whitehead with respect to metaphysical models is applicable with equal force here: it is commonly the unrecognized assumptions which are critical, as opposed to those explicitly recognized and stated. Both these difficulties are basically philosophical in nature.

(3) The system described here is fully deterministic. Extrapolations to probabilistic systems are necessary if the scope of usefulness in operations research of the symbolic methodology is not to be compromised. A set of consequences of some antecedent might read:

$$\text{if } a, \text{ then } b \text{ with a probability } p_{ab}$$
$$c \text{ with a probability } p_{ac}$$
$$d \text{ with a probability } p_{ad}$$

Such an extension will not, in general, compromise the usefulness of a truth table. It will not, however, indicate the most likely solutions; but these are the very solutions which merit the attention of the executive.

This limitation is not dangerous, for it leads to a consideration of a method whereby symbolic statements might be analyzed on existing computer systems. In adopting such a method of solution, a computer would be presented with a list of symbolic statements. These statements would be analogous to the mathematical formulae customarily the bill of fare for a computing machine. A further set of data would be those conditions which it is desired to examine. The conditions correspond to the values of the independent variables substituted in mathematical formulae. The problem presented to the computer would be that of compiling the probabilities that each of the possible solutions would occur. Computational techniques employed will vary with the size of the problem. The solution may be a formal one employing statistical methods for small problems; it may employ Monte Carlo methods in longer ones, which would give a sample distribution of outcomes.

(4) In many situations which the operations analyst needs to inspect, there may be no opportunity to specify the interrelationships between the component items in the problem. Indeed, it may be that the specification of those relationships is the goal, rather than the starting point, of the research. The propositional calculus employs a deductive approach. An inductive synthesis, however, leads to a set of generalizations whose implications can then be tested in the fashion proposed here.

Conclusion.

Operations research can enjoy considerable profit from invoking the methodologies of symbolic logic. Primary among the benefits to be expected is an increased clarity concerning the operation and a simplification of a complex problem. In general, it might be expected that symbolic logic would be most useful in the beginning, as contrasted with the end, of the analysis of an operation. It is a preface to operations research, not a substitute. The results obtained should be evaluated with full recognition of the assumptions which have been made, and in particular the realization that a formal model has been substituted for a process. It is possible, in large-scale problems, to employ high-speed computing machines in the " algebraic solution " of symbolic expressions. The duty of the operations analyst seems to parallel the duty of the philosopher as conceived by Whitehead: ". . . the true method of philosophical construction is to frame a scheme of ideas, the best that one can, and unflinchingly to explore the interpretation of experience in terms of that scheme." [3]

---

[3] Alfred North Whitehead, *Process and Reality* (New York: The Macmillan Company, 1929), p. x.

The Use of Computing Machines in Operations Research

JOSEPH O. HARRISON, JR.

OPERATIONS RESEARCH problems frequently require for their solution computing and data-handling on a very large scale. Under certain conditions, both of these processes may be facilitated by the use of large-scale computers. Hence it is of interest to those engaged in operations research to examine the capabilities and limitations of such computers with reference to their own work.

There are two types of large-scale calculating machines in common use: analogue or continuous variable machines; and digital or discrete variable machines. An analogue machine is a physical system— mechanical, electrical, or optical—designed in such a way that the variables of the system satisfy the same mathematical laws as do the variables of the problem to be solved. Computation proper is replaced by measurements of the physical quantities corresponding to values of the unknown variables. The best known analogue computers are: the REAC and the GEDA, produced by the Reeves Instrument Corporation and the Goodyear Aircraft Corporation, respectively, for the solution of systems of differential equations; network analyzers operated by the General Electric Company for the determination of the load characteristics of proposed power transmission systems; and numerous special-purpose analogue computers for finding the zeros of algebraic and transcendental functions and for solving large systems of simultaneous and linear equations.

Digital machines, in contrast to analogue machines, perform their operations by counting in a manner much the same as a person would count with a paper and pencil. The best known of these are: the ENIAC, the EDVAC, and the ORDVAC, all at the Aberdeen Proving Ground; Computers Mark I through Mark IV, constructed by the Computation Laboratory at Harvard University; IBM's Defense Calculator; and Remington Rand's UNIVAC System. At the most elementary level, the simplest analogue computer is the ordinary slide rule; the simplest digital computer, the abacus. This chapter will discuss the applications of large scale *digital* calculating machines.

The Large-Scale Digital Computer.

1)   Basically, the large-scale digital calculator will perform only the simplest types of operations—five of them. First, such a calculator will read. It cannot, of course, read a printed sheet, but it will read information which has been coded on punched cards, punched paper tape, magnetic tape, or similar media.

2)   Second, a large-scale digital computer will remember what it has read. For memory cells, most digital computers employ banks of relays, groups of vacuum tubes, magnetic drums, mercury delay lines, or electrostatic storage tubes. A relay computer remembers information by having certain relays in an energized or picked-up condition, while others are in the unenergized or dropped-out condition. When the memory apparatus consists of vacuum tubes, certain tubes will be conducting while others are non-conducting. Information is stored in a mercury delay line as a coded series of circulating pressure waves in a column of liquid mercury. An electrostatic storage tube remembers information by means of a combination of charged spots on the dielectric material of the tube.

3)   Third, a large-scale digital computer will do arithmetic. Most computers perform the operations of addition, subtraction, multiplication, and division.

4)   Fourth, the large-scale digital computer exercises choice. It is able to choose between one series of operations and another, depending upon the relative magnitudes of the quantities stored within its memory.

Finally, such a computer can write. It records upon punched cards, paper tape, or magnetic tape or, in contrast to the reading operation, on a sheet of paper. Virtually all digital computers have automatic typewriters or printers associated with them, and by such means, the computer records its results directly in a form which is suitable for manual evaluation.

Figure 1 illustrates this concept of a computer, a black box which will perform the operations of read, remember, do arithmetic, exercise choice, and write. The mathematician who uses the computer communicates with it by providing it with data and instructions and by receiving from it numerical results. The computer reads the data and instructions with which it is presented, performs operations upon the data according to the instructions, and writes out the numerical results so obtained for use by the mathematician.

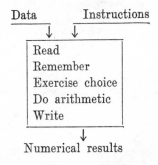

Figure 1. Idealized large-scale digital computer.

Large-scale digital computers vary greatly in their capacities and speeds. The earlier computers which used paper tapes read at speeds as slow as one ten-digit number per second. More modern machines, such as the UNIVAC, read from magnetic tape at a rate of up to 666 twelve-digit numbers per second. A machine such as the ENIAC will remember only 20 ten-digit numbers per second; newer machines produced by Engineering Research Associates, however, will remember over 16,000 such numbers. The speeds for arithmetic operations vary from one second for a multiplication or division in the case of the earlier relay machines, up to speeds of less than 100 microseconds for an addition, as in the case of the ORDVAC. Most machines make comparisons at a rate equal to the rate of speed for arithmetic operations. In the writing of information, computers show a similar variation, from one ten-digit number per second for printing on typewriters and punching on paper tape, up to 666 numbers per second for magnetic recordings.

Large-scale digital computers are frequently referred to as " giant brains." In view of the simplicity of the operations which they perform, this description is not particularly apt. It seems more reasonable to regard a large-scale digital computer as a mathematician's laboratory assistant, an assistant lacking originality but capable of executing calculations very rapidly and very accurately in accordance with the mathematician's instructions. Brain are required to solve complex problems numerically. These are, however, the brains of the mathematician who uses the computer, not those of the computer itself.

A simple example will serve to illustrate the way in which a mathematician uses a large scale digital computer. Let it be supposed that the mathematician desires to evaluate the definite integral

$$\int_a^b f(x)\,dx$$

where the form of the function $f(x)$ is given. Sufficient numerical analysis has been done to satisfy the mathematician that the integral can be approximated to a sufficient degree of accuracy by the finite sum

$$\sum_{i=1}^n f(x_i)\,\Delta x$$

where the interval size Δx is specified. This amounts to approximating the area under the curve $f(x)$ by the sum of the areas of a number of rectangles, each of width Δx.

The overall organization of the computation can be displayed conveniently in flow chart form, as shown in Figure 2. The mathematician preparing the problem for the machines constructs the flow chart as follows:

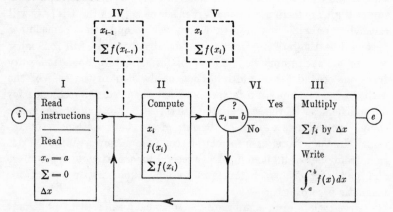

Figure 2. Flow chart of the evaluation of a definite integral.

He assumes the integration to be complete through $x = x_{i-1}$ and the quantities x_{i-1} and $\sum f(x_{i-1})$ to be stored within the memory of the computer, as shown in Storage Box IV. He then instructs the computer to compute x_i by adding Δx to x_{i-1}, to compute $f(x_i)$ according to the prescribed form of that function, and to compute $\sum f(x_i)$ by adding $f(x_i)$ to $\sum f(x_{i-1})$, as shown in Operation Box. II. He directs the computer to store x_i in the memory location in which x_{i-1} was previously stored, and to store $\sum f(x_i)$ in the same memory location in which $\sum f(x_{i-1})$ was previously stored as shown in Storage Box V.

Next, he asks the computer, in Alternative Box VI, to test whether or not $x_i = b$, in order to determine whether the integration process is completed. If x_i is not equal to b, the process is not yet complete and the computer is instructed to return to Box II and to repeat the calculations, this time using x_i instead of x_{i-1}, and $\sum f(x_i)$ instead of $\sum f(x_{i-1})$. The loop containing Box II is thus repeated until $x_i = b$ and the entire range of integration is covered. At this point, the computer is directed, in Operation Box III, to multiply $\sum f(x_i)$ by Δx, thus giving the desired approximation to the integral, and to write out this value. It is necessary now only to draw up the operations required to get the repetitive loop started. This is done in Box I. The computer is required to read in its instructions and to read in the data $x_0 = a$, $\sum f(x_0) = 0$ and Δx.

In the flow chart there are required only the simple operations which the computer is capable of performing. The computer is asked to read in Operation Box I, to remember in Storage Boxes IV and V, to do arithmetic in Operation Box II, to exercise choice in Alternative Box VI, and to write in Operation Box III.

A problem such as this one is economical for machine solution only if it is highly repetitive. In the example just described, the instructions in Operation Box II were repeated over and over again, each time upon different numbers. A computer does not solve a problem in the generally accepted sense of the word; what it actually does is to execute a series of instructions designed by the mathematician to solve the problem.

Contruction of Firing Tables.

A large-scale problem to which digital computers have been successfully applied is the making of firing tables. This was, in fact, one of the problems which motivated the development of the first electronic digital computers. Firing tables are required for each combination of gun and projectile used by the armed forces. They are no longer used in the field for aiming artillery, but are required by the makers of the automatic gun directors and are used in the field to check these directors. Firing tables are produced in large numbers, both at the Army's Aberdeen Proving Ground and at the Naval Proving Ground at Dahlgren, Virginia.

The following scheme is employed. First, a large number of trajectories are computed on the assumption that the projectile is a particle under the influence of gravity and air resistance. Through an equating of the vertical and horizontal forces acting upon the particle, one is led to a system of two simultaneous second-order non-linear differential equations. Certain parameters entering into these equations are found by range firings. A knowledge of these parameters, together with the initial velocity and angle of elevation enables one to compute the trajectory of the projectile. The firing table proper is constructed by inverse interpolation in a large family of trajectories. The effects of wind, rotation of the earth, non-uniform air density, etc., are applied to the completed firing table in the form of differential corrections.

In order to construct a family of trajectories, the computer is required to follow a number of different routines. First, it must execute an integration procedure which relates the position and velocity of the projectile at any instant of time to its position and velocity at several previous instants of time. Second, since this integration procedure cannot be carried out at the beginning of a trajectory, the computer must be able to follow an initial routine, such as an evaluation of a Taylor series solution, for the first several points on the trajectory. The projectile is relatively unstable at velocities in the neighborhood of the velocity of sound. This situation is evident from the computational point of view in requiring that smaller interval sizes be taken in this region. Thus, third, the computer must have a routine for shortening the length of a step, and fourth, another routine for lengthening a step. Fifth, the computer must recognize when the shell has finished its flight. This is done by making it test the sign of the altitude. When the altitude becomes negative, the shell is below ground and the mathematician has no further interest in its path. At this point, the computer is directed to interpolate so as to determine the exact time of flight, then to go back to the starting routine and begin a new trajectory with different initial conditions.

Clearly, these steps require a very elaborate program for the computer. When one considers, however, that hundreds of firing tables are needed and that each firing table requires the computation of many trajectories, each of which is repetitive as the shell moves from position to position, it becomes apparent that the program for the computer will be a highly repetitive one. It is interesting to note, in this connection, that, for high velocity artillery shells, the ENIAC can compute the path of the shell faster than the actual shell can get to its target.

Applications and Limitations of Digital Computers.

There are many other problems to which large scale digital computers have been or are being successfully applied. For convenience, these problems may be divided into five general classes.

First, there are those purely mathematical calculations which arise in engineering and the physical sciences. These consist of the making of mathematical tables, the evaluation of complex formulae, the differentiation, integration and smoothing of observed functions, the determination of the zeros of polynomials and transcendental functions, the solutions of linear algebraic systems and the execution of the associated matrix operations, and the numerical integration of ordinary and partial differential equations.

A second class of problems to which large-scale digital computers are being applied is a group of statistical or counting problems. An example of this class is the tabulation of the 1950 population census by the Census Bureau. The Bureau has collected statistics of age, sex, nativity, education, economic status, etc., on each of the 154 million residents of the United States. At present, a large-scale digital computer is being used to summarize these data and to compile tables from them. The tables give the structure of the American population, broken down into city, county, and state units. Such tabulation involves little formal mathematics, but requires extensive logical manipulation by the computing machine. The bulk of the work which this involves is enormous. Large-scale digital computers are being considered for a similar problem, namely, the summarizing of meteorological data. Both the Weather Bureau and the Air Weather Service have records of meteorological observations taken hourly at hundreds of stations at various altitudes; these records extend back over many years. In order that these data may be made useful, it is necessary that they be subjected to some automatic method of processing.

Logistic applications are a third class of applications. A large-scale digital computer is being considered for automatically monitoring a large military supply system involving over 300,000 different items. The computer is required to maintain a running inventory of all items, to record stock issues and stock receipts, and to keep track of the location of each item in the supply line. In addition, the computer is made to prepare a forecast of future requirements for the various items based upon a statistical analysis of their past rates of issue. Another type of logistic application is the computation of requirements for a large military or civilian operation using linear programming methods. The Office of the Air Comptroller makes extensive use of large-scale digital calculators in estimating the requirements of various Air Force operations. Certain of these operations require such extensive logistic support that their impact upon the country's whole economy must be considered. Large-scale digital calculators are in use to estimate this effect by a scheme based upon the theory of input-output economics developed by Professor Leontief and his associates at Harvard University. Recently, linear systems of order up to 192, based upon Bureau of Labor Statistics data, have been solved by a large-scale digital computer for this purpose.

A fourth type of application is the purely commercial. Life insurance companies have taken the lead in applying large-scale digital computers to their record-keeping and accounting operations. One study, made by one of the largest life insurance companies, involved the processing of six million policies. One phase of the processing, namely the premium billing, required the preparation of one and a half million bills per month. The digital computer was required to examine each policy and, on the basis of the type of insurance, method of payment, anniversary date, and similar data, to prepare a bill for the policy holder which would take account of the distribution of dividends and the deduction of the agent's commission. Similar record-keeping operations are required for banks, publishing houses, large retail stores, and other commercial establishments. The tremendous record-keeping and processing systems handled by the Social Security Administration and the Veterans Administration also present opportunities for the application of large-scale digital computers.

Finally, there is the class of real time control applications. The problem of aircraft traffic control was discussed in an earlier chapter in connection with queueing theory. Studies are being made of large-scale digital computers as a possible tool for aiding in the scheduling of aircraft traffic at an overcrowded airport. The computer can be made to keep a running record of all the planes in the vicinity and, on the basis of this information, to schedule landings and take-offs and to issue flying instructions which accord with the current degree of congestion. This is a real time problem since the computer must keep pace with the actual phenomenon which it is studying. Another potential real time control application is the use of a computer to direct an automatic factory or oil refinery. The computer can examine pressures, temperatures, and other critical parameters which affect the process and, on the basis of such readings, control the process so that optimum output is achieved.

Although a large-scale digital computer will theoretically perform any series of mathematical or logical operations which can be reduced to a firm set of rules, certain types of operations are not suitable for it. Once such process can be described by means of a simple illustration. Let it be assumed that there are a hundred points distributed at random in a rectangular plane. It is required to determine which pair of points is closest together, so that a certain reaction which takes place between the closest pair of points can be considered. If the computer is programmed so as to solve this problem in the most naive manner, it will compute the distances between each of the 4,950 pairs of points. It will then successively compare these distances and determine those two points associated with the shortest distance. Even though the computer can perform arithmetic operations and comparisons in a few microseconds each, the total of such operations will require something between a few seconds and a minute of computer time.

If one were to perform this operation manually, he would have the points plotted on a large sheet of graph paper and would, in most cases, be able immediately to identify the closest pair of points. He could certainly do it in several seconds. It is wasteful to use a computer costing nearly a million dollars to perform an operation which can be done just as well and as speedily without the computer. The reason that the computer is inefficient in this problem seems to be that, whereas it must examine each point in succession, the human problem-solver can look at all the points simultaneously. The computer, in short, possesses no peripheral vision.

A second kind of problem which the computer will not perform efficiently is one requiring random access to huge amounts of data. So long as the computer is required to refer only to information which can be held within its internal memory, the problem of random access to these data is not serious. If, however, the computer is required to have random access to more information than it can remember internally, a serious limitation is imposed upon the computer's utility.

One of the most advanced input-output systems in existence is that associated with Remington Rand's UNIVAC System. The UNIVAC reads its information from magnetic tapes. Each tape is wound on a reel about eight inches in diameter and contains about one and a half million characters, each character being a decimal digit or an alphabetic letter. One such tape will just about hold a novel the length of *Gone with the Wind*. The computer would then be able to read the novel and reproduce it on another tape in approximately three minutes. This is far faster than human performance of the same task.

Suppose, though, that the Baltimore telephone directory were recorded on such a tape and that the computer were then asked to look up the telephone number corresponding to a given name. If the tape were placed in such a way that the reading head was in the middle of it, the computer would take a maximum of a minute and a half or an average of about three-fourths of a minute to look up the number. This, then, is another operation which a human could perform manually just as rapidly. In this case, the computer, although it reads very rapidly, is restricted by the necessity for scanning each item on the tape before it can progress to the next item. The human, on the other hand, skips over many pages of the telephone directory without looking at them. These two examples demonstrate that a large scale digital computer can, generally, be used effectively only on problems which can be readily formulated as a linear sequence of the simple operations which the computer can execute.

Machine vs. Manual Computation.

A large-scale digital computer is capable of nothing which a human with paper and a pencil could not do provided that he lived long enough. The computer, however, can perform its operations more rapidly and more accurately. Hence, the utility of a large scale digital computer is largely a matter of economics. The economic question can be illustrated quantitatively by a simple example.

Let it be assumed that there is a problem which is amenable to solution by a sequence of the elementary operations which a computer can perform, and that the problem has already been analyzed numerically so that the exact operations required are known. It is desired to examine the relative merits of executing the operations by machine or by hand.

If a machine is used, the total elapsed time, T_{mach}, may be approximated by the formula:

$$T_{mach} = O \cdot t_{mach} + I \cdot t_{inst}. \tag{1}$$

The first term on the right, $O \cdot t_{mach}$, represents the number of operations which the problem requires multiplied by the machine time required to perform an operation; this term represents the machine time used. The second term on the right, $I \cdot t_{inst}$, represents the time spent in setting up the problem for the machine: a measure of the time required is given by I, the number of instructions required to direct the machine; the term t_{inst} represents the time per instruction that the mathematician spends in setting up the problem.

If, on the other hand, the problem were to be solved by hand, the time required for a person to execute the operations, T_{pers}, could be approximated by the formula:

$$T_{pers} = O \cdot t_{pers} \tag{2}$$

where t_{pers} is the time required for a person to perform an operation. Set-up time for the hand solution is omitted for two reasons: because the problem has already been analyzed numerically, the set-up time is small; and the formula, as it stands, is sufficiently accurate to illustrate the point which is being developed.

A measure of the effectiveness of the machine is given by

$$\text{Time Ratio} = \frac{T_{pers}}{T_{mach}}. \tag{3}$$

When this time ratio is evaluated in terms of formulae (1) and (2), one obtains

$$\text{Time Ratio} = \frac{\dfrac{O}{I} t_{pers}}{\dfrac{O}{I} t_{mach} + t_{inst}}. \tag{4}$$

Formula (4) illustrates that the effectiveness of the machine does not depend upon the degree of complication of the problem as represented by the number of instructions, nor upon the length of the problem as represented by the number of operations, but upon a ratio of these two quantities. For purposes of illustration, some typical numerical quantities can be substituted in Formula (4).

A hand computer, working continuously, can perform approximately one operation each fifteen seconds. A typical machine of the type under discussion requires, perhaps, one millisecond per operation. A mathematician preparing a program for this machine can perform all steps of the preparation and check the problem out on the machine at the rate of, perhaps, twenty minutes per instruction. These figures are presented in Table 1.

TABLE 1

	Time/op or Time/inst	Cost
Hand Computer	15 secs.	\$ 5/hr
Machine	1 msec.	\$100/hr
Mathematician	20 mins.	\$ 10/hr

Then, if figures are substituted in Formula (4), one obtains

$$\text{Time Ratio} = \frac{\frac{O}{I}\,15}{\frac{O}{I}\,(.001) + 1200}. \tag{5}$$

This function is plotted in Figure 3.

As the figure demonstrates, the potential time ratio of machine to manual computation is about 15,000; a near realization of this potential, however, requires an enormous ratio of operations to instructions. In short, for the machine to be economically effective, the computations must be highly repetitive.

Since a large scale digital computer costs much more per hour than does a person, it might be preferable to base this comparative estimate upon a cost rather than a time ratio. Typical cost figures, including overhead, are provided in Table 1. An expression similar to Formula (5) may be derived for the cost ratio as follows:

$$\text{Cost Ratio} = \frac{\dfrac{O}{I}\,.02}{\dfrac{O}{I}\,(.00003) + 3.33}. \tag{6}$$

This function is plotted in Figure 4.

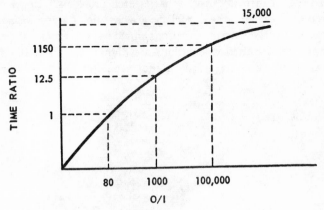

Figure 3. Time ratio of manual to machine solution as a function of the ratio of number of operations to number of instructions.

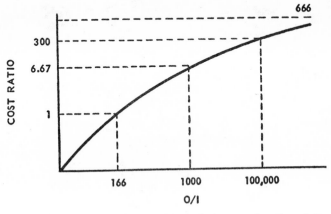

Figure 4. Cost ratio of manual to machine solution as a function of the ratio of number of operations to number of instructions.

Again, the same situation prevails: a tremendous potential saving in cost in favor of the machine, provided that the problem is highly repetitive.

It is hoped that these rather general observations concerning the uses of large-scale digital computers have suggested to those experienced in operations research several problems in which such a machine would have proved invaluable, and have assured those who are contemplating work in the field that computing machines will prove useful to them in many operations research problems. In operations research as elsewhere, when problems are capable of ready formulation in terms of the elementary operations which the computer can perform and when the required calculations are highly repetitive, the advantages offered by the large-scale digital computer should be seriously considered.

Linear Programming
and Operations Research

JOSEPH O. HARRISON, JR.

THE SUBJECT of linear programming will be introduced by means of an example. An entrepreneur has available to him fixed amounts of each of a number of different resources. These resources include raw materials, labor, equipment, and the like. He can combine these resources so as to produce any one of a number of different commodities or any combination of these commodities consistent with his resources. It is assumed that the total quantities of each resource used and the total return are linear homogeneous functions of the quantities of the various commodities produced. The unit return on each commodity and the amount of each resource required for one unit of that commodity are known. It is desired to produce that combination of commodities which will maximize the total return. The problem may be formulated mathematically in the following way. Let:

m = number of resources

b_i = maximum units of resource i available $(i = 1, 2, \cdots, m)$

n = number of commodities produced

c_j = unit return on commodity j $(j = 1, 2, \cdots, n)$

a_{ij} = units of resource i required for one unit of commodity j.

λ_j = units of commodity j to be produced in order to maximize the total return.

Since a_{ij} units of resource i are required for one unit of commodity

j, $a_{ij}\lambda_j$ units of resource i are required for the total quantity of commodity j. Hence $\sum_j a_{ij}\lambda_j$ units of resource i are required for all commodities. Since only b_i units of resource i are available, the λ's must be determined so that $\sum_j a_{ij}\lambda_j \leqq b_i$. An inequality of this type holds for each of the m resources. Since the return on one unit of commodity j is c_j, the return on all units of commodity j is $c_j\lambda_j$, and the return on all units of all commodities is $\sum_j c_j\lambda_j$. Hence the λ's are to be determined in such a way that $\sum_j c_j\lambda_j$ is a maximum. Finally, it is necessary to insure that non-negative amounts of each commodity be produced. Hence it is required that $\lambda_j \geqq 0$ for all j. The mathematical formulation of the problem may thus be stated:

Determine λ_j so as to satisfy the conditions

$$
\begin{aligned}
\lambda_j &\geqq 0 & (j &= 1, 2, \cdots, n) \\
\sum_j a_{ij}\lambda_j &\leqq b_i & (i &= 1, 2, \cdots, m) \\
\sum_j c_j\lambda_j &= \max.
\end{aligned}
\tag{1}
$$

This is a linear programming problem.

The general *linear programming problem* consists of the determination of non-negative variables which optimize a linear form subject to linear constraints. The linear form to be optimized is called the *objective* of the problem. The term *optimize* is understood to mean the determination of variables which make the objective a maximum or a minimum. A *linear constraint* in the variables λ_j is understood to mean an inequality in either direction or an equality between a linear form in these variables and a constant. Constraints of the form $\lambda_j \geqq 0$ are called *non-negativity constraints*. Constraints of the form $\sum_j a_j\lambda_j \leqq b$, $\sum_j a_j\lambda_j \geqq b$ or $\sum a_j\lambda_j = b$ which are not non-negativity constraints are called *functional constraints*. Any set of quantities which satisfies the non-negativity and functional constraints is called a *feasible solution* of the linear programming problem. Any feasible solution which optimizes the objective is called an *optimal solution*.

The general linear programming problem is thus of the form:

$$
\begin{aligned}
\lambda_j &\geqq 0 & (j &= 1, 2, \cdots, n) \\
\sum_j a_{ij}\lambda_j &\leqq, =, \geqq b_i & (i &= 1, 2, \cdots, m) \\
\sum_j c_j\lambda_j &= \max. \text{ or min.}
\end{aligned}
\tag{2}
$$

where the symbol $\leqq$, $=$, $\geqq$ means that any constraint may be an inequality in either direction or an equality independently of the remaining constraints.

Whether a particular application gives rise to a maximizing or minimizing problem is immaterial, since either one may be changed to the other by reversing the signs of the coefficients in the objective. Similarly, a functional constraint which is an inequality in either direction may be changed to one in the other direction by changing the signs of the coefficients on both sides of the inequality.

A constraint of the form $\sum_j a_{kj}\lambda_j \leqq b_k$ may be changed to an equality by adding to the system a new non-negative variable λ_{n+1} and supplying the artificial coefficients $c_{n+1} = 0$, $a_{k,n+1} = 1$, $a_{i,n+1} = 0$ for $i \neq k$. Thus the system

$$\lambda_1, \lambda_2 \geqq 0$$
$$a_{11}\lambda_1 + a_{12}\lambda_2 \leqq b_1$$
$$a_{21}\lambda_1 + a_{22}\lambda_2 \leqq b_2$$
$$c_1\lambda_1 + c_2\lambda_2 = \max.$$

may be transformed to

$$\lambda_1, \lambda_2, \lambda_3, \lambda_4 \geqq 0$$
$$a_{11}\lambda_1 + a_{12}\lambda_2 + \lambda_3 = b_1$$
$$a_{21}\lambda_1 + a_{22}\lambda_2 + \lambda_4 = b_2$$
$$c_1\lambda_1 + c_2\lambda_2 = \max.$$

Similarly, a constraint of the form $\sum_j a_{kj}\lambda_j = b_j$ may be changed to a $\geqq$ inequality by adding to the system a new non-negative variable λ_{n+1} and supplying the artificial coefficients $c_{n+1} = 0$, $a_{k,n+1} = 1$, $a_{i,n+1} = 0$ for $i \neq k$.

Consider a system of the form (1) with two variables and two functional constraints:

$$
\begin{array}{lll}
\text{(a)} & \lambda_1\lambda_2 \geqq 0 & \\
\text{(b)} & a_{11}\lambda_1 + a_{12}\lambda_2 \leqq b_1 & \\
\text{(c)} & a_{21}\lambda_1 + a_{22}\lambda_2 \leqq b_2 & (3) \\
\text{(d)} & c_1\lambda_1 + c_2\lambda_2 = \max. &
\end{array}
$$

Any pair of real numbers (λ_1, λ_2) may be represented as a point in the $\lambda_1\lambda_2$-plane (Figure 1). The set of all such points is said to constitute *solutions space*. The conditions (3) (a) that λ_1 and λ_2 be non-negative require that feasible solutions be represented by points in the first quadrant. The conditions (3) (b) and (3) (c) require that feasible solutions be represented by points simultaneously between the line $a_{11}\lambda_1 + a_{12}\lambda_2 = b_1$ and the coordinate axes, and the line $a_{21}\lambda_1 + a_{22}\lambda_2 = b_2$ and the coordinate axes, respectively. Thus

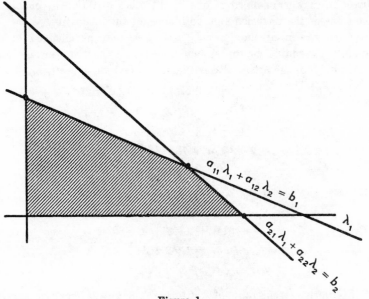

Figure 1.

the set of feasible solutions consists of those points in solutions space represented by the shaded portion of Figure 1 including the boundaries. These points constitute a convex set.

A set consisting of a single point is a *convex set*. A set consisting of more than one point is a *convex set* if every point on the line segment joining any two points of the set is contained in the set. An *extreme point* of a convex set is a point of the set that does not lie on any line segment joining two other points of the set. We have geometrically demonstrated the plausibility of:

Property I. If a linear programming problem is feasible, the set of all feasible solutions constitute a convex set in solutions space.

Let us now superpose on Figure 1 the set of contours of the objective (3) (d). Since the objective is linear and homogeneous in the λ's, this set is the family of parallel straight lines $c_1\lambda_1 + c_2\lambda_2 = M$. The superposition is shown in Figure 2. Let L be the maximum contour which contains at least one point in common with the convex set of feasible solutions. If L does not coincide with one of the

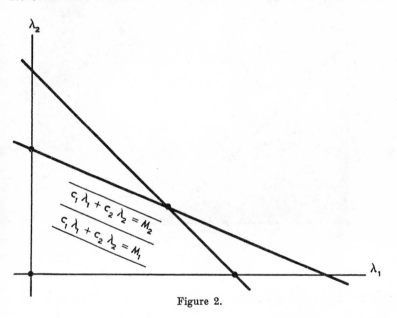

Figure 2.

boundaries of the convex set, it must intersect the convex set in an extreme point. The optimal solution of the problem is unique and this extreme point is that optimal solution. If L coincides with one of the boundaries of the convex set, every point on that boundary is an optimal solution. But this boundary includes at least one extreme point. We have thus demonstrated the plausibility of:

Property II. If a linear programming problem is feasible, an optimal solution occurs at one of the extreme points of the convex set of feasible solutions in solutions space.

We are now in a position to solve a simple numerical example. Suppose it is desired to determine λ_1 and λ_2 such that

$$\lambda_1, \lambda_2 \geqq 0$$
$$\lambda_1 + \lambda_2 \leqq 4$$
$$\lambda_1 + 3\lambda_2 \leqq 6 \qquad (4)$$
$$\lambda_1 + 2\lambda_2 = \max.$$

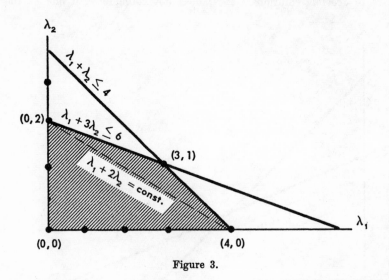

Figure 3.

The points, lines and regions concerned are plotted in Figure 3. It is seen that

a)   All feasible solutions lie within the convex set consisting of the shaded region and its boundaries.

b)   The extreme points of the convex set of feasible solutions are $(0, 0)$, $(0, 2)$, $(3, 1)$ and $(4, 0)$.

c)   The optimal feasible solution is $\lambda_1 = 3$, $\lambda_2 = 1$.

d)   The maximum of the objective is 5.

Duality Properties.

The following pair of related linear programming problems are known as *duals* of each other:

Problem #1	*Problem #2*
Determine λ_j such that	Determine μ_i such that
$\lambda_j \geqq 0$	$\mu_i \geqq 0$
$\sum_j a_{ij}\lambda_j \leqq b_i$	$\sum_i a_{ij}\mu_i \geqq c_j$
$\sum_j c_j\lambda_j = \max.$	$\sum_i b_i\mu_i = \min.$

where a_{ij}, b_i and c_j in the two problems are identical.

The two problems are sometimes written together in the form:

min.	λ_1	λ_j	λ_n	$\leq$
μ_1	a_{11}	a_{1j}	a_{1n}	b_1
μ_i	a_{i1}	a_{ij}	a_{in}	b_i
μ_m	a_{m1}	a_{mj}	a_{mn}	b_m
$\geq$	c_1	c_j	c_n	max.

Since these problems employ exactly the same coefficients, arranged in a different manner, one would expect there to be a close relationship between their solutions. Such indeed is the case.

The physical interpretations of the two problems are related as follows. Suppose:

$b_i =$ units of input i

$c_j =$ value per unit of output j

$a_{ij} =$ units of input i per unit of output j produced.

In this case, λ_j in Problem #1 represents the number of units of output j produced. We restate Problem #1 giving only the units of the quantities concerned rather than the quantities themselves.

$$(\text{output } j) \geqq 0$$

$$\sum_j \frac{(\text{input } i)}{(\text{output } j)} \cdot (\text{output } j) \leqq (\text{input } i)$$

$$\sum_j \frac{(\text{value})}{(\text{output } j)} \cdot (\text{output } j) = (\text{value}).$$

Since the coefficients of Problem #2 are the same as those of Problem #1, the corresponding statement of Problem #2 must be:

$$\mu_i \geqq 0$$

$$\sum_i \frac{(\text{input } i)}{(\text{output } j)} \cdot \mu_i \geqq \frac{(\text{value})}{(\text{output } j)}$$

$$\sum_i (\text{input } i) \cdot \mu_i = ?$$

These equations will be dimensionally consistent if and only if μ_i is in units of value per unit of input i. Hence, the two problems may be formulated in words as follows:

Problem #1. With a prescribed unit value for each output and a prescribed upper limit for the quantity of each input, how much of each output should be produced in order to maximize the value of the total output?

Problem #2. With a prescribed quantity of each input and a prescribed lower limit of unit value for each output, what unit values should be assigned to each input in order to minimize the value of the total input?

Problem #1 is a production scheduling problem. Problem #2 is a valuation problem.

The dual problems have a number of interesting and important properties. These properties may be derived from abstract mathematical considerations. However, each one has a physical counterpart in terms of the quantities which the mathematical variables represent. Considerable insight may be had concerning the intrinsic nature of a process under study by an interpretation of the dual relationships between the production and the valuation aspects of the problem.

Subject to certain conditions upon the boundedness of the sets of feasible solutions of the two problems, which we will not discuss here, the principal dual properties are the following: [1]

[1] D. Gale, H. W. Kuhn and A. W. Tucker, " Linear Programming and the Theory of Games," T. C. Koopmans (ed.), *Activity Analysis of Production and Allocation*, Cowles Commission Monograph 13 (New York: John Wiley and Sons, Inc., 1951), Chapter XIX.

G. B. Dantzig, " A Proof of the Equivalence of the Programming Problem and the Game Problem," Koopmans, *Activity Analysis*, Chapter XX.

G. B. Dantzig, and A. Orden, " A Duality Theorem Based on the Simplex Method," *Symposium on Linear Inequalities and Programming* (Planning

Property I. Feasible solutions of either problem exist if and only if feasible solutions of the other problem exist.

This property constitutes the fundamental existence theorem for the dual problems. It states that there is a basis for solving the valuation problem if and only if the production problem can be solved.

Property II. If feasible solutions to both problems exist, then the objective of the minimizing problem is greater than or equal to the objective of the maximizing problem.

This property is the second law of thermodynamis for linear programming problems. It states that the total value of the output cannot exceed the total value of the input.

Property III. If feasible solutions to both problems exist, the minimum of Problem #2 is equal to the maximum of Problem #1.

This property states that, if production is scheduled in the most efficient manner, and if the inputs are valued in the most efficient manner, then the total intrinsic value of the inputs is conserved.

Property IV. If, for an optimal solution of Problem #1,

$$\sum_j a_{ij}\lambda_j - b_i < 0,$$

then $\mu_i = 0$ for an optimal solution of Problem #2.

This property states that any resource which is not completely used must be assigned zero unit value. Such an assignment is consistent with our intuitive idea of value, since, if an arbitrarily small amount of the not completely used input is added to or subtracted from the total resources, the value of the total output will remain unchanged.

Let us consider now the dual of the problem treated on pages 221 and 222.

$$\mu_1, \mu_2 \geqq 0$$
$$\mu_1 + \mu_2 \geqq 1$$
$$\mu_1 + 3\mu_2 \geqq 2$$
$$4\mu_1 + 6\mu_2 = \min.$$

The points, lines, and regions concerned are plotted in Figure 4.

Research Division, Director of Management Analysis Service, Comptroller, Headquarters, U. S. Air Force, April 1952), pp. 51-55.

G. Dantzig, and A. Orden, *Notes on Linear Programming, Part II—Duality Theorems,* RAND Report P-393 (10 April 1953).

a) All feasible solutions lie within the unbounded convex set consisting of the shaded region and its boundaries.

b) The finite extreme points of the convex set of feasible solutions are $(0, 1)$, $(\frac{1}{2}, \frac{1}{2})$ and $(2, 0)$.

c) The optimal feasible solution is $\mu_1 = \frac{1}{2}$, $\mu_2 = \frac{1}{2}$.

d) The minimum of the objective is 5.

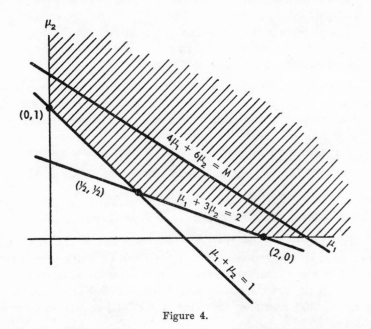

Figure 4.

Applications.

In 1945, the high cost of living motivated George Stigler [2] to consider the problem of determining the adequate diet of minimum cost. In order to handle the problem, Stigler was forced to neglect such aesthetic considerations as palatability and variety, which are difficult to measure. Also, he was forced to assume that the total effective nutrient content of a diet is a linear homogeneous combination of the effective nutrient contents of the individual foods of which that diet consists. This assumption is apparently not too far

[2] G. F. Stigler, "The Cost of Subsistence," *Journal of Farm Economics*, Vol. 27 (May 1945), pp. 303-14.

off from a dietary point of view. Stigler was then able to give a solution to the problem in terms of the costs and nutrient contents of the various available foods and the minimum nutrient requirements of the human body.

m = number of nutrients
b_i = minimum units of nutrient i required monthly
$\quad\quad (i = 1, 2, \cdots, m)$
n = number of foods
c_j = unit cost of food j $(j = 1, 2, \cdots, n)$
a_{ij} = units of nutrient i in one unit of food j
λ_j = units of food j to be consumed monthly.

By an argument precisely analogous to that employed previously in formulating the simple production problem, it may be shown that the quantities of the various foods which constitute the desired diet, λ_j, must be determined so as to satisfy the conditions

$$\lambda_j \geqq 0$$
$$\sum_j a_{ij}\lambda_j \geqq b_i$$
$$\sum_j c_j\lambda_j = \min.$$

The dual of this problem is the determination of μ_i such that

$$\mu_i \geqq 0$$
$$\sum_i a_{ij}\mu_i \leqq c_j$$
$$\sum_i b_i\mu_i = \max.$$

μ_i must have the dimensions of cost per unit of nutrient i. The dual problem may therefore be stated as follows. With a prescribed consumption of each nutrient b_i, and a prescribed upper limit of unit cost for each food c_j, what unit cost μ_i, should be attributed to each nutrient in order to maximize the total value of the nutrients consumed?

Stigler worked the problem out numerically for 77 different foods and 9 different nutrients, first on the basis of 1939 prices and again on the basis of 1944 prices. The nutrients considered were calories, protein, calcium, iron, Vitamin A, thiamine, riboflavin, niacin and ascorbic acid. He found that in 1939 the optimum diet consisted principally of wheat flour, cabbage, and dried navy beans and cost a total of $39.93 for the year. On the basis of 1944 prices, the dried navy beans were omitted, and a large amount of hog liver added. The total cost of the diet was $59.88 for the year, an increase of approximately 50 per cent over the 1939 cost.

The diet problem and the simple production problem are typical of a large class of problems requiring the combination of various input items into output items in the most efficient manner possible according to some specified criterion. Such problems are sometimes called mixing problems.

A large-scale problem of this type, for which results have been published,[3] is the problem of blending aviation gasolines into the most economical mixture. Aviation gasolines are obtained by blending straight-run gasolines, obtained directly from the refinery, with other refinery products such as isopentane, and chemical catalysts such as tetraethyl lead. The resulting aviation gasolines are graded according to their performance characteristics, the two most important of which are ignition properties, as measured by octane ratings or performance numbers, and volatility as measured by Reid Vapor Pressure. Under certain simplifying assumptions, Charnes, Cooper and Mellon succeeded in setting this problem up as a linear programming problem with 10 functional constraints and 22 unknowns. On the basis of 1950 market prices, they obtained numerically what appeared to be a very reasonable optimal solution.

A classical linear programming problem which arose from the consideration of an entirely different type of situation is the Hitchcock-Koopmans Transportation Problem. This problem was formulated independently by Hitchcock in 1941 [4] and Koopmans in 1947.[5] In its simplest form, the problem may be stated as follows:

A homogeneous product is available in specified amounts at each

---

[3] A. Charnes, W. W. Cooper and B. Mellon, " Blending Aviation Gasolines," *Symposium on Linear Inequalities and Programming*, pp. 115-46.

[4] F. L. Hitchcock, " The Distribution of a Product from Several Sources to Numerous Localities," *Journal of Mathematics and Physics*, MIT, Vol. 20 (1941), pp. 224-30.

[5] T. C. Koopmans, " Optimum Utilization of the Transportation System," *Proceedings of the International Statistical Conferences, 1947*, Vol. 5 (Washington, D. C., 1947). (Volume 5 reprinted as Supplement to *Econometrica*, Vol. 17, 1949.)

of a number of different origins. It is required to ship specified amounts of the product to each of a number of different destinations. The cost required to ship one unit of the product from any origin to any destination is known. What is the minimum cost shipping schedule?

m = number of origins

a_i = units of the product available at origin i
   $(i = 1, 2, \cdots, m)$

n = number of destinations

b_j = units of the product required at destination j
   $(j = 1, 2, \cdots, n)$

c_{ij} = cost of shipping one unit of product from origin i to destination j

λ_{ij} = units of product to be shipped from origin i to destination j.

Mathematically, the problem reduces to the determination of λ_{ij} satisfying the following conditions:

$$(a) \qquad \lambda_{ij} \geqq 0$$
$$(b) \qquad \sum_j \lambda_{ij} \leqq a_i \qquad\qquad (5)$$
$$(c) \qquad \sum_i \lambda_{ij} \geqq b_j$$
$$(d) \qquad \sum_i \sum_j c_{ij}\lambda_{ij} = \min.$$

Constraints (5) (a) are the non-negativity constraints which state that negative amounts of the product cannot be shipped. Constraints (5) (b) are functional constraints which specify that not more than a_i units of the product may be shipped from origin i. Constraints (5) (c) are functional constraints which specify that at least b_j units must be shipped to destination j. The objective (left-hand side of (5) (d)) is an expression for the total cost of transportation.

The Hitchcock-Koopmans Transportation Problem is a member of a class of algebraically equivalent linear programming problems which may appropriately be called assignment problems. This class of problems is characterized by the fact that the elements of the matrix of coefficients of the functional constraints consist entirely of zeros and ones. This feature may be capitalized upon in the numerical solution of such problems.

A personnel assignment problem [6] may be formulated as follows. A specified number of persons are available in each of a number of mutually exclusive personnel categories. A specified number of jobs are available in each of a number of mutually exclusive job categories. Quantitative measures of the productivity (scores) of persons in each personnel category at jobs in each job category are given. How should the persons be assigned to the jobs in order to maximize the total productivity of all persons on all jobs?

m = number of personnel categories

a_i = number of persons in personnel category i ($i = 1, 2, \cdots, m$)

n = number of job categories

b_j = number of jobs in job category j ($j = 1, 2, \cdots, n$)

c_{ij} = productivity of a person in the ith personnel category on a job in the jth category

λ_{ij} = number of persons in personnel category i to be assigned to a job in job category j.

The λ_{ij} are to be selected in such a way that

$$\lambda_{ij} \geqq 0$$
$$\sum_j \lambda_{ij} \leqq a_i$$
$$\sum_i \lambda_{ij} = b_j$$
$$\sum_i \sum_j c_{ij}\lambda_{ij} = \text{max.}$$

Linear programming problems of the assignment type may arise whenever general purpose equipment or material is to be used for specific tasks. In particular, the problem of the allocation of different types of military aircraft to different missions [7] has been treated.

The problems mentioned so far have been static in the sense that

[6] D. F. Votaw, Jr. and A. Orden, "The Personnel Assignment Problem," *Symposium on Linear Inequalities and Programming*, pp. 155-63.

J. Von Neumann, "A Certain Zero-sum Two-person Game Equivalent to the Optimal Assignment Problem," H. W. Kuhn and A. W. Tucker, *Contributions to the Theory of Games*, Annals of Mathematics Studies 24 (Princeton University Press, 1951), pp. 5-12.

[7] J. L. Holley, "Suitability Scales for Allocation Problems," *Symposium on Linear Inequalities and Programming*, pp. 192-93.

time has not entered explicitly. However, a class of dynamic problems can be handled by linear programming methods.

The simple static production-scheduling problem considered earlier treated the production operation as a one shot affair. Had the functional constraints of that problem been set up so as to limit rates at which the various inputs were made available rather than the total quantities of the inputs which could be used, and the objective of that problem defined so as to represent rate of total return rather than quantity of total return, the solution could be interpreted as a production schedule for a steady-state continuing operation.

To represent reality in any degree of detail, however, transient phenomena must usually be considered. In production scheduling, one of the important problems in the transient case is the balancing of inventory levels with production levels.

In producing a commodity for which there is seasonal demand, management must accept one of three alternatives: (1) maintain a constant level of production and allow inventory to fluctuate; (2) maintain a constant inventory level and adjust production to it; (3) allow both the inventory level and the production level to fluctuate so as to optimize some measure of effectiveness consistent with the company's overall objectives. In general, alternative (1) represents the production manager's point of view; alternative (2) represents the comptroller's point of view; alternative (3) represents the stockholder's point of view.

A simple example will show how linear programming helps to resolve this type of conflict. Consider a company that has one production line upon which it produces a single homogeneous commodity. We suppose that the commodity sells for a fixed unit price; that the costs for regular time production, overtime production, and storage are known; that the rate of production per unit time is known; and that an accurate sales forecast in the form of demand during each of a number of successive time periods is known. It is desired to formulate a production schedule which will meet the sales forecast and minimize the combined costs of production and storage.

$k = $ number of time periods

$S_i = $ number of units of finished product to be sold during ith time period

$I_0 = $ initial inventory

$\Lambda =$ maximum number of units which can be produced each time period on regular time

$U =$ maximum number of units which can be produced each time period on overtime

$C_I =$ cost of storage of 1 unit of product for 1 time period

$C_\lambda =$ cost of production of 1 unit on regular time

$C_\mu =$ cost of production of 1 unit on overtime

$\lambda_i =$ regular time production during i^{th} time period

$\mu_i =$ overtime production during i^{th} time period.

For concreteness, it will be assumed that each time period is one month in length, and that the inventory for each month is taken on the last day of that month. This is equivalent to adding the month's production to inventory and withdrawing the month's sales from inventory at the end of each month.

The linear programming formulation of the problem is then the following:

$$\text{(a)} \qquad \lambda_i, \mu_i \geqq 0$$

$$\text{(b)} \qquad \lambda_i \leqq \Lambda$$

$$\text{(c)} \qquad \mu_i \leqq U \tag{6}$$

$$\text{(d)} \qquad \sum_{\alpha=1}^{i} (\lambda_\alpha + \mu_\alpha) \geqq \sum_{\alpha=1}^{i} S_\alpha - I_0$$

$$\text{(e)} \qquad \sum_{i=1}^{k} (C_I I_i + C_\lambda \lambda_i + C_\mu \mu_i) = \min.$$

where

$$\text{(f)} \quad I_i = I_0 + \sum_{\alpha=1}^{i} (\lambda_\alpha + \mu_\alpha - S_\alpha) \qquad i = 1, 2, \cdots, k. \tag{6}$$

Constraints (6) (a) are the non-negativity constraints. Constraints (6) (b) are functional constraints which state that the regular time production during any month shall not exceed Λ units. Constraints (6) (c) are functional constraints which state that the overtime production during any month shall not exceed U units. Constraints (6) (d) are functional constraints which state that the sales forecast for each month must be met by the inventory at the end of that month. Constraints (6) (d) are derived from the following considerations. Let the inventory during the αth month be denoted by I_α. Then, since the inventory at the end of any month is equal to the inventory at the end of the previous month plus the monthy production minus the monthly sales,

$$I_\alpha = I_{\alpha-1} + (\lambda_\alpha + \mu_\alpha) - S_\alpha.$$

Summing this relation from $\alpha = 1$ to i yields expression (6) (f). The requirement that the right hand side of expression (6) (f) be non-negative yields the constraints (6) (d). This requirement is the equivalent of the statement that a non-negative inventory must remain after subtracting the sales at the end of each month. The objective (left hand side of (6) (e)) is an expression for the total cost of production and storage.

In theory, there is no difficulty in extending the dynamic production scheduling problem to accommodate a multiplicity of products and a variety of different types of functional constraints.[8] In practice, difficulty may be expected in formulating objectives and company policies in quantitative terms, in approximating the complex constraints of reality by linear relationships, in obtaining reliable numerical coefficients, and finally in numerically evaluating solutions of the problem in time for them to be of use. Most of these difficulties, however, are shared by any scientific attempt to schedule a production process on a rational basis and hence should be interpreted as intrinsic difficulties of the problem rather than deficiencies of the linear programming approach.

Linear programming appears to be applicable to production scheduling on three distinct levels of detail. First, coarse optimal overall levels of activity for long-range planning purposes may be worked out from a steady-state model. Second, schedules with monthly time periods may be worked out a year in advance for budgetary and annual planning considerations on the basis of best predicted data. Third, daily computations may be made for detailed process control using short range predictions of requirements and current reports on the status of the process.

[8] J. F. Magee, *Studies in Operations Research I: Application of Linear Programming to Production Scheduling* (Cambridge, Mass.: Arthur D. Little, Inc., n. d.).

Further Topics.

Two broad topics in linear programming have not yet been touched upon. Limitations on time prevent us from doing more than merely mentioning them here. The first of these topics is the relationship between finite zero-sum two-person games and linear programming problems. The basic properties relating these two types of problems are the following: [9]

Property I. To every finite zero sum two person game with positive value (positive value is not an essential restriction in generality), there corresponds a linear programming problem.

Property II. To every linear programming problem, there corresponds a symmetric finite zero-sum two-person game.

Property III. In both cases I and II above, the correspondence is such that a solution of the game exists if and only if a solution of the associated linear programming problem exists.

Property IV. If solutions to both problems exist, these solutions are related to each other by trivial transformations of variables.

These relationships are important for two reasons. First, additional conceptual understanding of either type of problem may be gained by studying the associated problem of the other type. Second, numerical methods for the solution of finite zero-sum two-person games are applicable to linear programming problems and numerical methods for the solution of linear programming problems are applicable to finite zero-sum two-person games.

The second topic which should be mentioned is the subject of the numerical solution of linear programming problems. The graphical method of solution discussed earlier is valid for problems in two variables with any number of functional constraints. By considering the dual of a given problem, the method can be made to apply to the case of two functional constraints and any number of variables. Persons who are clever at making three-dimensional drawings will have little difficulty in extending the graphical technique to the cases of three functional constraints or three variables. It is theoretically

[9] Gale, Kuhn and Tucker, " Linear Programming and the Theory of Games." Dantzig, " Proof of Equivalence, etc."

J. C. C. McKinsey, *Introduction to the Theory of Games* (New York: McGraw-Hill Book Co., Inc., 1952), Chapter XIV.

possible to solve problems in four or more dimensions graphically by considering successively 2 or 3 dimensional sections of the higher dimensional space. In practice, however, the graphical method ultimately becomes prohibitively complicated.

The problems of greatest practical interest are generally those having both a large number of variables and a large number of constraints. In order to solve such problems various numerical methods have been devised. Since the technique of linear programming developed concurrently with the development of large-scale digital calculating machines, most of the methods are designed for suitability for machine calculation. Hence, these methods, in general, possess the attributes of simplicity and generality, at the expense of a large amount of numerical manipulation.

The best known numerical method for the solution of linear programming problems is the Simplex Method.[10] The method requires as a starting point the coordinates of one of the extreme points of the convex set of feasible solutions. A sequence of extreme points is then obtained, each one being computed from its predecessor in such a way that (1) the value of the objective is not decreased, and (2) the same extreme point is never repeated. Since there are only a finite number of extreme points, and since an optimal feasible solution occurs at one of them, an optimal solution is obtained in a finite number of steps. The indicated operations are carried out by means of a simple arithmetic algorithm.

Other published numerical methods include (1) The Method of Fictitious Play [11] for symmetric finite zero-sum two-person games, (2) The Relaxation Method [12] for systems of linear inequalities, and

[10] G. B. Dantzig, "Maximization of a Linear Function of Variables Subject to Linear Inequalities," Koopmans, *Activity Analysis*, Chapter XXI.

A. Charnes, W. W. Cooper and A. Henderson, *An Introduction to Linear Programming* (New York: John Wiley and Sons, Inc., 1953). (This volume is devoted almost entirely to the derivation, execution and application of the Simplex Method.)

G. B. Dantzig, *Notes on Linear Programming Part III—Computational Algorithm for the Simplex Method*, RAND Report P-394, 10 April 1953.

[11] G. W. Brown, "Iterative Solution of Games by Fictitious Play," Koopmans, *Activity Analysis*, Chapter XXIV.

[12] Charnes, Cooper and Henderson, *Introduction to Linear Programming*, pp. 70-74.

(3) The Solution of a System of Ordinary Differential Equations [13] whose asymptotic values give the solution of a symmetric finite zero-sum two-person game. The relative merits of various of these methods have been investigated empirically.[14]

For the operations analyst, linear programming constitutes a powerful tool. Although subject to various types of limitations, it is applicable to many broad classes of problems.

The intrinsic mathematical limitations are the postulates upon which linear programming is based. These have been called the postulates of (1) linearity, (2) divisibility, (3) additivity, and (4) finiteness. Dorfman [15] discusses in considerable detail the extent to which these postulates limit the application of linear programming. Suffice it to say here, first, that these limitations are shared by most of the models which operations analysts have found useful in the past, and, second, that iterated application of the linear programming technique will in many cases result in adequate approximations for problems to which the postulates clearly do not apply.

The practical difficulties encountered in applying linear programming are threefold: (1) the expression of realistic objectives and constraints in measurable terms; (2) the determination of suitable numerical values for coefficients; and (3) the computational labor required to execute numerically large-scale linear programming problems. The extent to which the first of these difficulties is encountered is a function of the operation being studied, not of the technique used to study it. A man who treats practical problems in a rational manner must be able to meet successfully this type of difficulty. The extent to which the second and third types of difficulties occur is dependent upon the level of detail with which the operation is studied. In general, the study of the details of an operation requires

[13] G. W. Brown and J. Von Neumann, " Solutions of Games by Differential Equations," Kuhn and Tucker, *Contributions to the Theory of Games*, pp. 73-79.

[14] A. Hoffman, M. Mannos, D. Sokolowsky and N. Wiegmann, " Computation Experience in Solving Linear Programs," *Journal of the Society for Industrial and Applied Mathematics*, Vol. 1, No. 1 (September 1953), pp. 17-33.

A. Orden, " Solution of Systems of Linear Inequalities on a Digital Computer," *Proceedings of the Association for Computing Machinery* (Pittsburgh, May 1952), pp. 91-95.

[15] R. Dorfman, *Application of Linear Programming to the Theory of the Firm* (University of California Press, 1951), pp. 79-88.

detailed data and detailed manipulation of this data. Thus the practical difficulties encountered in applying linear programming are in a sense an indication of the level of difficulty of the problems which linear programming can treat.

The obvious type of application for linear programming is the construction of a numerical action schedule using available resources. In addition to this type of application, however, linear programming may be used, under certain circumstances, to aid in policy control. For example, a firm may have under consideration the investment of surplus capital to increase its material resources. Linear programming provides a technique for qualitatively estimating the theoretical increase in the selected measure of the firm's objective due to this proposed increase in material resources. As another example, the firm may wish to evaluate quantitatively the cost of some personnel policy, such as the elimination of scheduled overtime work. Linear programming provides a technique for quantitatively estimating the cost of the policy change in terms of the firm's objective.

Quite aside from its use in determining numerical answers, linear programming can be a conceptual aid to the operations analyst. The linear programming approach, even if it is not carried through the data-gathering and computational phases, points up the necessity for clearly formulating objectives and focuses attention upon those parameters upon which optimization of the objective depends.

There seems to be no universally accepted definition of operations research. However, if one uses a definition which has been proposed, that operations research is the selection by rational means of an optimum course of action from among a set of courses of action, then linear programming is a powerful tool of operations research. For, in situations where linear programming applies, this is exactly what linear programming does.

Game Theory

DAVID H. BLACKWELL

THOSE ENGAGED in operations research often begin the investigation of a problem by describing a model of the situation which they are trying to analyze. Frequently, the model which they describe has the following skeleton. There is a set of mutually exclusive alternative actions, $A_1, \cdots, A_n$, of which one and only one must be taken. It is the purpose of the analysis to make a selection from the group of alternatives. One examines each possible action, A_i, and determines its consequences, C_i. The operations research worker describes the consequences of these various actions in such a form (e. g. dollar profit, number of ships sunk) that the customer can readily decide which consequences he prefers and then select the appropriate action. Many problems have this basic structure; the analysis consists essentially of describing the consequences of each action in a way which makes possible a clear, quantitative comparison of their merits.

In game theory also, the aim is to establish a clear basis for decision. The game situation, however, is more complex, since the actions of an opponent or competitor must also be taken into account. The consequences of an action by one party, therefore, depend not only on that action but also upon the action which the opponent chooses from among his alternatives. This type of conflict situation is, obviously, essentially different from the simple maximization problem where there is but one decision maker.

Von Neumann's Theory of Games.

In 1928, Von Neumann [1] first demonstrated a method for describing such conflicts and developed the famous minimax principle for making decisions in these situations. The model for a conflict situation is called a *game.* The description of a very simple kind of game will serve to illustrate the construction of such a model. Let A be any matrix of numbers; that is, A consists of mn numbers, arranged in a rectangle of m rows with n numbers in each row. The number in the ith row and the jth column is designated A_{ij}, so that the matrix has the following appearance:

$$
\begin{array}{ccccc}
A_{11} & A_{12} & A_{13} & \cdots & A_{1n} \\
A_{21} & A_{22} & A_{23} & \cdots & A_{2n} \\
\cdot & \cdot & \cdot & \cdots & \cdot \\
A_{m1} & A_{m2} & A_{m3} & \cdots & A_{mn}.
\end{array}
$$

Any matrix of numbers corresponds to a game between two players, I and II, which is played in the following way. Player I chooses one of the rows of the matrix; he chooses a number, i, any number from 1 to m inclusive, and writes it on a sheet of paper. Player II, simultaneously and without knowing what I has selected, chooses one of the columns by writing a number, j, any number between 1 and n inclusive, on his sheet of paper. Their two choices are then examined and II pays I the amount A_{ij}, the number in the row chosen by I and in the column chosen by II.

Such a game is a clear example of the conflict situation mentioned previously. Player I cannot predict the consequences of his choosing row 1; he can predict only the joint consequences of his choosing row 1 and II's choosing a particular column. In such a case, the maximization principle fails and a new basis for decisions is required.

Von Neumann's first achievement was to show that every game could be reduced to a matrix game of the kind just described, that there were no kinds of games other than matrix games. This remarkable demonstration was made possible by the concept of *strategy* in the sense in which Von Neumann used the word.

[1] See John Von Neumann and Oskar Morgenstern, *Theory of Games and Economic Behavior* (2nd ed.; Princeton University Press, 1947).

One might, for example, wish to describe chess in the rectangular form. This could be achieved by handing each player a list of all the possible situations which might arise in the course of the game in which it would be his turn to move, and by requiring him to list opposite each situation the move he would select should that situation arise. Thus the many little decisions made during a chess game can be replaced, conceptually, by one big decision by each player, namely the decision of how to fill in the list. Each legitimate way of completing the list constitutes what is called *strategy* for chess. Once the two players have chosen their strategies, i. e. filled in their lists, their papers can be handed to a referee who can carry out the play of the entire game and announce the result. If $S_1, \cdots, S_m$ are the possible strategies for White, i. e. the different ways of filling in his list, and $T_1, \cdots, T_n$ are the possible strategies for Black, and one defines

$$A_{ij} = \begin{matrix} 1 \\ 0 \\ -1 \end{matrix} \text{ if the result of choices } S_i, T_j \text{ is } \begin{matrix} \text{White wins} \\ \text{draw} \\ \text{Black wins,} \end{matrix}$$

the m by n matrix A with elements A_{ij} determines a matrix game equivalent to chess.

The concept of strategy as an overall plan, specifying what to do in every contingency, can be applied to any game, reducing it to a matrix with as many rows as there are strategies for Player I and as many columns as there are strategies for Player II; A_{ij} denotes the numerical worth to I of the consequences of his choosing strategy i and II's choosing strategy j.

Once the game is described in rectangular form, which row should Player I choose? A simple example from baseball will illustrate the problem. Let it be assumed that there is a pitcher against a batter with a 3-1 count; there are three balls and one strike against the batter. To simplify the problem rather artificially, it is also assumed that the pitcher can throw only two kinds of pitches, strikes and balls, and that he can throw either as he wishes. The batter must decide in advance whether or not he is going to swing at a particular pitch. If he decides to swing and the pitch is a ball, he will miss it. If he decides to swing and the pitch is a strike, three possible consequences may be assumed: he will miss it; he will make a hit; or he will fly out. To simplify the illustration, these three results will be regarded as equally likely.

The batter is trying to get on base and the pitcher is trying to get the batter out. How should each behave? One can begin by considering the possible strategies which are open to the batter. Let H denote the decision to swing at a particular pitch and N the decision not to swing. He may decide to hit at the first pitch, and then, if he is still at bat, hit at the second. Or he may decide to hit at the first pitch and, if he is still batting, not hit at the second. Or he may decide not to hit at the first and to hit at the second, or to hit at neither. His strategy NH, for example, would mean, " I will not swing at the first pitch and, if it should happen to be a strike, which would put me in a 3-2 situation, I will swing at the next pitch."

Four strategies are available to the pitcher. He can decide to throw a strike both times, a ball both times, a strike and then a ball, or a ball and then a strike. Now a matrix can be constructed and the numbers in it will be the probabilities that the batter gets to base for the various pairs of strategies. The matrix of the situation is, after each element is multiplied by 9 to simplify writing:

	SS	SB	BS	BB
HH	4	3	3	0
HN	3	6	0	9
NH	3	0	9	9
NN	0	9	9	9

The 4 in the first row first column is obtained in the following way. The probability that the batter hits the first pitch is 1/3. The probability of his missing the first pitch and hitting the second is $1/3 \cdot 1/3$ or 1/9. Therefore, his probability of getting on base is $1/3 + 1/9$ or 4/9. The other numbers in the matrix are similarly obtained, all being multiplied by 9 to avoid fractions.

If the pitcher could know what the batter was going to do, he would know what to do himself. In other words, if he knew which row the batter would select, the pitcher could simply look across that row and find its smallest element, then select that column. Since each row contains a 0, a pitcher who knew the batter's strategy could surely keep that batter from reaching base; the pitcher would simply throw a ball at each pitch when the batter intended to swing and a strike otherwise.

Similarly, if the batter knew what the pitcher was going to do, he would examine the column of the pitcher's choice, select its largest element, then play the row containing that element. The largest element in the second, third, and fourth columns is 9 and the largest in the first column is 4. Therefore, if the pitcher knew that the batter was going to find out his strategy, he would choose column 1; any other choice would allow the batter to get 9, but, even knowing the pitcher's choice, the batter can do no better than 4 in the first column. There is, then, a gap, 0 to 4, between what the batter could get if he found out what the pitcher was going to do and the limit to which the pitcher could restrict the batter if he knew what the batter was going to do.

Two questions then arise. Can the batter do anything to improve over 0? Can the pitcher do anything to bring the outcome below 4? Any batter would sometimes swing and sometimes not swing at the first pitch, since it is an essential part of the situation to conceal one's signals and intentions from the opponent. It would not be practical to use a theory which required the choice of a single row; if such a theory were announced, the opponent too could consult the matrix and select the designated countermeasure. It becomes necessary, therefore, to introduce some new concept and Von Neumann has provided the concept of *mixed strategy*. Mixed strategy requires that a probability be assigned to each strategy and that these probabilities be used to determine which strategy should actually be used in a particular play.

This can be illustrated by consideration of a particular set of probabilities. One might consider, for example, the numbers 27/44, 9/44, 6/44, and 2/44, whose sum is one. Next, 44 balls can be placed in an urn: 27 of them are labeled HH; 9 are labeled HN; 6 are labeled NH; and 2 are labeled NN. The balls are then mixed up inside the urn. One reaches in then, pulls out a ball, and does what the label on the ball instructs. It is impossible to say what will happen in a given play, because it is not known which ball will come up. One can, however, predict what will happen on the average, since the average frequencies with which the various kinds of balls will come up are known.

When these numbers are used against strategy SS by the pitcher, the probability of the batter's getting on base is:

$$\frac{\frac{27}{44}(4) + \frac{9}{44}(3) + \frac{6}{44}(2) + \frac{2}{44}(0)}{9} = \frac{153}{44(9)} = .386.$$

A similar computation yields the same probability, $153/44(9)$, of his getting on base against each of the pitcher's three remaining strategies. If the pitcher used the same probabilities, $27/44$, $9/44$, $6/44$ and $2/44$, he would find that there was the probability of $153/44(9)$ that the batter would get on base no matter what strategy the batter chose.

The essence of the Von Neumann minimax theory is that, no matter what matrix is used, it is always possible to find the probabilities for playing the strategies and to find a number which corresponds to the $153/44(9)$ developed in the above example. Such a number, which is called the value of the game, has the following property: if Player I chooses the strategies according to the specified probabilities, he is certain to achieve at least the value of the game regardless of what the other player does; and if Player II chooses the strategies specified for him, he guarantees that Player I will not get more than the value of the game, regardless of what Player I does. This number, V, then, which is the value of the game, is a reasonable evaluation to place on the game: Player I can guarantee V, and Player II can guarantee that Player I achieves no more than V. Moreover, the specified probabilities are reasonable prescriptions for the game, since they assure one player an amount which his opponent can prevent him from exceeding. Those probabilities which guarantee the value or better are called good strategies for the two players. The basic Von Neumann theorem is that every game has both a value and good strategies.

One can sketch the proof of this theorem. The discussion will be for the case in which Player I has two strategies, but the argument can be extended to any number. Consider then, a 2 by n matrix A:

$$A_{11} \cdot A_{12} \quad \cdots \quad A_{1n}$$
$$A_{21} \quad A_{22} \quad \cdots \quad A_{2n}.$$

The n points can then be plotted in a plane:

$$P_1 = (A_{11}, A_{21}), \qquad P_2 = (A_{12}, A_{22}), \cdots, P_n = (A_{1n}, A_{2n}).$$

Let $q = (q_1, \cdots, q_n)$ be any set of non-negative numbers with sum 1; let $s(q) = q_1 P_1 + \cdots q_n P_n$; and let S consist of all points $s(q)$

obtained by varying q. The point $s(q)$ is the center of gravity of the system of weights q_1 at P_1, q_2 at P_2, $\cdots q_n$ at P_n. The set S of all centers of gravity obtained by varying the weight distribution q has the property of *convexity*; that is to say, if any two points of S are joined by a line segment, all points of this line segment are in S. S is, in fact, the smallest set with this property containing $P_1, \cdots P_n$.

Among all points of S, there is one with a maximum coordinate which is as small as possible. If $s(q_0) = s_0 = (x_0, y_0)$ is such a point, and V is the larger of (x_0, y_0) (or their common value if $x_0 = y_0$), then:

(a) $x_0 \leqq V$, $y_0 \leqq V$ and

(b)   for every $s = (x, y)$ in S, either $x \geqq V$ or $y \geqq V$.

Let T consist of all points $t = (x, y)$, both coordinates of which are less than V:

(c) $x < V, y < V$ for $t = (x, y)$ in T

The set T also has the convexity property, and does not intersect S, since the inequalities (c) are incompatible with those of (b).

One next invokes the general proposition that any two nonintersecting convex sets in the plane can be separated by a line (in three dimensions, by a plane, etc.). There is a line $Ax + By = C$ which is such that:

(d) $Ax + By \leqq C$ for (x, y) in T, and

(e) $Ax + By \geqq C$ for (x, y) in S,

as shown in Figure 1.

One first observes that s_0 is on the line, i. e.:

(f) $Ax_0 + By_0 = C$, since s_0 is in S;

but there are points arbitrarily close to s_0 (e.g. $(x_0 - e, y_0 - e)$, $e > o$) in T. Next $A \geqq o$, $B \geqq o$, since:

$$A(V - n) + B(V - 1) \leqq C$$

for all positive n, which would be impossible for $A < o$. Since $A \geqq o$, $B \geqq o$, one rewrites the equation of the line so that $A + B = 1$

and writes $P_o = (A, B)$. With this normalization, $C = V$, since, from (a):

$$C = Ax_o + By_o \leqq AV + BV = V,$$

while, since $(V - e, V - e)$ is in T for every $e > o$:

$$V - e = A(V - e) + B(V - e) \leqq C.$$

One can now assert that P_o, q_o are good strategies in the game and that V is the value of the game, i. e. that:

$$Aa_{1j} + Ba_{2j} \geqq V \text{ for all } j = 1, \cdots, n;$$

and

$$q_{o1}a_{i1} + \cdots + q_{on}a_{in} \leqq V \text{ for } i = 1, 2.$$

The first inequality follows from the fact that $P_j = (a_{1j}a_{2j})$ is in S, and from (e), while the second inequality is inequality (a) with x_o, y_o expressed in terms of q_o and a_{ij}. This completes the proof of the theorem.

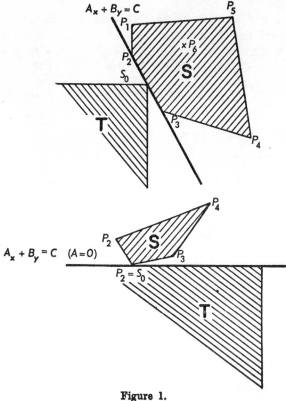

Figure 1.

Methods for Solving Games.

The preceding pages have described briefly the Von Neumann theory of games. Consideration will now be given to some of the methods which are used for solving games, to those techniques by which the value of the game is ascertained and its good strategies determined. Four such methods will be discussed.

1. *Solution in Normal Form.* The minimax theorem asserts that, for every m by n matrix $A = \| a_{ij} \|$, there exist vectors

$$p = (p_1, \cdots, p_m), \qquad q = (q_1, \cdots, q_n)$$

and a number v, such that:

(a) $p_i = 0, \ \sum_i p_i \geqq 1; \qquad q_j \geqq 0, \ \sum_j q_j - 1$

(b) $\sum_i p_i a_j \geqq v$ for all j

(c) $\sum_j q_j a_{ij} \leqq v$ for all i.

Those p, q and v satisfying (a), (b) and (c) are *good strategies* for Players I and II and the *value* of the game with matrix A. To solve a game means to find p, q and v. Two facts which are helpful in solving games are listed below.

Theorem 1. If p, q, v are a solution of the game with matrix A, then:

(d) $\sum_i p_i a_{ij} = v$ for all j with $q_j > 0$;

(e) $\sum_j q_j a_{ij} = v$ for all i with $p_i > 0$.

Theorem 2. Every matrix A has a square submatrix B, such that:

(f) *the good strategies p, q for B are the unique solutions of the system of equations:*

$$\sum_i p_i b_{ij} = constant$$

$$\sum_i q_j b_{ij} = constant$$

$$\sum_i p_i = \sum_j q_j = 1, \ and$$

(g) *the vectors p^*, q^* obtained from p, q, by supplying o for the components corresponding to rows and columns of A not in B are good strategies in A.*

The usefulness of these theorems can be simply illustrated by the following example. Player I is to look for Player II in one of the locations A, B, C. Player II is now at A, but, at a cost of one unit, he may move to B or C, or, at a cost of two units, to D. The cost of moving, if any, is paid to Player I after the search is over; Player I also receives an additional three units if he succeeds in locating his opponent.

Solution: The matrix is

	A	B	C	D
A	3	1	1	2
B	0	4	1	2
C	0	1	4	2

It is not clear whether a good strategy for Player II necessarily involves his choosing each of A, B, C, D with positive probability; it seems likely, at first glance, however, that a good strategy for Player I involves his searching each of A, B, C with positive probability. If this is the case, equation (e) indicates that a good strategy q is among the solutions of:

$$3q_1 + q_2 + q_3 + 2q_4 = 4q_2 + q_3 + 2q_4 - q_2 + 4q_3 + 2q_4;$$

$$q_1 + q_2 + q_3 + q_4 = 1.$$

This system has the two linearly independent solutions,

$$q^* = (0, 0, 0, 1) \text{ and } q^{**} = (1/3, 1/3, 1/3, 0),$$

with constant incomes to Player I of 2 and 5/3 respectively. Thus, q^* cannot be a good strategy for Player II, although q^{**} may be. If q^{**} is, indeed, a good strategy for Player II, equation (d) indicates that any good strategy p for Player I satisfies the equations:

$$3p_1 = p_1 + 4p_2 + p_3 = p_1 + p_2 + 4p_3 = 5/3;$$

$$p_1 + p_2 + p_3 = 1.$$

This system has the unique solution $p = (5/9, 2/9, 2/9)$. Next, one checks $(p, q^{**}, v = 5/3)$ against (a), (b) and (c) to determine whether they are, in fact, a solution. Requirement (a) is clear and inequalities (b) and (c), as equalities, are guaranteed by the method used to determine p, q^{**}, except for (b) with $j = 4$. This inequality becomes $2 \geqq 5/3$ on substitution, so that this is a solution.

The reader has undoubtedly noticed that the method just described is a tentative one and works only if the initial guess about the i's for which $p_i > 0$ is correct. Such guesses are, however, often easy to make; in any case, it is a simple matter to check a given triple, however it is arrived at, to test whether it is a solution. *Theorem 2* provides a systematic method which is certain to yield a solution: for every square submatrix B, the system may be solved (f); if it has a unique solution, one should check the corresponding p^*, q^* described in (g) to determine whether it is a solution of A. This tentative method, then, consists essentially in trying the most likely submatrix first.

2. *Solution in Stages.* It sometimes happens that the solution to a complicated game can be reached by dividing the game into stages. This involves the solving of several games, each of which is simpler than the original. The method is as follows. A game G is considered as a succession of moves, $M_1, \cdots, M_n$. Let $c = (c_1, c_2, \cdots, c_n)$ be any possible set of choices at these moves; c_1 is a possible (i. e. legal) first move, c_2 is a possible next move in the situation created by choice c_1, and so forth. Any such $c = (c_1, \cdots, c_n)$ is called a *play* of the game. A particular play c is said to end a *stage* at the kth move if, after that move, both players are informed of the choices $c_1, \cdots, c_k$ made during the first k moves, or, at any rate, of all aspects of $c_1, \cdots, c_k$ which are relevant in determining the outcome of the play. In any play of chess, for example, a stage is completed after each move, since both players see each move as it is made. In a rubber of bridge a stage is ended at the conclusion of each hand.

If one follows each play c until a stage is ended, say after $k(c)$ moves, the resulting situation is, in itself, a game $G(c_1, \cdots, c_{k(c)})$, involving fewer moves than the original. If each of these games is solved and their values are denoted by $v(c_1, \cdots, c_{k(c)})$, and if the new game G is considered which is played according to the rules of G until a stage is ended, whereupon G^* ends with payoff $v(c_1, \cdots, c_k)$, it is immediately clear that the value of G^* is the value of G, and that good strategies in G consist of using a good strategy for G^* followed by a good strategy in the resulting game

$G(c_1, \cdots, c_{k(o)})$. Games in which a stage is ended after each move are called *games of perfect information.*

The solution to the following game will serve to illustrate this method. Players I and II alternately choose integers, each choice being 1 or 2 and made with the full knowledge of all preceding choices. As soon as the sum of the preceding choices exceeds 10, the last player to choose pays his opponent one unit.

Solution. The game resulting from the first move is exactly like the original, except that Player II now has the first move and the critical number, instead of 10, is now 9 or 8, depending on whether Player I has selected 1 or 2. If the value of the game when the critical number is n and Player I moves first is designated as $v(n)$, $-v(n)$ becomes the value of the game with critical number n when Player II moves first. The game G^*_n has the following 2 by 1 matrix:

$$\begin{vmatrix} -v(n-1) \\ -v(n-2) \end{vmatrix}$$

so that

$$v(n) = \max[-v(n-1), -v(n-2)]$$
$$= -\min[v(n-1), v(n-2)].$$

Clearly $v(0) = -1$, $v(1) = 1$, so that successively one obtains:

n	0	1	2	3	4	5	6	7	8	9	10
$v(n)$	-1	1	1	-1	1	1	-1	1	1	-1	1, etc.

The first player should win G_{10}, and he wins by always presenting his opponent with a critical number which is a multiple of 3.

3. *Infinite Games. Theorem 1* has an analog for infinite games (i. e. games in which each player has an infinite number of good strategies) which suggests that the tentative method of looking for strategies yielding constant income often produces a solution. Such is, in fact, the case, which can be illustrated by the following example, called the *silent duel.*

Players I and II are each equipped with a gun holding exactly one bullet. Each may fire at the other at any time t, $0 \leq t \leq 1$. If a player fires at time t, he kills his opponent with probability t and misses with probability $1 - t$. The guns are silent, so that neither player knows whether his opponent has fired. Player I is paid 1 if he kills Player II and is not himself killed; he receives — 1 if Player II kills him and is not himself killed; the payoff to Player I is 0 if either both are killed or both survive.

Solution. The strategies are numbers $x, y, 0 \leqq x, \ y \leqq 1$, specifying the times at which I, II plan to fire. The payoff to I from choices x, y is

$$M(x, y) = \begin{cases} x - (1 - x)y = x - y + xy & x < y \\ 0 & \text{if } x = y \\ -y + (1 - y)x = x - y - xy & x > y. \end{cases}$$

One type of mixed strategy for infinite games is a probability density $p(x)$, i.e., a non-negative function $p(x)$ with $\int_0^1 p(x)\,dx = 1$, with $\int_a^b p(x)\,dx$ representing the probability of choosing x between a and b. If I uses density p, his expected payoff is

$$M(p, y) = \int_0^y (x - y + xy)p(x)\,dx + \int_y^1 (x - y - xy)p(x)\,dx$$

$$= m_1 - y + y\left(\int_0^y - \int_y^1\right)xp(x)\,dx$$

$$= m_1 - y + y\left[2\int_0^y - \int_0^1\right]xp(x)\,dx$$

$$= m_1 - y(1 + m_1) + 2y\int_0^y xp(x)\,dx,$$

where $m_1 = \int_0^1 xp(x)\,dx$.

If $M(p, y)$ is to be constant in y, $\dfrac{dM}{dy}$ and $\dfrac{d^2M}{dy^2}$ are identically zero, i.e.,

$$\frac{dM}{dy} = -(1 + m_1) + 2y^2 p(y) + 2\int_0^y xp(x)\,dx = 0$$

and

$$\frac{d^2M}{dy^2} = 2y^2 p^1(y) + 4yp(y) + 2yp(y) = 0;$$

$$yp^1(y) = -3p(y),$$

$$\frac{p^1(y)}{p(y)} = -\frac{3}{y},$$

$$\log p(y) = \log \frac{c}{y^3},$$

$$p(y) = \frac{c}{y^3}.$$

Unfortunately no choice of c makes p a density, since $\int_0^1 dx/x^3$ is infinite. If, however, one chooses a number a, $0 < a < 1$ and defines

$$p(x) = \begin{matrix} 0 & x < a \\ & \text{for} \\ \frac{c}{x^3} & x \geqq a \end{matrix}$$

where $1/c = \int_a^1 dx/x^3$ so that $\int_0^1 p(x)\,dx = 1$, he obtains for $y \geqq a$,

$$M(p, y) = m_1 - y(1 + m_1) + 2yc \int_a^y dx/x^2$$

$$= m_1 - y(1 + m_1) + 2yc \left[\frac{1}{a} - \frac{1}{y}\right]$$

$$= m_1 - 2c + y\left[\frac{2c}{a} - 1 - m_1\right].$$

Since

$$c = 1/\int_a^1 dx/x^3 = 2/\frac{1}{a^2} - 1 = \frac{2a^2}{1 - a^2} \text{ and}$$

$$m_1 = c \int_a^1 dx/x^2 = \frac{c(1-a)}{a} = \frac{2a}{1+a},$$

the coefficient of y in $M(p, y)$ is

$$\frac{4a}{1-a^2} - 1 - \frac{2a}{1+a} = \frac{4a - 1 + a^2 - 2a + 2a^2}{1 - a^2} = \frac{3a^2 + 2a - 1}{1 - a^2}$$

$$= \frac{(3a-1)(a+1)}{1-a^2}, \text{ which vanishes for } a = 1/3.$$

Thus, for $a = 1/3$, $M(p, y)$ is constant for $y \geqq 1/3$. The constant is $m_1 - 2c = 0$. It is easily checked that $M(p, y) > 0$ for $y < 1/3$. (This is obvious anyway; if Player I never fires until after time $1/3$, Player II is clearly worse off in firing before $1/3$ than in firing at $1/3$.) Since the game is symmetric, the value is zero and the specified p with $a = 1/3$ is a good strategy for either player.

4. *Solution by Guessing.* Guessing at solutions is a worthwhile method for solving games, especially in those cases where other methods fail. As indicated in regard to the other techniques, it is usually a simple matter to check a guess to test whether it is correct. For example, Player II chooses a y, $0 \leqq y \leqq 1$ and Player I chooses x, $0 \leqq x \leqq 1$. If $|x - y| \leqq 1/5$, Player I wins one unit; otherwise he wins nothing.

Solution. Player I may be thought of as choosing an interval of length $2/5$ in 0, 1, and winning when the interval covers y. Clearly, by specifying three intervals covering $(0, 1)$, i. e., $(0, 2/5)$, $(2/5, 4/5)$, $(3/5, 1)$ and choosing one of them at random, he has at least a $1/3$ probability of covering y; therefore, $v \geqq 1/3$. On the other hand, no interval covers more than one of the three points, 0, $1/2$, 1, so that Player II can, by choosing of these points at random, reduce to $1/3$ or less for any interval the probability of his being covered. Thus, $v = 1/3$ and the specified strategies are good strategies.

In addition to the methods for the solution of games which have just been described, others have been devised for cases where machine computation is used. For exact solutions, the Dantzig simplex method is an example, while the Brown fictitious play method can be used for approximate solutions.

Conclusion.

Game theory is potentially a valuable addition to the body of method available to the operations research worker. It is readily apparent that some of the problems to which operations research turns its attention are of the kind where the simple maximization principle cannot be applied. In military contexts, a tactical situation can be considered a *game* in which each of the opposing commanders, together with his men and materiel, is a player. In strategic situations, the players are the entire forces of nations or, more probably in modern warfare, entire nations themselves. Similarly, wherever deliberate competition exists in the world of business, there is a game situation. The application of game theory to such situations depends, in large measure, on how accurately and exhaustively the choices of moves for the players and their consequences can be determined and expressed. The challenge facing the operations research worker will be to describe such choices and consequences in a way that enables the solution of the game to be meaningful from the point of view of its application.

PART III

Case Histories

Case Histories

In Operations Research

JOSEPH F. McCLOSKEY

T0 THE EXTENT that each problem requiring executive decision is
unique, each solution proposed by operations analysts must likewise be unique. As a result, operations research resembles law and
medicine in that much of the body of knowledge that has been, is
being, and will be built up in this relatively new field of endeavor
must be of the " case book " variety.

Just as law and medicine have developed systematic approaches
in their fields, and have moved on to fundamental principles, so will
operations research. The preceding chapters on the methods of
operations research show clearly that systematic approaches have
emerged. More such approaches—and fundamental principles—are
undoubtedly on the way.

For the present, however, the simplest way to " explain " operations research is to describe cases which have been handled by its
techniques. By tracing the steps in defining the problem, accom-
plishing the research, completing the analysis in terms of the problem,
and evolving the appropriate conclusions and recommendations, the
reader gets an insight into the attitude of mind that distinguishes the
operations research worker from other types of research workers and
the approach to problems that distinguishes him from other types of
problem solvers available to management.

A corollary virtue of the case book method of "explaining" operations research is that it helps to strip away the "magic" with which the exigencies of wartime security tended to clothe the early work in the field. It is worth noting that much of this magic is also the product of a serious problem of communication—a problem that is serious for users, for students, and for practitioners of operations research.

Communication Problems in Operations Research.

In the present century, physical scientists, aided by powerful mathematical tools, have reduced to principle many phenomena little known and less well understood by their predecessors. Unfortunately, these principles defy depiction or description in the ordinary sense. They can be expressed only in mathematical terms which are far beyond the grasp of most individuals, no matter how well educated, who have not been trained in this "language" of physical science.

Operations research has turned the interest and attention of many people trained in the physical sciences away from the laboratory and the classroom toward the "real" world of decision-making. These scientists can make a unique contribution in this new environment specifically because they command the mathematical tools that make possible the reduction to principle and formula of many of the variables that enter into consideration when major decisions must be made. But this still leaves them with the problem of communicating their results both to their colleagues and to the executive who has requested that the work be done.

One symptom of this difficulty of communicating results to persons untrained in the language of mathematics is the tendency of practitioners in the field either to oversimplify their examples, thus stripping them of meaning, or to exemplify operations research by citing cases in which little more than common sense has been applied.

If one were to carry this latter tendency to its logical conclusion, every housewife would be listed as an operations analyst because she strikes an optimum balance between available funds and the menu for the evening meal! The oft-cited example of rearranging mess cans in order to speed up service at a mess hall on Guam [1] is cut from

[1] For example, see Philip M. Morse and George E. Kimball, *Methods Of Operations Research* (New York: John Wiley and Sons; and Cambridge: The Technology Press, 1951), p. 3.

the same cloth—with three reservations. First, the experienced operations analyst who recommended the rearrangement was merely an interested bystander. Second, he had some leisure time in which to study the problem; those responsible for the unsatisfactory system were probably too busy to be aware that anything could be done about it—if, indeed, they recognized that anything was wrong. Third, the analyst in this case had sufficient prestige that those responsible for the system were willing to listen to him and to act on his suggestion.

These three conditions—detachment from direct responsibility for the operation under study, sufficient time for research (as opposed to expert opinion or snap judgment), and the confidence of the executive who has the responsibility for the decision—are *sine qua non* to successful operations research.

Another symptom of the communication problem posed by the mathematical language of the physical scientists has been the tendency on the part of some operations analysts, trained as physical scientists or mathematicians, to conclude that " real " operations research must be confined to problems, or those parts of problems, which yield to mathematical treatment. This is in contrast to the point of view which insists that operations research organizations should make use of the specialized knowledge from any discipline that can be employed usefully in solving problems.

In support of the latter position, one may point out that the variety of highly trained specialists making contributions in operations research is now such that the staffs of some of the larger groups could well be transformed into the faculties of fair-sized universities offering curricula in mathematics and statistics, the physical, life, and social sciences, and business and engineering. The humanities would probably suffer in such a hypothetical university, even though there have been examples of language and literature specialists and historians who have made valuable contributions as members of operations research teams. Obviously, an operations research group so staffed has many hurdles to overcome before teams—genuine mixed teams— can work harmoniously and effectively, primarily because of the problem of communication.

" Explanation " through Case Histories.

But it is time to end this digression on the problem of communi-

cation and to return to the case method of "explaining" operations
research. The cases which follow in the remaining chapters of this
book, as well as those which have been presented as exemplification
of techniques, have a number of elements in common:

Each has defined the problem.
Each has considered the specific problem at hand in terms of the
system of which it is a part.
Each has required intensive research, usually by specialists
drawn from more than one or two academic disciplines.
Each has involved use of the scientific method.
Each has come to specific conclusions and to explicit or implicit
recommendations for executive action.

The importance of defining the problem is touched on elsewhere in
this volume. It is well to point out here, however, that considerable
research is sometimes required before the problem can be defined,
because it is frequently necessary to construct some sort of model of
the entire operation before the problem area or areas may be defined
with any degree of certainty and with proper appreciation of the
possible impact on the whole system of a change in one or more of
its parts. This point will be elaborated later in this chapter.

Once a problem has been defined, it may be simple enough (or
related closely enough to the training of one kind of specialist) that
one operations analyst may be capable of handling it, given sufficient
time. More frequently, a mixed team is put to work on the problem,
usually because the problem is so complex as to require the specialized
skills of, for example, physicists, statisticians, economists, psychologists, and engineers, but sometimes because the time within which an
answer must be given is so short as to require the efforts of more
than one or two persons.

There is considerable debate about the size and composition of
teams of operations analysts. Naturally, both size and composition
must be related to the magnitude, complexity, and importance of
the problem. On the other hand, size and composition must also be
related to the best way of getting the job done.

Thus, for example, an experienced mixed team of operations
analysts will usually be more effective as a group than the sum of
effectivenesses of the individual members. Each team member tends

to look at a problem from the point of view of the skills which he possesses, and his approaches and part-solutions will tend to spark the other members of the team, just as he is being sparked by them. This situation tends to set a minimum size for an effective team. From the experience of most groups working in the field, this minimum number appears to be three, whenever circumstances permit.

Obviously, as the size of team goes up, factors tending to establish a maximum number begin to operate. In the experience of the Operations Research Office, this maximum number is surprisingly close to the minimum: five. Larger teams are used, again whenever circumstances permit, but examination of these larger teams usually shows that three to five of the analysts are operating as such and that the remainder of the group is performing near-clerical, routine functions. In the exceptional cases, examination usually shows that sub-teams of three to five have been organized to handle sub-areas of the problem up to the point where the sub-team leaders take over to achieve a final synthesis. It is, of course, important that these teams be part of larger groups from which they may derive advice, help, and criticism.

There is also the question of whether the team should be made up exclusively of " outsiders " or whether people with work-experience in the area should be included on the team. A man drawn from the system under study may speed the matter of the whole group's coming to understand the system; on the other hand, he may be so aware of many variables, policies, and personalities as to inhibit the group's effectiveness. Many operations research groups compromise by using such experienced people as advisers or consultants, rather than as team members.

There is also the debate about whether the team should work at a home office or at the site of the problem. Again, most groups have compromised by doing some of both.

These teams apply the scientific method in that all are seeking out the elements of order in a system so that these elements may be reduced to some degree of predictability as a guide for action. This approach guarantees continuation of the central importance of probability and statistics in operations research, but does nothing to preclude the use of other tools and techniques, for many systems and parts of systems simply do not generate the kinds of data required for the application of mathematical techniques, and so must be analysed by the techniques of other types of specialists.

After the essential predictables in a system have been analysed and the unpredictables have been considered, if only intuitively, the analysis is then applied to the problem at hand in order to arrive at conclusions about the causes of, and correctives for, the problem. These conclusions must be in a form that permits their ready translation into action, whether or not specific recommendations for action are made.

All this sounds rather simple and straightforward. Usually, the work that goes into solving a problem is neither simple nor straightforward. One of the elements that adds greatly to the complexity of solving operational problems is that the analysis is usually done on a going operation (although some work is always being done on systems that are to be established at some future date), and a going operation cannot be " stood still " like the specimens on a biologist's slide or the year-end financial statement of a corporation.

Some operations lend themselves to simulation in counterpart or miniaturized systems. These may be analysed to identify problems, changed in a variety of ways in order to approximate an optimum, and then the altered system may be imposed on the full-scale operation. Dr. Thornthwaite's experimental garden is an example of such miniaturization.

But other systems lose all meaning when they are " stood still " or when counterparts or miniatures are devised. Just as the bit of living tissue that is to be examined under the microscope must be divorced from the system of which it was a part, so battle, for example, when it is to be subjected to analysis by operations research workers, loses much of its meaning as soon as it is simulated out of contact with the enemy.

The Importance of Models.

Considerations such as these emphasize the necessity for the development of a model of the whole system of which the problem under study is a part. This model may be nothing more formal than a thorough understanding of the system. Or, it may be a word-description. Or, it may be a diagram showing organizational relationships and the flow of material and data within the system. Or, it may be a series of equations, curves, and formulae that describe all or most of the operation. In any case, the whole system must be comprehended.

Dr. Thornthwaite's work at Seabrook Farms is classic in this respect. He was employed as a consultant on supplemental irrigation, but before he made any recommendations, he studied the whole Seabrook operation and became fully acquainted with the interaction of the parts. Had he taken his original directive literally, he could have made only those recommendations which he subsequently did make regarding supplemental irrigation; the result could have been catastrophic in terms of imposing an even greater agricultural production on an already overburdened work force and processing plant. Or he could have reasoned that the additional production could be handled by increasing the capacity of the processing equipment; this would have entailed a large capital outlay for plant and equipment that might be used for only a few weeks a year. Other recommendations of this sort could have been made to reduce specific problems in particular parts of the system. However, because Dr. Thornthwaite understood the whole system, he was able to see that the existing problems were interrelated and could be traced ultimately to the planting schedules that were being used at Seabrook.

Models of some systems are, of course, extremely difficult to construct. Probably none is more difficult to construct than a model of conflict, especially armed conflict. Here there is interaction within each system and between the two or more contending systems. Armed conflict not only produces its own peculiar tensions, but requires careful study of the things that are aggregated under the heading of attrition, and the effects of tension and of attrition are the very things which cannot be simulated, except approximately, and then only by the introduction of historical evidence and theoretical calculations into the analysis of the data derived from the simulation of the action.

The fact that military systems are large and complicated and that model-making, even of the intuitive kind, is so difficult, helps account for the relatively large size of military operations research groups. It also helps account for the rather limited scope of many analyses of military operations, for, in such large systems, those problems which can be isolated to some extent must be isolated and studied in order to make simpler the ultimate task of constructing meaningful models of larger and larger aggregates, and ultimately of the whole systems.

This is one reason why military operations research has tended to move from technological, to tactical, and then to strategic studies.

It is hoped that the foregoing considerations will enable the reader to place the case histories which follow into proper perspective—for these few cases can scarcely represent any considerable fraction of the kinds of work that have been done or may be done by future operational analyses.

Experiences in Commercial
Operations Research

HORACE C. LEVINSON

THE OPERATIONS RESEARCH practitioner who studies problems of
industrial or business operations may be either external or internal
to his customer's organization; that is, either he may be working under
contract to the company (as an individual or as a member of an
independent firm), or he may actually be an employee of the company.[1]
Most of my own experience has been in the latter situation, my
research being directed to the analysis of operations of the company
with which I was associated. I shall therefore take that point of
view here.

What can the internal operations research department contribute
to its company? To be thoroughly successful it should make three
kinds of contributions. First, it should develop solutions to those
problems that are susceptible to solution by operations research alone.
Such problems are exceptional, but they occasionally arise. Second,
the more usual situation is one in which the operations research
department can solve those fragments of a total problem that are
amenable to quantitative formulation. The suboptimized solutions
can then be considered by top management together with the intangibles, the unquantifiable elements of the problem. The executive

---

[1] This chapter has been published in *Journal of the Operations Research
Society of America*, Vol. 1, No. 4 (August, 1953), pp. 220-39.

decision will, in such cases, be based partly on the operations research solutions, partly on other data produced by the company, and partly on the judgment and intuition of management. Third, the successful operations research department can render an invaluable service by keeping top management informed of significant trends, either inside the business or in the business's relation to its environment, which may have an impact on executive decisions. Top management is usually too pressed for time to study fully all the reports emanating from various parts of the company or to consider thoroughly all those outside problems involved in the company's relations to its environment. The research department, however, is equipped with the statistical techniques for handling a wide range of data from which can be distilled facts of importance to the business that may assist the executive. One simple example would be the removal of the inflationary or deflationary effects from sales figures so as to provide management with a more meaningful picture of its sales record. This is a simple, common economic device, but one that is rarely used in retail organizations, which typically rejoice when dollar sales figures rise and mourn when dollar sales figures fall regardless of inflationary or deflationary trends.

As previously stated, the principal contribution that the operations research department of a company can make is in solving those portions of large problems that are susceptible to operations research methods so that management can use these solutions along with other factors in reaching decisions. In some cases such problems come to the research department as an assignment from top management, but more often they are proposed by the director of research as a result of his exposure to the policy-making boards and committees of the business. A third alternative is that problems crystallize out of discussions between management and research people. In my experience there was always an oversupply of problems for the research department, and the assignment of priorities was no easy task. My own invariable practice was to consult on this question with one or more members of top management, usually the president of the company, and I never undertook a research job without his wholehearted approval. On the other hand I cannot recall that I was ever turned down on a job that I felt was both urgent and important.

I have been asked to present here some examples of operations research from my own experience in the mail-order and retail businesses. I accepted this assignment after considerable hesitation. As everyone knows, it is difficult to find examples of commercial operations research that are of general interest and at the same time can be adequately presented without violation of professional ethics. Some examples are of such simplicity that they leave the reader with a "so-what" feeling; others are so specialized that the reader becomes bored; still others require such condensation, because of space restrictions, that they become unintelligible. In selecting the three case histories that follow I have tried to steer a course between these various rocks and can only hope that I have at least partly succeeded. The fact that these cases date back many years has made it possible to present them here.

The first study comes from a mail-order house during the twenties. The second and third have to do with a department store in the thirties and forties, respectively. In the two latter I have omitted certain facts the knowledge of which could conceivably be of advantage to competitors.

Operations Research in a Small Mail-Order Business.

A small mail-order house offers ideal opportunities for business research or, as it is called today, "operations research." In such a business, all the important data are quantitative. Buying habits of customers are easily studied, for, with few exceptions, every bit of sales action can be traced back to its source, namely, printed matter of some sort that is dispatched to former customers or prospective future customers. Each catalog, each order blank, and each newspaper or magazine advertisement carries its own code designation so that the sales it produces can be readily identified. All in all, the nature of the business is such that it lends itself almost ideally to experimental techniques, so that new and promising ideas can be tested at relatively little cost. As an example, one of the most powerful of these techniques is the so-called "split-town" test, in which the two advertisements (catalogs) to be tested are mailed to the same town on the same day, each to a random half of the names on the list. Seasonal, meteorological, and economic variations are effectively eliminated. Apart from chance fluctuations, there remain only the differences between the advertisements that are under test.

I became associated with a small mail-order house in 1924. Its typical mail-order transaction was C.O.D., which, because of its appeal to low-income families, enabled small mail-order houses to compete with the larger houses requiring cash with the order.

One of the problems that faced the company with which I was associated was the fact that just over 30 per cent of the dollar volume of its gross sales represented returned goods. This figure included two types of returns. One, which was not unique to C.O.D. business, was the "customer return"; this transaction occurred after the customer had received and paid for the goods if he later returned them because of dissatisfaction with size, color, quality, or some other factor. The second type, representing a very much larger volume and unique to C.O.D. business, was the "unclaimed return," in which the customer refused to accept the package when it was delivered by the postman. According to postal regulation the package was held at the local office for two weeks. If not accepted by the end of this period, it was supposed to be returned to the mail-order house. Actually, the average interval between shipment and return was over five weeks, so that much of the merchandise became unseasonal and had to be sold out at a heavy loss. But this was only one of the losses involved. There were the operating expenses connected with filling and shipping the original order and handling the returned package. There was a large bill for postage, both outgoing and incoming. Furthermore, in addition to the merchandise losses referred to above, there were others. For in order to avoid serious customer dissatisfaction it was necessary to buy more of each item than the net sales requirement, and much of this extra merchandise had to be sold at a loss.

An offset to these serious disadvantages was the simple fact that, under the C.O.D. method of doing business, sales resistance was remarkably low; in other words, gross sales per catalog mailed were remarkably high. The profits yielded by such a business, however, depended to a large extent on the percentage of unclaimed returns.

In this small business doing a gross volume of between $6,000,000 and $8,000,000 a year, each increase of 1 per cent of returns represented a loss of net profit of approximately $40,000. Therefore the company's directors watched with genuine apprehension the red line on a chart which traced the percentage of unclaimed returns. They were aware that an increase of returns by a few percentage points could wipe out their entire net profit; they also knew that a corresponding decrease would significantly enlarge their profits. Therefore, from the time I joined the company in 1924, I devoted a major effort to finding methods of reducing these unclaimed returns.

Returns were entered on the index of customers' names so that habitual refusers of merchandise could be located and eliminated. Unclaimed returns were broken down by states to determine the relation between the geographical location of customers and their proneness to refuse C.O.D. deliveries. Returns were studied as a function of the value of the order; as one might expect, the average returns percentage increased rapidly with the value.

In describing the research department's work on the interesting problem of unclaimed returns, I shall have to confine myself to a particular phase of the effort. At one of the directors' meetings the ever-present problem of unclaimed returns was introduced. An argument developed concerning the effect that speed in shipping had on the returns percentage. Although all members of the board except myself were long experienced in the mail-order business, they were almost equally divided into two camps. One group maintained that the more quickly the order reached the customer the more likely it was to be accepted; that the longer the delay between ordering and receiving of goods the more opportunities for the customer's money to be spent in other ways. The other group contended that speeding shipment would merely increase operating expenses without reducing the percentage of returns. Since the argument appeared to be stalemated, I suggested that an appropriation for analysis of the problem might determine the answer; this suggestion was accepted and money was set aside for the study.

Fortunately there was statistical material at hand, since the company maintained an IBM installation both for research purposes and to provide a basis for improved buying estimates. A sample of several hundred thousand shipments was selected; a large number was required because it was necessary to separate out the effect of the value of the order on returns, which relation had already been determined. It was found that delay in shipment had a profound effect on the likelihood of the package's being returned.

The data indicated that, for orders of average size, when shipment was made on the same day as the receipt of the order, the returned proportion was only 20 per cent, two-thirds of the overall normal returns percentage. If the package was held for 5 days prior to shipment, the returns jumped to 40 per cent; for 10 days, they reached the level of 60 per cent. A straight line fitted these points very well.

The marginal break-even point for returns was around 40 per cent. This meant that, if there was a shipping delay of more than 5 days, that shipment entailed a loss. This immediately suggested the rule that all orders be shipped within 5 days, even if doing so involved cancellations or substitutions of one item of merchandise for another. But still more important was the possibility of materially reducing unclaimed returns by faster shipping. The board of directors decided to continue the study along these lines.

There were available, of course, the frequency distributions for shipments in terms of the days elapsed between receipt of the customer's order and its shipment. The problem facing the research department was that of shifting the distribution to the left by an optimum amount, that is, to cut the average time that an order was held (thus incurring the extra expenses that acceleration necessarily entails) in such manner as to maximize net profits. The operating and merchandising problems involved in speeding up shipments were severe and were company-wide in scope. But, since unclaimed returns represented a hidden profit differential of about $40,000 per percentage point, the problem merited the attention it required. It was a simple matter to compute the increase in profits due to the decrease in returns for each improved distribution of shipments. The next step was to find the answers to two questions: Which of the possible theoretical distributions was capable of practical realization from an operating and merchandising point of view? How much marginal expense was involved in each such distribution? Through the answers to these questions an optimum solution was found.

This study provides an example of an early and in some ways typical operations research effort in the world of business. Although the problem was of importance to management, it was formulated quantitatively by the research director rather than by the board of directors as such. It could be solved because the company had a research department, statistical data, IBM equipment, and funds available for research. The technical requirements of the problem exceeded elementary statistics, and its full solution demanded the cooperation of all departments of the business.

The Effect of Night Openings on Department Store Sales.

As noted in the preceding case example, statistics concerning customers' buying habits are immediately available in a mail-order business. In department stores, however, such statistics are incomplete and often misleading. This is due to the fact that, in every store, there is a large volume of sales on a "cash-taken" basis, in which the customer pays cash for goods and takes them with her, so that there is no record of her name. As a result, most studies of customer buying habits are confined to the group of charge-account customers. But even such statistics are not complete, for special tests have repeatedly shown that charge customers, as a group, make many cash purchases.

This is not to imply, however, that there is a lack of statistics in a department store. In a large store there are from 50,000 to 200,000 transactions each day and, in the mountain of sales checks and related records that these generate, there are valuable clues to better and more profitable management. One problem that faces the research man within the store is to identify and extract these clues. The aim of the department store, along with other business concerns, is to maximize sales and minimize costs so as to obtain an optimum long-term net profit within such limiting conditions as customer relations, ethics, regulations, and so on; the function of store research is to assist management in reaching this objective.

In September, 1938, L. Bamberger & Co. and the other Newark department stores began the practice of remaining open Wednesday nights until 9:00 P. M., store hours normally being from 9:00 A. M. to 5:30 P. M. These night openings, however, were discontinued during the summer months. In July, 1939, I was asked to make a study to throw what light I could on the soundness of this policy. My first step, obviously, was to inquire what was known concerning the profit of night openings during the other 10 months of the year. I found that a study had been made of the extra sales volume due to the Wednesday night opening. It was based on a method that at first sight seemed reasonable, but that actually involved unjustified assumptions about customer behavior. The method identified the extra

Wednesday business as that done after an arbitrary cutoff time, in this case 5:45 P. M. I therefore made a preliminary study of " winter " night openings, using a different method of attack. This is the part of the problem of some general interest, and I shall confine myself to it here.

These were the essential features of the problem. Clearly, if store hours were extended, some business would be conducted during the additional period. We wanted to know how much of this extra sales volume was true *plus* business, in other words, business that would not have been conducted at any time had there been no extra store hours. If none of the extra Wednesday sales represented true plus business, then such sales had necessarily been transferred to Wednesday from other days in the week. In this case the store would merely be spreading a given quantity of dollar intake over a larger number of hours, scarcely a profitable procedure.

If it were assumed that a part of the extra Wednesday business was true plus business, what did it amount to in sales dollars? It was clear that this question could not be answered by measuring the amount of Wednesday night business conducted after a certain time, such as 5:30 or 5:45, for we did not know in advance what effect the night opening had on customer buying habits. Some customers might shop during the evening hours who would have made purchases in the afternoon had the store closed at 5:30. Others might reverse this procedure and shop in the late afternoon, knowing that they would not be interrupted at 5:30. In addition, there would be customers who shifted some of their shopping from other days in the week to Wednesday night or late afternoon. One purpose of the study was to determine these changes in customer habits, to the extent that this was possible.

The next step in solving the problem consisted in estimating as accurately as possible the marginal expense induced by the night opening in the form of selling costs, heat, light, power, housekeeping, and so on. This involved close cooperation with store management executives. The marginal expense, so determined, was to be subtracted from gross profit on those sales which represented *true plus business*, as a measure of the profits involved in night openings.

Such are the quantitative elements of the problem. In addition there were three essentially nonquantitative or intangible elements. The first, favorable to night openings, was the fact that they were an obvious convenience to certain classes of customers, for example, those who were employed and preferred Wednesday night to Saturday shopping. The second and third, both unfavorable to night openings, were the unpopularity of night openings with employees,[2] and the fact that keeping the store open 11½ consecutive hours involved difficulties in scheduling of work hours that reflected adversely on customer service.

Top management proposed to make its own appraisal of the relative importance of these intangibles in reaching its decision. What it wanted from the research department was whatever indications could be discovered concerning the dollar profits yielded by night openings.[3]

We first introduced, in attacking the problem, the concept of *add-on* Wednesday business, defined as the difference between total Wednesday sales, with a night opening, and total Wednesday sales had there been no night opening. The Wednesday add-on business obviously would include any true plus business the night opening produced.

[2] While this article was being prepared for the *Journal of the Operations Research Society of America*, the *New York Times* published a summary of a survey on retail-store-employee attitudes conducted by the School of Retailing of New York University. The report is quoted as stating: " Evening openings ' acceptable ' to but 25 per cent of employees polled."

[3] The work reported here was done long ago. In the meantime there have been many changes, including the introduction of the 5-day work week in retailing, with further complications in scheduling. Nevertheless the problem, and therefore perhaps the method of the study, are of special interest today. And retailers are even less in agreement about the value of night openings than formerly, as the following facts indicate. In October, 1952, Macy's, New York, adopted the policy of staying open Monday nights, in addition to the Thursday night opening, which dates back to 1935. In February, 1953, three leading New York stores announced that they were discontinuing Monday night openings but retaining those on Thursday. A week later two others announced the discontinuance of all night openings. The president of one (De Pinna) made the following statement as quoted in the *New York Times*: " We believe better store service can be afforded during peak daytime hours if we do not stagger our personnel schedules. . . . Night openings are not popular with store employees. . . . Our experience, after a very reasonable experimental period, does not justify, financially or otherwise, the difficulties which it (night opening) entails."

In order to implement this definition of Wednesday add-on volume it was necessary to make a statistical study of daily sales in relation to weekly sales for selected periods prior to the inauguration of night openings. A similar study was made for a set of weeks in the spring of 1939, in which there were night openings. In order to attain comparability and sufficient accuracy it was necessary to make a detailed analysis of company history, so that weeks distorted by special events or sales promotions such as direct mail could be identified and eliminated. In this way we finally arrived at two sets of figures showing the distribution of sales by days in typical weeks, before and after the inauguration of night openings. They are given in Figures 1 and 2. For convenience we have labeled the comparison period 1938, although actually it was a composite based on several years.

We can now return to the definition of Wednesday add-on business, which we denote by A. Let w represent the ratio of Wednesday sales to total weekly sales in the comparison period (the numerical value of w is 0.16). Let S equal total sales for a given week in 1939 (with night opening). Finally, let P equal the amount of plus sales in this given week. Now if there had been no night opening in 1939, total sales for the week would have been $S - P$, and total Wednesday sales would have been $w(S - P)$. By the definition of A we have, therefore,

$$A = W - w(S - P),$$

where W represents total Wednesday sales in 1939. Putting $P = pA$, and solving for A, one derives

$$A = (W - wS)/(1 - wp). \tag{1}$$

There exists, therefore, a simple algebraic relation between A, the amount of add-on business, and p, the ratio of plus business to add-on business.

The range of A is given by

$$W - wS \leqq A \leqq (W - wS)/(1 - w).$$

When we substituted the proper numerical values for s, W, and w, and compared the range of A with the Wednesday night sales (as measured by the cutoff method) we found that the latter were some 20 per cent below the smallest possible value of A. This indicated that the

Wednesday night openings were producing extra sales during the daytime hours of Wednesday.

It might be of interest to point out that later, when we applied this method to Macy's in New York, the result was very different. In that case the Thursday night sales, determined by a sales cutoff, were well above the top of the range of A, indicating that there was, relatively, far more night shopping than at Bamberger's. Thursday daytime was losing sales to Thursday night.

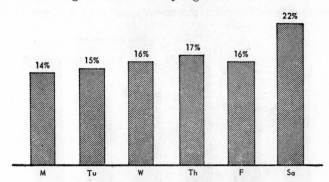

Figure 1. Percentage of Total Week's Sales Transacted on Each Day of the 1938 Average Week (Comparison Period).

If we could determine the amount of add-on business, we would know from (1) the amount of plus business, and vice versa. But we could not know either a priori. It was necessary to proceed indirectly. Our argument ran as follows: Whatever part of the add-on business A that is not plus business necessarily represents transfers of sales into Wednesday from other days of the week. If $T(p)$ is the amount of such sales transfers, we have

$$T(p) = (1 - p)A = (W - wS)(1 - p)/(1 - wp).$$

Now let us make various assumptions as to the value of p over its range from 0 to 1. For each such value the corresponding numerical value of $T(p)$ can be computed; for example, for $p = p_1$, one can compute $T(p_1)$. We ask whether it is possible to transfer an amount of sales equal to $T(p_1)$ out of Wednesday and into the other 5 days of the typical week in such manner as to reproduce the distribution of sales by days for the comparison period, as shown in Figure 1. Only if this can be accomplished is p_1 a possible value of p. If p_1

is a possible value, it is clear that all values of $p \leqq p_1$ are also possible values. It follows that the best that we can expect from this method is a limitation on the possible range of p. The process is illustrated in Figure 2.

For $p = 1$ we have $T(1) = 0$. All the add-on is plus business. To test this hypothesis we need merely subtract A from both the sales for the week and from Wednesday's sales and compute the ratios of daily sales to weekly sales, as adjusted. If these ratios do not differ significantly from those for the comparison week (Figure 1), then

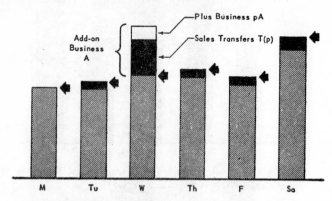

Figure 2. Percentage of Total Week's Sales Transacted on Each Day of the 1939 Average Week (Corresponding to Comparison Period). The arrowheads indicate 1938 distribution of sales as in Figure 1. The solid black area for Wednesday represents sales transferred from other days. It equals the sum of the other four solid black areas.

$p = 1$ is a possible value, as are all values of p. In this case, the limitation on the amount of plus business is merely that it cannot exceed A, the amount of add-on business.

Application of this method to the Bamberger night-opening problem determined the range of possible values of p to be from 0 to 0.4. The highest values did not give a very satisfactory fit, but they could not be rejected with confidence.

We found, from our studies of marginal expense, that the break-even point for the Wednesday night operation corresponded to $p = 0.22$, or approximately the mid-point of the range of possible values of p. For this value of p, the plus business P is approximately 1.3 per cent of weekly sales.

As a by-product of the method we learned some interesting facts about the origin and amounts of the sales transferred into Wednesday as a result of the night opening. These are summarized in Table 1. As will be seen, the percentages for each day are nearly constant over the range of values of p. We therefore, for mnemonic reasons, abbreviated the table to its last line. The largest transfer came from Saturday, as expected. In Table 2 the same results are presented in a different form, as percentages of total sales of the day that gave up sales to Wednesday. Expressed in this way, the variations between the days (except Monday) are much reduced.

As previously remarked, the method of this study was subsequently applied to the Macy Thursday night openings. The differences in the results reflected major differences between the stores, their customers, and their environments. At Macy's the range of possible values of p was larger than at Bamberger's, attaining a somewhat doubtful value of 0.7. But the most interesting comparisons were those of the amounts of sales volume transferred into the night-opening day. Tables 3 and 4, for Macy's, correspond respectively to Tables 1 and 2 for Bamberger's. We see that the Saturday situation in New York was a quite different one. In fact there is little correspondence between the figures for the two stores. But perhaps the most striking difference is this: Friday at Macy's corresponds to Thursday at Bamberger's, as far as its relation to the night opening is concerned; yet there is no appreciable transfer from it, while there is a transfer of some 30 per cent of the total from Thursday to Wednesday at Bamberger's. The behavior of Friday at Macy's suggested to us at the time that it must attract a quite different class of customers from those of other days. This observation, if verified, would have a bearing on newspaper advertising policy.

Department-Store Newspaper Advertising.

This study, like the preceding, involves the problem of *true plus business*, defined in general as additional sales procured as a result of some definite action that would not have been procured except for that action. The problem of determining *true* plus volume, as distinguished from *apparent* plus volume, is one of the fundamental problems of business. And, since businesses appropriate hundreds of millions of dollars annually with the expectation of securing profitable

TABLE 1

VOLUME LOST TO WEDNESDAY, EXPRESSED AS A PERCENTAGE OF
TOTAL VOLUME TRANSFERRED, T (p), FOR VARIOUS
VALUES OF p (BAMBERGER'S)

p	M	Tu	W	Th	F	S	Total, %
0	2	17	—	28	17	36	100
0.1	0	17	—	29	17	37	100
0.2	0	17	—	29	16	38	100
0.3	0	16	—	29	16	39	100
0.4	0	15	—	30	15	40	100
Values Adopted	0	15	—	30	15	40	100

TABLE 2

PROBABLE VOLUME LOST TO WEDNESDAY, EXPRESSED AS A PER-
CENTAGE OF THE TOTAL DAILY VOLUME (BAMBERGER'S)

M	Tu	W	Th	F	S
0	4.0	—	6.9	5.6	7.0

TABLE 3

PROBABLE VOLUME LOST TO THURSDAY AS A PERCENTAGE
OF TOTAL VOLUME TRANSFERRED (MACY'S)

M	Tu	W	Th	F	S
8	22	43	—	0	27

TABLE 4

PROBABLE VOLUME LOST TO THURSDAY AS A PERCENTAGE
OF TOTAL DAILY VOLUME (MACY'S)

M	Tu	W	Th	F	S
1	3	6	—	0	3

plus volume, it is clear that any method that establishes a criterion
as to whether a definite action does or does not produce plus volume
is of considerable practical value.

In the case of certain types of action it is self-evident that any
extra volume procured is true plus volume. For example, if a firm
opens new territories or develops foreign markets, it is safe to assume
that sales in these new territories or markets represent true plus
volume. In most cases, however, it is extremely difficult to determine
after the fact, let alone before the fact, whether true plus business is
obtained. This is particularly the case with many types of advertising.

This study deals with department-store newspaper advertising
aimed at producing an immediate sales response (as distinguished
from advertising designed to promote long-term good will). For
brevity we shall call it "R-advertising." There are two types of
R-advertising: in the first, merchandise is offered at a price below
its normal selling price; in the second, medium- or low-priced merchandise is offered at its normal selling price. In the original study
these two types were treated separately. So as to avoid unnecessary
complications, however, we shall not distinguish between them here.

When R-advertising appears in a newspaper it usually produces
an immediate response, often large enough so that sales of the parent
department as a whole are perceptibly increased. In such cases it is
not difficult to estimate the amount of this sales increase, which is
what we will call the *apparent* plus volume, as distinguished from the
true plus volume. In most stores this distinction is not made; it is
tacitly assumed that apparent plus volume consists entirely of true
plus volume.

It is clear that whatever part of the apparent plus volume is not
true plus volume is made up of sales that are transferred in space
(from one selling department to another) or in time (from one week
or month to another). Each department is competing for the consumer's dollars with: (1) corresponding departments in other stores;
(2) itself in the weeks and months that follow; (3) other departments
in the same or other stores; and (4) lines of goods not sold in department stores. In general, the amount of money available for buying
department-store type merchandise is in proportion to the available
income of customers. If a customer buys a $2000 fur coat this fall,
she is not likely to undertake the refurnishing of her home during the

same period. The sale of the coat may, in effect, represent a transfer from the Home Furnishings Department. Or if the store offers a $2400 coat at $2000 in August, it may attract buyers who would have purchased the same coat later at $2400. This is a transfer in time, together with a loss of $400. On the other hand, if the store does not offer the coat at $2000, one of its competitors might get the business, or the group of stores as a whole might lose it. The problem is: Does the store gain or lose in this process, on balance?

The answer to this question clearly cannot come from a study of one or more departments, nor from a study confined to a few weeks. It can come, if at all, only from an analysis of newspaper R-advertising for the store as a whole over periods of several months.

A word as to the genesis of the attack on this problem may be in order here. Like many operations research studies, this one began with nothing more than the desire to learn something that would obviously be of considerable value, in many directions, to my company. Looking back, I can see that it required what seems a long period, perhaps a year and a half, for me to realize that the problem was soluble and that I had before me, or could get, the necessary data. The curious feature of this problem was that it apparently could not be solved by using only data internal to the store. It was necessary to reach out to the competing department stores in our area and to include their weekly sales and R-advertising expenditures in the initial data. This was done without their consent or knowledge. (I might add, parenthetically, that it was not done by bribery or stealth, but by computation and measurement. That is to say, we computed weekly sales of the total district from data available to us, and we measured the competitive advertising in the newspaper file.) As a result of this approach, from the conclusions of the study we learned as much about the effectiveness of our competitors' R-advertising as we did about our own.

The data on which the study was based were as follows: weekly sales of our store (Bamberger's); combined weekly sales of the other department stores in the Newark group; weekly expenditures for R-advertising in newspapers (cost of space only) for Bamberger's, and for all of the other stores as a group. In addition, it was necessary to conduct extensive historical research in order to identify and eliminate weeks during which there were direct-mail promotions or other distorting factors. For such reasons, we found it necessary to eliminate something over 50 per cent of the weeks. As a partial compensation, the results of the study enabled us to go back later over the weeks with direct-mail promotions and to measure, with considerable accuracy, the sales produced by these mailing pieces.

The method of attack on the problem depended first of all on the observation that weekly R-advertising expenditures, both for Bamberger's and for the other Newark stores, had fluctuated irregularly over the past few years. Now if these expenditures were in fact producing appreciable amounts of true plus volume, there should have been corresponding fluctuations in the sales of Bamberger's, on the one hand, and in those of the remaining stores of the group, on the other. If it had been possible to run controlled experiments, in which R-advertising was discontinued for arbitrary periods, the situation would have been similar, except that the sales fluctuations would presumably have been larger. The problem was to isolate these admittedly small sales fluctuations produced by fluctuations in R-advertising from fluctuations due to seasonal effects and to the impact on sales of such factors as weather and changes in economic conditions.

Let B_i represent Bamberger's sales for the ith week *not* produced by R-advertising, O_i the same for the other stores. (It is assumed that the ith week is free of direct-mail and other distorting factors referred to above.) Consider the ratio B_i/O_i. It is reasonable to assume that its fluctuations in value are small, in other words that it is a statistical constant, since the two groups of stores are located in the same small geographical area, and are, therefore, subject to the same external influences, such as weather and changes in economic conditions. It is reasonable to assume that changes in these external conditions will affect sales in proportion, at least over properly selected limited intervals of time. As for sales fluctuations due to R-advertising, they do not enter, by definition of B_i and O_i. We therefore put

$$B_i/O_i = c. \tag{2}$$

We define the *pulling power* of R-advertising *as the amount of sales produced per dollar of expenditure,* and we make two further assumptions as follows:

A₁. The pulling power of the R-advertising of each group of

stores is approximately constant over periods of the order of a few months.

A$_2$. Transfers of sales in time, because of R-advertising, as discussed above, are negligibly small.

In connection with the first of these assumptions, it should be mentioned that the average number of separate advertisements per week for each group was from 100 to 200. Both these assumptions are in the category of *sine qua non*. For if either one turns out to be incorrect, the method of the study will fail, in the sense of yielding estimates of the parameters (the pulling powers and the constant c) with high standard deviations. In fact, the results of the study showed that both these assumptions were justified, within the required limits of accuracy.

We now introduce the following notations:

	Bamberger's	Other Newark Stores
Total store sales for i^{th} week	S_i	S_i^o
Expenditure for R-advertising for i^{th} week	z_i	z_i^o
Average pulling power for period	p	p^o

By definitions of B_i and O_i we can write

$$B_i = S_i - pz_1; \quad O_i = S_i^o - p^o z_i^o.$$

Equation (2) can now be written, after clearing of fractions,

$$S_i - pz_i + p^o cz_i^o - cS_i^o = 0.$$

Put

$$p_1 \equiv p; \quad p_2 \equiv p^o c; \quad p_3 \equiv c.$$

We wish to minimize the function

$$F \equiv \sum_i [p_1 z_i + p_2 z_i^o - p_3 S_i^o - S_i]^2,$$

where the sum is taken over the "admissible" weeks in the period under study, usually half a year. The conditions for a minimum are

$$\partial F/\partial p_j = 0, \qquad (j = 1, 2, 3),$$

which lead in the usual manner to three normal equations for the determination of p_1, p_2, p_3, and therefore of p, p^o, and c.

I will illustrate this theory as applied to the first season of 1943, February to July inclusive. Of the 26 weeks, only 11 were admissible, 11 being rejected because of direct-mail promotions (Bamberger's being the chief offender) and 4 for other reasons. Numerical solution of the normal equations gave $c = 1.37$; $p = 12$; $p^o = 7$. In other words, the pulling power of Bamberger's R-advertising was 12, that of the other Newark department stores, as a group, 7. It will be recalled that pulling power represents dollars of sales produced by R-advertising per dollar of expenditure for such advertising. Advertising percentage, as usually defined, is the reciprocal of the pulling power, expressed as a percentage. In terms of advertising percentages the results were: Bamberger's, 8.5 per cent; other Newark stores, 14 per cent.

The numerical results indicate that, at least under certain conditions, newspaper R-advertising produces substantial amounts of true plus business. The value $c = 1.37$ shows that Bamberger's, with sales produced by R-advertising and by direct mail omitted, was doing more than one third more business than the other four Newark stores combined. Also its R-advertising was outpulling the other stores by more than 50 per cent. It was not possible to determine to what extent this superior pulling power was due to Bamberger's outstanding reputation in the community, and how much to the inherent appeal of its advertising. Our guess was that both factors were involved.

The reliability of the numerical conclusions depended, first of all, on the extent to which c deviated from its mean value over the admissible weeks. For we had assumed that $B_i/O_i = c$ was a statistical constant. For Spring, 1943, the standard deviation of c was 0.03, so that we can write $c = 1.37 \pm 0.03$.

The question of reliability can be approached from another direction, which lends itself to visual representation. We have computed the pulling powers for Bamberger's and for other Newark stores, and can therefore remove from the weekly sales of each of the two groups those sales produced by R-advertising. In this way we obtain weekly values of B_i and of O_i, and the resulting 11 ratios can be exhibited graphically. We have done this in Figure 4, except that instead of showing the ratios B_i/O_i we have preferred to plot the ratios $B_i/(B_i + O_i)$, namely the ratios of Bamberger's adjusted sales to those of the Newark Federal Reserve District. In Figure 3 the values of the ratios $S_i/(S_i + S_i^o)$ are shown for each of the 26 weeks of Spring, 1943. It will be recalled that S_i and S_i^o are, respectively, the total weekly sales of Bamberger's and of other Newark stores, the crude data from which we started. It is interesting to compare these two charts, giving the same ratios before and after removal of sales produced by R-advertising. We will also add a few explanatory comments that may give a clue to certain by-products of this study.

In Figure 3, the abnormally high weeks, like 3, 5, 10, 15, 16, 18, 19, and 21, are weeks in which Bamberger's had direct-mail promotion. Although such weeks were eliminated from the basic study, and therefore do not appear in Figure 4, the results of the study could be applied to them in such manner as to yield a measurement of the sales produced by the direct-mail pieces. This was accomplished by removing from such weeks the sales due to the R-advertising of both groups. The difference between the result and the "normal" sales for the week, when the computed value $c = 1.37$ was used, represented sales due to direct mail. In those weeks when the other group had no direct mail, the results enabled Bamberger's advertising and merchandising people to study the effectiveness of these promotion pieces.

The low weeks in Figure 3 are, in general, weeks when other Newark stores had direct mail. The sales this direct mail produced could be measured in the same manner, but the results had little interest for us. One low week, namely 22, deserves special comment. It included the Fourth of July weekend when Bamberger's, in order to give employees a long weekend, closed its doors on Friday, as well as Saturday. The other stores were closed only on Saturday. It was easy for us to compute the gross sales lost by this good-will gesture; they were approximately $55,000. The loss of sales would have been much greater had we been unable to announce to the public, through newspaper advertising, that the store would be closed. We learned this on a later occasion when the store had to be closed for one day without previous announcement. Under the latter circumstances we found, using the method of this study, that the loss of sales was approximately equal to total predicted sales for the day in question.

In addition to Spring, 1943, several other seasons were studied by these methods, with comparable results. All of them were during

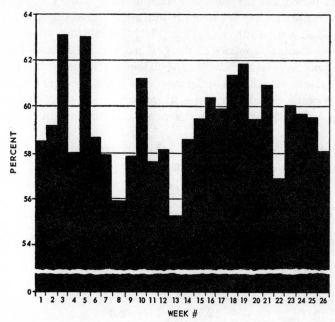

Figure 3. Bamberger's Competitive Sales Position, Spring 1943. Percentage of Bamberger's sales to those of the Newark District by weeks.

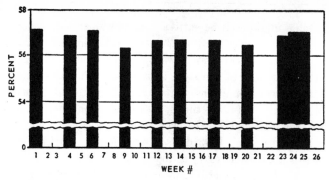

Figure 4. Bamberger's Competitive Sales Position, Spring 1943. Percentage of Bamberger sales to those of the Newark District by weeks, with sales due to direct-response advertising eliminated.

the war period and the work was made difficult by the many regulations and restrictions. We found it impossible, for example, to apply
this method successfully to Spring, 1942. During that period, there
were two disturbing events of the first magnitude: Federal Reserve
restrictions on consumer credit (Regulation W); and gasoline rationing. Because of inherent differences between Bamberger's and the
other Newark department stores, these restrictions affected the two
groups differently, so that there were wide fluctuations in the ratios
B_i/O_i.

Results of the computations of pulling powers and of c for several
seasons, including 1943, are shown in Table 5.

TABLE 5

THE PULLING POWER OF DIRECT-RESPONSE ADVERTISING FOR SELECTED PERIODS

Season	Pulling Powers		
	Bamberger's	Other	c
Fall 1941	12.5	8.3	1.48
Spring 1943	12.0	7.0	1.37
Fall 1943	8.3	4.2	1.38
Spring 1944	5.0	2.6	1.35
Fall 1944	—	—	—
Spring 1945	10.1	6.3	1.42

This table might well be entitled: How war and its concomitant
regulations, restrictions, and consumer goods shortages affect the
economics of department-store newspaper advertising, which in part
reflects the economics of the store as a whole. The table shows that
the effects of war conditions were cumulative, reaching maximum
intensity in early 1944. It shows, also, that a sharp recovery took
place towards the end of the war, when advertising effectiveness
apparently headed back toward its prewar levels. Further interpretation of this table would carry us too far afield.

The methods just described were successfully applied to various
particular problems at Bamberger's. Our basic assumption, that the
ratios B_i/O_i had approximately the same values over periods of at
least a few months provided that economic conditions were moderately

stable, was verified by the successful application of the theory. The variance of the ratios was very small, as indicated by Figure 4 for Spring, 1943. Similarly, the two other assumptions, designated as A_1 and A_2, were verified by the results of the study and hence can be expressed as conclusions: (1) the average weekly pulling power of the R-advertising of each group of stores was approximately constant throughout the separate periods studied; and (2) transfers of sales in time because of R-advertising were, for each of the groups, negligible.

The values of the parameter c, as computed for successive seasons, are an important measure of the relative good-will of the two groups of stores in their community, for they indicate the relative sales positions of the two groups apart from their short-term efforts to increase sales by newspaper R-advertising and direct mail. Sales due to advertising of these types can clearly be increased (up to a point) by increasing expenditures; such increases, however, are not necessarily profitable. The remaining sales, those which enter the ratio $c = B_i/O_i$, on the other hand, depend only on longer-term operations, which, in the last analysis, depend on the general reputation of the stores in their community. If the trend of values of c from season to season is upward, it means that Bamberger's (in this special case) is improving its long-term sales position in its area, and hence its good-will. If the trend is downward, the opposite is the case; a well-managed store, once advised of this trend, will immediately initiate efforts to determine the causes of the decline. Furthermore c as a function of time is a sensitive measure which can detect an unfavorable trend before it reaches such proportions that it appears glaringly in the last line of the profit and loss sheet.

For the sake of brevity and clarity the theory, as presented here, has been greatly simplified. I should, therefore, emphasize that it is capable of generalization in several directions. First, as previously noted, it is important, in normal times, to break down R-advertising into two categories: off-price and on-price. This requires the introduction of two new parameters. The theory was applied in this form prior to August, 1943, at which time government restrictions abolished "sale" advertising, thus virtually eliminating the off-price category. Second, it is usually essential to treat R-advertising separately for each newspaper used. There will be a full set of parameters representing pulling power of the advertising for each newspaper. Because of circumstances, it was possible to carry out the Bamberger study as though there had been only one newspaper. Third, it is possible to introduce more than two groups of stores. In this case it is preferable to introduce a set of parameters c_j, corresponding to c in the above theory, defined by $c_j = B_i^j / D_i$, where B_i^j represents the sales of the jth group for the ith week, after sales due to R-advertising are removed, and D_i the corresponding sales for the ith week for all the groups combined.

The number of independent equations corresponding to (2) will be one less than the number of groups, since $\sum c_j = 1$. In order for this formulation to have practical content, it is necessary to know sales and advertising expenditures by weeks for each group. This would be the case, for example, if in the analysis Bamberger's were divided into two "stores," the Upstairs and the Basement Store. Since each of these divisions carries a full line of goods, aimed to appeal to different economic levels, such an investigation would have great interest.

Even when the problem is confined to two groups of stores and two types of newspaper R-advertising, it is clear that the number of parameters increases rapidly with the number of newspapers. Calling the latter N, and the number of parameters n, we have

$$n = 2.2N + 1 = 4N + 1.$$

If this theory were applied to a typical large department store located in a large city, one could expect the value of N to be 3, 4, 5, or even higher. The corresponding values of n are 13, 17, 21, or still larger. Even with the smallest of these values, the calculations involve the solution of sets of 13 linear equations. In practice it would be necessary to use high-speed electronic calculators to solve problems of such magnitude.

Opportunities for Operations
Research in Supermarkets

SEYMOUR T. R. ABT

S INCE OPERATIONS RESEARCH is a relatively new form of research activity, those who practice it are intensely interested in each example of its application to new problems or to old problems in new contexts. Sometimes the public in general is also interested, but it often happens that the nonscientist is ill-equipped to appreciate fully the work of operations researchers in atomic energy, guided missiles, or other areas in which training in the sciences is a prerequisite to understanding. Such is not the case with operations research for supermarkets; everybody is familiar with supermarkets and, to some extent, interested in their operation. Many people, even those not engaged in some kind of research or engineering, wonder, as they go through the process of pushing a grocery cart, selecting their purchases, and ending up at the checker's stand, whether there isn't a better way to perform at least some phases of the operation. Operations research is always looking for "better ways" and, in its attempts to improve supermarket operations, is, therefore, thinking along the same lines as supermarket customers, though in a more direct manner.

This chapter will deal with operations research in supermarkets with emphasis on the Giant chain, consisting of twenty-four supermarkets in Washington, D. C., and its suburban environs, and independent of stores of similar name in other parts of the country. It might be well, before describing the opportunities for operations research in supermarkets, to prefix some definitions. The recognized

trade definition for a supermarket is " a retail food store which carries
food in various departments, which does an annual volume of business
of at least half a million dollars, and in which there is self-service
at least in the grocery department." The only part of the definition
which is likely to be new to the layman is the half-million-dollar
requirement. This is a more or less arbitrary cutoff which divides
the large markets from smaller stores which have adopted self-service
selling. The important thing about supermarkets is not their dollar
volume but what they purport to do, namely to bring together under
one roof and to channel through one money transaction the wares
of the specialized food stores which were once the only retail outlets
for provisions. All adults remember butcher shops which were separate
from grocery stores which were separate from produce or green-
grocery stores which were separate from bakeries. These specialized
establishments still exist, but, whereas they once accounted for
virtually all of the retail food trade, they now handle only a fraction.
A second distinguishing feature about supermarkets is self-service.
The process whereby a clerk used to sell the customer merchandise
has been replaced; the customer now sells to herself, or to himself
(for many men are now doing the family shopping). One can readily
see that this change introduces a new complex or problems centered
in the question, " How can the customer be made to sell himself
merchandise ? "

The supermarket is composed of several departments. There is the
Grocery Department. Groceries, in this instance, is not the generic
term for food in general, but applies, rather, to such nonperishable
items as canned goods and packaged goods (breakfast cereals, gelatin,
etc.). The *Meat* Department handles perishable meatstuffs as distinguished from canned meats which are " groceries." Different supermarkets have different practices in respect to what they consider
Delicatessen items. In the Giant chain, along with some other markets,
delicatessen refers to smoked meats and to all the dairy products,
including butter, eggs, milk, cheese and others. The *Seafood* Department handles the fresh fish products, and the *Tobacco* Department
carries cigarettes. The *Bakery* Department in the Giant stores sells
only those goods baked by Giant in its own plant, the Heidi Bakery.
Packaged baked goods supplied by outside vendors, such as crackers,
are within the province of the Grocery Department. The *Produce*
Department handles perishable fruits and vegetables.

The supermarket's "mission," if one may borrow this term, is that of any food store, namely to buy food as cheaply as possible and to sell it at the retail level. Actually, the aim might be to sell at the highest possible price, but supermarket enterprises have very little control over how high to price their merchandise. This is because the supermarket industry is highly competitive. So far as is known, there is no collusion among competing supermarkets. There is no such thing as the joint fixing of prices by rival chains. The Giant stores employ personnel whose primary job is to visit the stores of competitors to do comparative pricing; and Giant stores are similarly visited by the representatives of other supermarkets. As soon as a Giant scout discovers that Safeway or A & P is selling beans a penny less than Giant, the alarm goes out, and Giant stores lower the price of their beans a penny. It may be assumed that these other chains make a like response when they discover that Giant is selling an item at a lower price.

The supermarket industry is relatively new, since the concept of the supermarket is only about twenty years old. Consequently, supermarket operations have all the vigor of youth, and there is very little that is traditional or inflexible in this form of retailing. When a supermarket finds that it has stopped being progressive, stopped looking for and putting into practice new ideas, it also finds that it has ceased to draw customers. The receptivity to new ideas which characterizes the supermarket industry makes it fertile ground for many kinds of research, including operations research.

A supermarket is in business to buy food, and such related items as kitchen utensils, and to sell them to the public. Its function is strictly distributive. There is, of course, a small amount of processing connected with the business. Meat must be sliced and wrapped for self-service. Certain produce items, such as lettuce, may be put into bags. Basically, however, the job involves distribution rather than fabrication. In certain supermarket chains, the Giant stores among them, there is an intermediate function between buying and selling, namely storage. When a chain reaches a certain size, it finds that there is a cost differential between having items delivered to each of its stores by the various vendors and having all items delivered to a central warehouse from which they can be distributed among the stores. The cost differential is usually large enough to justify the chain's setting up a warehouse and arranging its own distribution. In the growth of a supermarket chain, the stage is quickly reached where certain items are being warehoused; as the chain grows larger, more and more items are introduced, until nearly everything is being channeled through the warehouse. Buying, storing, and selling are the three phases of operation in the typical supermarket chain.

Buying for Supermarkets.

The buying function in a supermarket is a highly skilled art. A good buyer of foodstuffs is an invaluable asset to a supermarket chain. It is difficult to describe the qualities which make a buyer good; it is not necessarily a matter of formal education or diversified talents. It seems, rather, to involve a capacity for hunches and the other inspirations which make a good gambler, as well as a detailed knowledge of commodities and markets based on long experience. Buying is especially hazardous in perishable foodstuffs, the prices of which fluctuate widely and rapidly. The lettuce buyer in Washington talking by phone to his supplier in California is quoted the price for that day; he knows that the lettuce won't arrive for ten days or so, and guesses on whether to order lightly or heavily, trying to predict the direction of price fluctuations in the interim. If tomorrow's price is likely to be lower than today's, delaying a large order might make the difference between final profit and loss.

This is, indeed, a precarious operation. There have been developed, however, many forms of scientific research for assisting the food buyer. Buyers get various reports on market conditions, studies of price fluctuations, and indices of seasonal phenomena. The informed buyer will know, at any time, the size and quality of a crop in which he is interested in one part of the country as opposed to another. Thus the hunch or lucky guess is more and more becoming an auxiliary to decisions based on quantitative information and the comparison of alternatives. But although there are numerous quantitative aids which help the buyer to decide where to buy and how much to buy, he receives very little help in deciding what to buy. In the last analysis, the answer is to buy what sells. This appears, at first glance, to be a simple problem, but it is full of inherent complications.

In any supermarket, there is only so much space. Each new item which is added, or each new brand of an old item, or each new size of an old brand of an old item, takes its place on the shelves only at the expense of something else. There is a continuous vying for space among the various products which the market carries and among those not carried, but constantly being offered in tremendous numbers by salesmen.

Most supermarket chains are doing some kind of analysis on this problem, either informally or through designed studies; such efforts are usually referred to as market research, and they use some of the methods and techniques of operations research. Usually, the research takes the form of setting up an experiment to determine whether or not a product sells well enough to justify its being bought in quantity. Generally, the experiment involves taking a limited number of cases of a product and putting them up on the shelf in one store, then watching the speed with which they sell. This seems simple enough, until one considers the various factors which must be considered in the design of the experiment. The procedure must be arranged so that the test item has neither more nor less display space than its competing items so that it has the same quality of display as its competitors. The conditions of the experiment must be clearly recognized and stated, so that the results are weighed in relation to the season of the year, if it is applicable, to the income level of the store's customers, and to any of the other variables which have an impact on sales. Most buyers would not refer to these studies as operations research, but the approach to the problem is obviously similar to that in many operations research studies.

The Giant chain has given intensive study to a problem related to the buying operation, namely the ordering by stores from the chain's baking plant, the Heidi Bakery. Rigid adherence is paid to the bakery's slogan, "Baked Today—Sold Today." This means that the baking must be done as nearly as possible to the time that goods are shipped from the baking plant to the various stores. Although a day's baked goods are not put into the ovens until very early the same morning, doughs must be mixed the preceding afternoon in order to allow the necessary time for fermentation. On any given day, therefore, the bakery must have all the stores' orders for the next day.

Each store must, therefore, predict its sales of each bakery item one day in advance. Underprediction results in lost business and dissatisfied customers; overprediction yields stale merchandise and dollar losses. Studies have indicated that the day of the week, the sales for that day in previous weeks, the weather, and the size of the government payroll that day are the major determinants of what will be sold. All these data are, of course, obtainable, and they are furnished to the stores. Then, by means of a rather intricate system of forms, orders are able to be placed by phone in the morning for dough which will be mixed that afternoon and which will, in turn, become the next day's baked goods stock available for sale.

This system has proved quite accurate in matching the stores' orders from the bakery to their customers' demands for baked goods. The success of the ordering procedure pointed up two values, namely the predictability of sales and the dollar cost of time lag between the placement and delivery of orders. Now that the stores are provided with historical sales records and the fluctuations caused by weather and government payrolls, they are able to estimate their needs much more closely than was formerly possible. The loss rate for bakery goods, which are highly perishable, has been lowered appreciably by a reduction in overordering. Sales have risen because of reduced underordering. Finally, the narrowing of the time gap between ordering and delivery has allowed the stores to make use of the order day's sales activities as well as a later prediction of the next day's weather.

Warehousing and Delivering.

In respect to its storage function, the supermarket industry is outstandingly progressive. Some of the most modern and best equipped warehouses are to be found in the supermarket chains. It is no longer meaningful to discuss with a supermarket operator whether or not unit load is the most effective method for warehousing stock; that it is the best method has long since been established. But progress continues far beyond the decision to " palletize." Supermarket opera- tors are eager to work with equipment still better than the good equip- ment they now have; as a result manufacturers are continually striving to develop better fork lift equipment, better conveyors, and so on. The warehouses themselves are laid out by professional warehousemen who, although they may be totally unaware of the term, " operations research," are constantly seeking for ways of improving their clients' warehousing function within the total operation.

Operations research has, however, been consciously applied to one of the Giant stores' problems in the warehousing of its groceries. The grocery procedure is a well-organized one. Each store's order is recorded on IBM sheets listing each item and the quantity desired by the store. The warehouse receives a book of IBM pages for a particular store, and that book is distributed among the various order selectors in the warehouse. One selector goes down the juice aisle with his pages and picks out the juice items; the next man does the same in the vegetable aisle; the next, in the canned fruit aisle, and so on through the whole list. After the entire order has been accumulated, it is loaded into a trailer. This much has been standard procedure for some time; the method of getting the unit loads at the warehouse onto shelves in the individual stores, however, was changed significantly about a year ago.

Formerly, a driver would be standing by at the warehouse to deliver a loaded trailer to a store. When the driver had made his delivery and returned, another trailer would probably be ready for delivery to another store. Eventually, the first store would phone to inform the warehouse that it had emptied the trailer, and a driver would be dispatched to collect it. This operation was carried on during the normal business day, five and a half days a week. The selectors and drivers were all working at the same time.

Under this system, the set-up pattern in the various Giant stores was erratic. Theoretically, the shelves in a store should always be at the same level of depletion. In actual fact, however, a supermarket will do almost one half of its week's business in one-third of the week, Friday and Saturday. It is almost a physical impossibility for a store's employees to keep the shelves looking as neat and well-stocked on Saturday as on Monday, simply because of the irregular traffic flow. Giant decided, some time ago, that all stores should be set up completely on Thursday night in preparation for the week-end rush.

The system of delivery that was being used, however, did not make it possible for all stores to be set up on Thursday night, especially those which were receiving their trailers on Friday or Saturday. A check with store managers revealed, moreover, that they had a serious grievance against the grocery delivery system, namely the uncertainty as to when the trailer would arrive. Each store was informed about the day of the week its delivery would arrive, but not about the time when the trailer was to be expected. This caused considerable inconvenience. Under the terms of the union contract, only grocery clerks are permitted to unload a grocery trailer. The use of porters for this job is specifically forbidden. The result is that the grocery clerk, whose principal job is to put merchandise on the shelves, must also be available to unload the trailer, a job which takes three hours and more. The store's practice was to schedule its help so that the bulk of the grocery men would be on duty on the day that the trailer was expected. But it was impossible to anticipate whether the trailer would arrive at 9 : 00 A. M. or 5 : 00 P. M., so that the entire crew came in early. Time was wasted whenever men waited for the trailer. If the trailer arrived too late in the day to be unloaded, the same full complement of grocery clerks had to be called in again on the next morning. This involved shuffling the help schedule for the week, overtime payments, and other irregularities. Added to this was the fact that the drivers were obliged to work under conditions which were far from favorable in terms of speed and general efficiency. At 8 : 00 A. M., the drivers would leave on their first trip from the warehouse, which is located in northeast Washington close to the Maryland border. Some had to go as far as Virginia and they, as well as the other drivers to a lesser degree, were generally bucking heavy traffic nearly all the way. The delivery system was, in fact, full of problems and the source of some degree of irritation.

The system was, therefore, overhauled. It was quickly realized that there was no reason for the drivers to deliver their trailers during the hours of the working day, nor carry on their work at the same time as the selectors. Accordingly, the two groups were put on separate schedules. The selectors now select an order, load a trailer, select a second order, load a second trailer, and so on through the day. The trailers stand loaded and ready until the drivers arrive at midnight. During the hours between twelve and seven, the drivers make their deliveries, leaving the loaded trailers at the appropriate stores.

This simple change has accomplished at least three improvements. Whereas drivers were formerly able to make only two, perhaps three round trips a day, they now make four or five, simply because they work in minimum-traffic hours. Secondly, every store manager now knows that, when he comes to work on the day he is supposed to receive his delivery, a loaded trailer will be ready and waiting for him. He knows, therefore, exactly when to have his maximum work force in the store, and they can begin their unloading before customers arrive to begin shopping. Some managers actually bring their work crews in as early as 4:30 A. M. on delivery days; by 9:00 A. M. none of the usual telltale signs of a recent delivery, such as cartons strewn about the floor, are evident.

Finally, since the drivers are no longer alerted to take away each trailer as it is loaded, deliveries of trailers to stores are concentrated on Mondays, Tuesdays, Wednesdays and Thursdays; Friday and Saturday deliveries of groceries are entirely eliminated so that, on these days, each store's personnel can devote full time to taking care of the store, with no interruptions for unloading. All stores now have their groceries by Thursday night, and the shelves can be stocked adequately to take care of the week-end influx of customers.

The change in the delivery system has not necessitated the addition of any new equipment or the increase in numbers of any item of old equipment. And a more effective use is being made of the drivers. Perishable merchandise, in contrast to groceries, must be delivered to the stores daily, and must be delivered in larger quantities on Fridays and Saturdays than on the less busy weekdays. Under the new system, drivers who have completed grocery deliveries by Thursday are available to help with the peak load of perishables on the last two business days of the week. The individual stores are receiving much more satisfactory delivery service and the warehouses too are able to operate more efficiently because of the better utilization of driver personnel.

Selling Operations in Supermarkets.

It is the selling phase of the supermarket which is generally referred to as store operations, and the opportunities for operations research in this area are numerous. The highly competitive nature of the supermarket industry makes the need for more efficient and effective operation an absolute necessity. The margin of profit in supermarkets has been driven down, through competition, to what is practically rock bottom. The margin, or gross profit percentage, is the difference between the cost and the retail selling price of an item, expressed as a percentage of the retail price. For supermarket chains generally, this margin is something like 17 per cent. From this 17 per cent, the costs of labor, rent, overhead, storage, advertising, taxes, remodeling of old stores, and all other charges must be met. After all these expenses are deducted, what remains is the stockholder's profit, the net profit, which must provide funds for expansion as well as dividends.

The net profit is now roughly 1 per cent of sales. This means that, for every dollar a customer spends in a supermarket, the stockholder is left with a penny. The store must sell one hundred dollars worth of merchandise to compensate the owners for every dollar's worth which is damaged or pilfered by customers. As recently as a few years ago, supermarkets were operating on a net profit margin of 2 or 2.5 per cent; this, however, is no longer possible.

The largest item of cost, one which consumes roughly 35 to 45 per cent of the gross profit, is store salaries. Except for the cost of the merchandise itself, there is no cost in the entire operation which is comparable in magnitude. For this reason, a great deal of effort has been expended toward the cutting of payroll costs, both by the supermarkets themselves and in studies by industrial engineers and the Department of Agriculture.

When one walks through a Giant store, one can usually find, somewhere in the aisles, a grocery clerk with an open carton lying at some crazy angle on the floor. The clerk is removing a can from the carton with his right hand, switching it to his left hand, then placing it on the appropriate shelf. This goes on all day—right hand, left hand, shelf. This pattern of activity is a hard one to change. One can show the clerk that it is plainly more efficient to move the case right up against the counter, to stand facing the counter and to reach down with both hands and place two cans on the shelf at once. He will probably agree that it's a better way of doing the job. But, the next day, the carton will be back in the middle of the aisle and the clerk will have reverted to the same familiar motions—right hand, left hand, shelf. One clerk, having been shown the advantages of the two-hand system, remarked, "Maybe it's a better way of doing it, but what's the point? As soon as I get through this, they'll find something else for me to do." It is clear that something in addition to the time-and-motion approach is needed if this problem is to be solved.

There is a tight labor market in the Washington area, where Giant stores are located, and it is difficult to find competent personnel, despite the fact that the pay is reasonably good. The constant need for personnel is made more complicated by the fact that Giant is always opening or on the verge of opening a new store. Where are the personnel to be found? One good source is from other stores where personnel can be spared. In short, it is to the benefit of the Giant chain, as it is to chains everywhere, to conduct its selling operations with the minimum personnel needed in each store; this enables the available supply of personnel to be stretched farther and, furthermore, reduces the payroll per store, which is always a significant item in the budget.

Giant has been putting a great deal of effort into improving the store-salaries situation. All twenty-four Giant stores are different from each other. Some larger chains have been able to develop fixed patterns of store layout so that, when a new store is to be opened, a blueprint is available which has been used before and will be used again. Giant does not follow this procedure: for one thing, Giant stores do not open in such quick succession; secondly, the chain has found that, with every new store that is opened, something can be changed or added in order to make it somewhat better than the last. Not only are the stores different in respect to the actual plant, but also in other important ways. Some are located in areas where the income level is high, and others where it is low; and, although all carry the same line of merchandise, the rate at which a given item sells often depends on the income level of the clientele. Some stores are located in thickly populated residential areas and the flow of business is fairly evenly spread through the week; others, especially those located at good road intersections where traffic comes from a distance, tend to do a large fraction of their business on Fridays and Saturdays. Some stores do 25 per cent of their week's business on Saturday alone.

The volume of each store's weekly business is fairly constant. A store which does $40,000 business one week, may do $38,000 or $42,000 the next, but not $35,000 or $45,000. Giant has found, by a continuing study over several months' time, that the payroll in each store can be correlated with the volume of sales in that store. Whatever the layout of the physical plant, the income bracket of its customers or the curve of its weekly business activity, there is a fairly constant linear relationship between the volume of sales and the total of store salaries. Having found this relationship, management was tempted to make it a fixed matter of policy, to say to each store manager, " Here is your volume of business, therefore here is the line which establishes your payroll."

Actually, this has never been put into practice. Although the correlation remains, the position of the curve moves upward with the passage of time. By the terms of the various union contracts, for example, each employee receives a raise every six months until he has been with the company two and a half years. The contracts also contain cost-of-living escalator clauses. Furthermore, contracts are occasionally renegotiated. So, whereas the volume of sales remains fairly constant, payroll tends to rise. This explains in part the fairly recent and rapid drop from 2 to 1 per cent in net profit. It is, therefore, not possible to put too strict an upper limit on a store's payroll.

Giant proceeded, therefore, along a new line, reasoning that, if there was a correlation between volume of sales and salaries, there must be a correlation between volume of sales and man-hours expended. After some months of accumulating figures, it was established that there was a correlation between man-hours and sales in each major department, although each department had its own line of relationship, and that the position of each curve changed only slightly in time. Figure 1 demonstrates, for example, the relationship for the Produce, Meat, and Grocery Departments.

The ratios indicated by these lines seem thoroughly reasonable to anyone acquainted with supermarket operations. The Grocery Department has a lower base than the Meat Department because the very nature of meat department operations requires more personnel: butchers are needed to cut the meat, girls, to slice and wrap; and the cuts must be individually weighed and priced. The steep rise for the Produce Department is easily explained. The moment that business in produce increases, there is that much more merchandise to be washed, trimmed and sorted. Furthermore, there is a rotation procedure whereby spoiled pieces of produce must be moved before the spoilage spreads. The Produce Department involves many problems with which the Grocery Department is unconcerned. A customer can walk to a grocery shelf, select a can of tomatoes, change her mind and return it, and nothing has happened to the item which makes it less attractive for sale to another customer. The same customer, however, may pick up a fresh tomato and throw it back on the rack or drop it on the floor so that it is no longer salable. The produce manager's bonus and the chain's success depend on the volume of produce sales and the rate of spoilage. It is necessary, therefore, that produce be carefully watched so that the least bit of spoilage

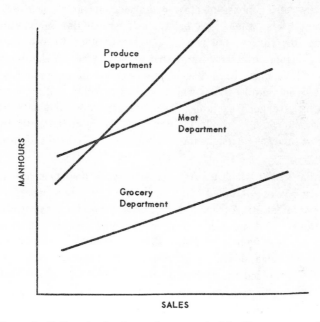

Figure 1. Ratio of sales to manhours worked in three supermarket departments.

can be removed before it spreads. This requires man-hours. In respect to some other types of personnel, for example porters and parking lot attendants, manhour requirements are dictated by local conditions. These include the distribution of business through the week and the proximity of checkout booths to the parking lot.

These studies have enabled Giant to set up, for all stores, two sets of man-hour standards, one "localized," the other general. The emphasis throughout the stores is now on manhours, not dollars, and it is to the reduction of man-hours that Giant managers and supervisors are devoting their energies. The payroll is at an all-time high and is still rising. Each store, however, now reports its man-hours for each department weekly. By relating these reports to the dollar payroll, Giant is able to know how much of the rise is accounted for by the increase in average wage per man-hour. It can also discover, by store and department, where inefficiencies exist, and is able to correct them much sooner than had been previously possible.

In the selling phase of store operation, one area for research is in display. The whole idea behind self-service lies in making the customer buy things—not the things she intended to buy when she started to shop, but extra things that appeal to her as she makes the rounds of the market. A tremendous amount of research has been conducted on impulse-sales, which this unexpected selling is called. Packaging is a good example; the more attractive and enticing the container in which a product is set out, the more likely it will be to find a market through impulse-sales as well as in determined customers.

Similarly, the whole question of how much display space to give each item has been studied. The Giant chain has been working with the Department of Agriculture on some aspects of this problem.[1] (The Department of Agriculture works with various supermarket chains on experiments, provided that the expected results will be generally useful and can be published.) A study conducted in this way recently yielded the conclusion that the first two rows of selected canned goods will sell five times as much per row as each additional row up to six. In short, two rows sell a certain amount; the third row sells one-fifth as much as each of the first two rows; the third, fourth, fifth and sixth rows each contributes the same amount to the total sales volume for the item.

These results, coupled with the fact that the shopper likes to see as many brands as possible represented for each item, suggest that no item should be carried in more than two rows. Implementing this suggestion, however, would introduce operational problems for fast-

[1] U. S. Department of Agriculture, Production and Marketing Administration, *Better Utilization of Selling Space in Food Stores*: Part I—*Relation of Size of Shelf Display to Sales of Canned Fruits and Vegetables*, Marketing Research Report No. 30 (Washington, D. C., November 1952).

selling items; grocery clerks would spend a great deal of time restocking depleted space if only two rows were displayed. It is necessary, therefore, to compromise between operating efficiency and space efficiency.

The investigation of space efficiency continues and will eventually, it is hoped, provide some valuable guidelines towards the improvement of the selling operation. There are opportunities for operations research in another aspect of this operation, namely minimizing the losses in profit through damage. All supermarkets are aware, for example, that canned goods which are dented or which have damaged labels will not sell, regardless of the fact that the contents are unimpaired. Most stores, therefore, have a rack or basket containing these damaged items marked down in price.

One supermarket chain, on discovering that its rate of dented cans was significantly higher than that of other markets, began to investigate the problem. Management hired, for this investigation, a firm of industrial engineers, and requested that a thorough analysis of the operation be made so that the source of damage could be spotted. Actually, no such thorough analysis was necessary. The investigator very soon observed a basic difference between the damaged goods policy of the chain and that of its competitors; dented cans at reduced prices were, in this chain, sold to employees rather than to customers. Employees were deliberately denting cans! A simple change in policy, whereby these marked-down items were made available to customers rather than employees, quickly resulted in a reduction of dented cans.

As in other operations, of course, supermarkets cannot necessarily base their policy decisions on cost-effectiveness criteria alone. Other factors such as good will, which are less quantifiable but not less significant, must be taken into account. A simple illustration will demonstrate that the operations research answer forms only part of the basis for decisions, albeit an important part. The cost of packaging paper is high enough to constitute a matter of some concern in the supermarket industry. A brief preliminary study of the correlation between the dollar volume of sales and the cost of paper bags required to wrap these sales yielded some promising results for the Giant chain. It was found that the packers normally used the largest bag available regardless of the size of order they were wrapping. A great many unfilled large, heavy bags, therefore. were leaving the store while smaller, less expensive bags would have sufficed. For experimental purposes, the largest-sized bag was removed entirely from one store on one busy day. The result was that there was, in that day, more of the second-size bag used than the usual total for the first two sizes combined; this was, however, accompanied by a measurable saving in cost. The maximum profit criterion indicated that further experiments should be conducted with a view to extending this paper-saving effort. Management protested, however, that good will might be impaired through customers' being irritated by being burdened, in some cases, with two small bags instead of one large one. There was, furthermore, some indication that customers depended on the large size bags for garbage and trash can liners.

As the preceding discussion has indicated, there are numerous opportunities for operations research in all three phases of the supermarket's operation, in buying, in storaging, and in selling. In any or all of these phases, the principal contribution of operations research will be in presenting, for management's consideration, those alternative procedures or policies the effectiveness of which can be expressed quantitatively. In the last analysis, however, management will make its decisions on the basis of a complex of factors, in which those which are numerical, though of great importance, cannot stand alone.

The Effect of Promotional Effort on Sales

JOHN F. MAGEE

THE GENERAL AREA of marketing and sales management,[1] removed as it is from the factory and the highly developed fields of engineering and the physical sciences, is the one in which, perhaps, the least precise and complete information has been available for the guidance of administrative decisions. Yet the management of an industrial enterprise is constantly faced with the problem of deciding how much advertising, selling, or promotional effort is economically justified. A reasonable response to this question implies at least an intuitive knowledge of the relationship between sales volume and promotional effort; the following case history describes the development of such a relationship in explicit and quantitative form.

This case history consists of the application of research methods to a study of the effects of promotional efforts on sales, which was performed at Arthur D. Little, Inc. Arthur D. Little, Inc., is a privately owned, profit-making company whose business is research—primarily research in the physical sciences and related engineering problems. Although the company has done considerable work in economics related to technological problems, it has not entered the fields of management or industrial engineering, principally because of the wish to remain a physical research company. About four years

---

[1] See also Mr. Magee's article, " The Effect of Promotional Effort on Sales," *Journal of the Operations Research Society of America*, Vol. I, No. 2 (February 1953), pp. 64-74.

ago, an operations research group was formed within the company. It was thought that the technical training of various staff members, coupled, in some cases, with experience in military operations research, might thereby be utilized toward the solution of appropriate problems presented by industrial clients. Although the operations research work started on a very modest scale, the successful application of operations research methods to clients' problems has resulted in the group's becoming a firmly established and rapidly growing section of the company.

The case study which follows describes the work undertaken for one of the firm's clients. Industrial security requires that it be disguised, but the camouflage has been achieved, it is hoped, without distortion of the methodology involved. Naturally, the summary presentation of a case history suffers somewhat by being telescoped, a process which condenses into a few sentences the reasoning and analysis which actually consumed many months. The full flavor of an operations research study can be appreciated only if the mistakes and unsuccessful approaches are understood together with the successes. This description of the work omits some of the intriguing byways and techniques into which the problem led those who were tackling it.

The study involved research into the intricacies of industrial operations. It met the criteria which Arthur D. Little, Inc., would like to apply in order to keep the meaning of " operations research " fairly well restricted. First, the analysis undertaken and the results obtained were quantitative. Furthermore, the results were capable of being verified by experimental methods, and the analysis included the establishment of two types of experiments, informational and critical. The primary goal of the analysis was the understanding of the operation, although that understanding, once achieved, ultimately provided a basis for action. The results were not restricted to the specific questions asked, but the model developed became one component of a more general model of the client company's whole operation.

The Problem.

The company for which the study was conducted is engaged in distributing coffee to a large number of retail grocery stores throughout the country. The main promotional effort for this activity is carried on by a group of salesmen who travel from store to store and work with the individual dealers. These salesmen distribute point-of-sale advertising and displays, try to obtain from dealers favorable display locations for their product, and educate the dealers in the merits of the merchandise.

The cost of the salesmen is such that the distributing company has felt that promotional calls on all dealers were not justified. It was determined, therefore, that promotional salesmen could profitably call on about 40 per cent of the dealers. The problem which faced the company, once this determination was made, was to select those dealers who should receive the visits; this problem had been under consideration for some twenty years at the time the investigation was initiated.

When Arthur D. Little, Inc., was first introduced to the problem, the company was selecting dealers for promotion in any given month on the basis of their sales records for the two previous months. For example, the 40 per cent of the dealers purchasing the greatest volume during April and May would be subjected to the promotional program for June. The company wanted to determine the effects of the existing promotional effort on the dealers' accounts. Only this much was known: that the promotional effort appeared, on the average, to have some effect on orders from those dealers who were promoted. Business from individual dealers was subject, however, to wide, random fluctuations. Furthermore, the effect of promotional activities was confounded with the fact that only dealers from whom a relatively large amount of business was expected were visited.

As the problem was originally posed to Arthur D. Little, Inc., it encompassed three major questions:

1. How can the existing procedure of selecting dealers for promotion be improved?

2. How good is this procedure? Can an " ideal " be set, and, if so, how close to " ideal " is the present system? How much further effort in refining this dealer-selection method is warranted?

3. How much promotional effort is justified so long as the present method of directing this effort is unchanged?

Available Data.

The distributing company had various sets of records which were available for the investigation. The purchase record over a one-year period for each of the many thousands of dealers was on file. These records indicated the name, location, sales route number, and promotional territory code of each dealer, the date of each of his purchases, and the size of each order; they further included a note as to what promotional attention, if any, had been given to each account in each month.

Also available were records of special promotional experiments. Such experiments had been complicated by the variety and numbers of dealers, and the various random influences affecting the purchase orders of each. A method had been used whereby two large groups of dealers from a single region had been selected, the groups roughly equally composed of several classes and types of dealers, and also roughly equal in respect to their purchases during several preceding time periods. The normal promotional procedure was then given to the eligible dealers in one group, while those experimentally eligible in the other received an experimental promotional program. Conclusions were based on a comparison of the amounts of total business ensuing from the two groups. The time required to set up each experiment together with random errors in the results made this type of experiment both costly and inflexible. Furthermore, the data which were provided were of limited usefulness for studying the workings of the operation, since the experiments were designed to provide comparisons between specific promotional programs.

One particular type of experiment which the distributing company had conducted, however, proved particularly valuable to the analysts who began studying the total operation. In a series of tests, the company had promoted all of its dealers in a particular area in an attempt to improve, by statistical analysis, the method of distribution and promotion. When some applications of multiple correlation methods to the resulting records failed, however, the data were filed away, presumably permanently. The discovery of these records and analysis of them eventually provided the first break in the construction of a general model for the operations research study of the problem.

The distributing company's products were sold to dealers by the case and the cost of each case was fixed. Whether a dealer purchased frequently in small quantities or less frequently in large quantities did not matter. Neither was the particular product or products which he purchased important. The significant characteristic of a dealer for determining the amount he would buy was the expected number of cases he would order in a specified time.

When the average number of cases ordered per month per individual dealer was computed from several months' observations and compared with the number of cases ordered in later months, a substantial degree of persistence was observed. Nonetheless, a large amount of random variation between past and future performance remained to be accounted for. This combination of persistence and randomness had been the most confusing characteristic of the operation in the company's past attempts to improve performance. One member of the operations research group assigned to the problem suggested that this combination might be explained if the dealer's customers were regarded as purchasing individually and collectively at random, with a rate of arrival characteristic of the dealer's outlet, so that the dealer's purchases reflected this randomness. Thus, each dealer would order at random intervals in time, but the expected length of these intervals would be governed by the arrival rate of his customers.

The Study Procedure.

The hypothesis was proposed that the distribution of the actual number of cases ordered could be approximated by the Poisson distribution,

$$E(n) = \frac{e^{-c}c^n}{n!}, \tag{1}$$

where $E(n)$ is the probability that a dealer with an expected frequency of ordering, or characteristic order, c, will actually order n cases in a given unit time period.

This hypothesis was not simple to verify. The values of c for individual dealers were not known; they could only be estimated from past records. Unfortunately, however, the estimate of c depended not only on the average number of cases ordered by the individual dealer, but also, where the number of the time periods was small, on the distribution of c's for the dealer group as a whole.

One simple check was made. The average number of cases and the observed variance were computed for each of several hundred dealers. If the hypothesis was correct, these should have been approximately equal. Without such a check, validation of the hypothesis would have depended on more general tests of consistency. The question was, in short: If the Poisson distribution was assumed to be the proper one, would further analyses of dealer behavior yield results consistent with the data obtained in any manipulations made in the model? This served as a check on whether errors introduced by the Poisson assumptions were satisfactorily compensated for in other parts of the model, rather than as a check on the model itself.

A second question then arose: If an individual dealer could be characterized, at least in part, by his expected number of cases purchased (his characteristic order), could groups of dealers be similarly characterized; for example, the group of all dealers, or the group of dealers in a particular area? It was known that there were "excellent" dealers who averaged many cases a month and "poor" dealers with small average orders; the remainder, of course, fell somewhere between these two extremes. If the dealers were arranged according to their characteristic orders, c, it was possible to show some sort of probability density of dealers against their expected number of cases ordered, which was called $Y(c)$.

It was assumed that the density function, $Y(c)$, of dealers according to their expected number of cases ordered, or characteristic order, c, would depend in some fashion on the promotional program followed by the distributing company. For convenience, $Y(c)$ was defined as the density function of the expected values, c, under the condition that all dealers received the typical promotional aids.

The fraction of dealers in the whole group who would order no cases, one, two, or, in general, n cases would be given by the equation:

$$f(n) = \int_0^\infty \frac{e^{-c}c^n}{n!} Y(c)\,dc. \qquad (2)$$

This equation simply expresses the fact that the fraction of dealers ordering three cases in a given month (if, for example, n is set to equal 3) is the sum of the fractions who will order three times from the groups of dealers whose average number of orders, c, is between 0 and 1, between 1 and 2, between 2 and 3, and so on.

Results of past experiments in which all dealers had been given promotional help yielded information on the form of $Y(c)$. Figure 1 shows the observed values of $f(n)$ for one such experiment. The form of the plots in Figure 1 suggested that $Y(c)$ should be an exponential or sum of exponentials in form. The simple exponential form,

$$Y(c) = \frac{1}{s} e^{-c/s} dc \qquad (3)$$

was tested, where s is the average number of cases per month for the group of dealers as a whole. Substituting the form (3) for the fundamental distribution of dealers according to their characteristic case orders in (2) yielded

$$f(n) = \frac{s^n}{(s+1)^{n+1}}. \qquad (4)$$

The values of $f(n)$ calculated from (4) are shown in Figure 1. In each case, the value of s used was simply the total number of orders from the group divided by the total number of dealers in the group.

The validity of the Poisson distribution to describe the behavior of individual dealers was tested by means of equation (3). If an individual dealer orders n_k cases in k months, the expected value of his characteristic order, c, is

$$E(c/n_k, k) = \int_0^\infty c' \frac{(ks+1)^{n_k+1}(c')^{n_k}}{s^{n+1} n_k!} e^{-c'} \left(\frac{ks+1}{s}\right) dc' = \frac{n_k+1}{k+1/s}. \qquad (5)$$

Since the expected value of the number of cases ordered in a future month, n_f, is c, the number of orders n_f should be related to the number of orders in k past months by the equation

$$E(n_f) = \left(\frac{s}{sk+1}\right) n_k + \left(\frac{s}{sk+1}\right). \qquad (6)$$

When tested on several hundred dealers in the experimental groups, the slope and intercept of equation (6) were found to agree with the observed values.

The sales organization used a routine procedure for ranking the dealers to whom it distributed the cases of coffee. The top 40 per cent of the dealers, as indicated by this ranking, were then normally given promotional attention. The system was sufficiently flexible, however, so that fractions ranging from 30 per cent to 100 per cent of the total group had been given promotion in some instances. Where fractions larger than 40 per cent had been promoted, though, it was still possible to isolate the records of that 40 per cent of the dealers who would have received promotion under normal conditions.

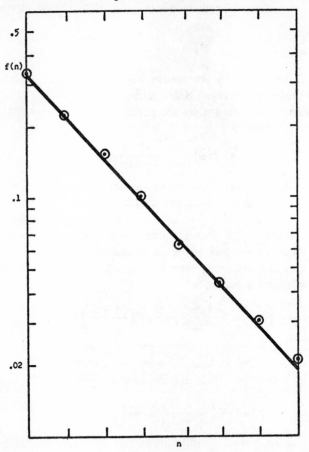

Figure 1. The observed fractions of dealers ordering n cases in a month. All dealers given special promotional help. The curve is a plot of equation (4) with $s = 2$.

The probability density function $Y_p(c)$ for this eligible top 40 per cent was unknown, but it was presumably different from that of the group as a whole, $Y(c)$. Plots were made of the fractions of these groups ordering n cases, $f_p(n)$, as shown by the circles in Figure 2.

Various predictions of $Y_p(c)$ were tried, but the one which gave the best prediction of $f_p(n)$ was

$$Y_p(c) = \frac{1 - e^{-g(c/s)}e^{-c/s}}{as},$$ (7)

where a is the fraction of the dealers promoted and $g = (a/1 - a)$. The values of $f_p(n)$ would then be given by

$$f_p(n) = \int_0^\infty E(n)Y_p(c)dc$$

$$= s^n \left\{ \frac{1}{(s+1)^{n+1}} - \frac{1}{(s+g+1)^{n+1}} \right\}.$$ (8)

A comparison of equations (3) and (7) indicates that $Y_{np}(c)$, the distribution of characteristic orders of dealers normally not promoted (the lower 60 per cent), is approximated by

$$Y_{np}(c) = \frac{e^{-((g+1)/s)c}}{(1-a)s},$$ (9)

and the fraction of these dealers ordering n cases by

$$f_{np}(n) = \frac{s^n}{(1-a)(s+g+1)^{n+1}}.$$ (10)

The fit of equation (8) to observed values is plotted by the solid line in Figure 2.

Equations (7) and (8) were tested by application to the records of several groups of dealers subject to the normal promotional campaigns. The checks described previously were also made with the substitution of equations (7) and (8) for (3) and (2) respectively. In all cases, the agreement was found to be excellent, which lent considerable support to the conclusion that equation (7) accurately described the effect of the selection process in picking dealers for promotion.

The functions discussed above were derived from experiments in which *all* dealers were promoted. If the promotional effort had no effect on business, equations (9) and (10) would describe the non-promoted dealers. By comparing the observed fractions of non-promoted dealers ordering a given number of cases with those values calculated from equation (10), one derives a basis for estimating the

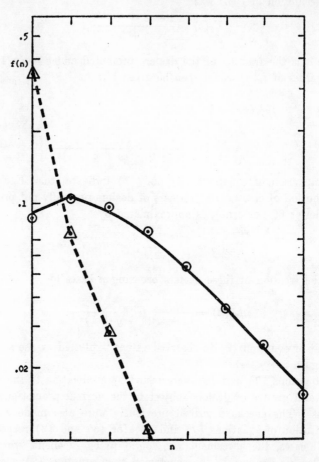

Figure 2. The observed fractions of dealers ordering n cases in a month.
Those normally receiving promotional help are plotted in circles;
those normally not receiving promotional help are plotted as
triangles. The solid line is a plot of equation (8); the dashed
line, of equation 10(a).

effect of the promotional effort. When this comparison was made, two differences were found:

(1)   According to equation (10), the ratio of $f_{np}(n)$ to $f_{np}(n+1)$ is $(s+g+1)/s$. When the observed values of these ratios for $n \geq 1$ were used to determine s, the average number of cases ordered by one dealer per month, the value found was equal to 0.71 times the value expected from study of the promoted dealers.

(2)   When the value of s determined above was substituted in equation (10) for calculating the values of the fractions ordering n cases, $f_{np}(n)$, the observed values of $f_{np}(n)$ for $n \geq 1$ were found to be 0.7 times the calculated values.

Equation (10) can be adjusted to account for these two effects as in equation (10a), which is shown as a broken line in Figure 2.

$$f_{np}(n) = \frac{0.7(0.71s)^n}{(0.71s + g + 1)^n}, \qquad n \geq 1,$$

$$f_{np}(o) = (1 - a)\{1 - \sum_{n=1}^{\infty} f_{np}(n)\}. \qquad (10a)$$

These two effects can be summarized as follows: When a dealer is given no promotion, the probability is 0.3 that he will act as if his characteristic order, c, were zero; moreover, the probability is 0.7 that he will act as if c were 0.71 of his frequency if promoted. The net effect is a reduction in his expected business of 50 per cent.

Once the effect of promotion is isolated, it becomes possible to write down the sales resulting from any given level of promotional effort. Let it be assumed that there are N dealers, of which Na are to be selected by the usual means for promotion. The resulting number of cases ordered will be

$$O(a) = N\{a \int_0^\infty cY_p(c)dc + 0.5(1 - a) \int_0^\infty cY_{np}(c)dc\}$$

$$= \frac{Ns}{2}(1 + 2a - a^2). \qquad (11)$$

Since the value of a case is fixed, the resulting business will be

$$B(a) = \frac{Nsv}{2}(1 + 2a - a^2), \qquad (12)$$

where v is the value per case.

The best that could be expected from a system of the type used for the selection of dealers would be a system which always picked the upper tail of the distribution $Y(c)$ in equation (3). In this case, the resulting business would be

$$B'(a) = Nv \left\{ \int_{-s\ln a}^{\infty} \frac{c}{s} e^{-c/s} dc + 0.5 \int_{0}^{-s\ln a} \frac{c}{s} e^{-c/s} dc \right\}$$

$$= \frac{Nsv}{2} \{1 + a - a \ln a\}. \tag{13}$$

The poorest reasonable method of selecting dealers for promotion would be random selection, for which the resulting business would be

$$B''(a) = \frac{Nsv}{2} (1 + a). \tag{14}$$

The relative efficiency of the present selection method might be defined as the gain in business over that resulting from random selection, compared with the potential gain from use of an ideal method of selection. The efficiency necessarily must depend on a, the level of promotional activity, since any system would be "ideal" if no dealers or if all dealers were promoted. The relative efficiency $E(a)$ is, therefore, defined as

$$E(a) = \frac{B(a) - B''(a)}{B'(a) - B''(a)} \tag{15}$$

or, in this case,

$$E(a) = -\frac{(1-a)}{\ln a} ; \ 0 < a < 1. \tag{16}$$

$E(a)$ is shown in Figure 3.

The relative potential gain from improvement of the selection of dealers is given by

$$G(a) = \frac{B'(a) - B(a)}{B(a)}$$

$$= \frac{a(a - 1 - \ln a)}{1 + 2a - a^2}, \tag{17}$$

also shown in Figure 3.

It should be noted that both the measure of relative efficiency, $E(a)$, and the measure of relative potential gain, $G(a)$, are independent of the factors influenced by economic conditions, namely the average number and value of cases, s and v.

The Impact of Research Results.

This theoretical analysis of promotional methods, based on existing data and requiring no special experiments, yielded the following useful

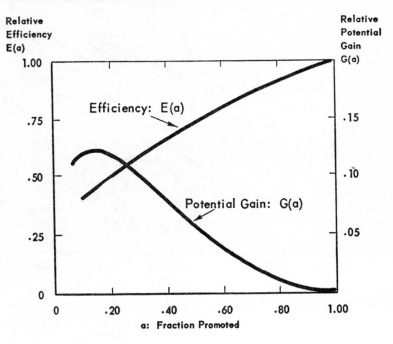

Figure 3. Relative efficiency and potential gain.

results: measures of the relative efficiency of distribution of promotion and potential gain in sales through better distribution; a measure of the effect of promotion on individual accounts; and a broad view of the whole operation forming an important part of a general theory of company operations.

The insight into the process which was gained made it possible to suggest a new basis for selecting dealers for promotion which concentrated attention on purchases during a series of past months, while neglecting extraneous factors which the distributing company had previously felt were important. The effect on total sales is demonstrated by Figure 4. The straight line indicates the sales resulting from a given level of promotion if dealers are selected at random; the other solid line shows the sales volume which is theoretically possible as predicted by the model. Of the two broken lines, the lower shows the amount of business obtained under the old method of dealer selection, whereas the upper shows the results obtained under the new method.

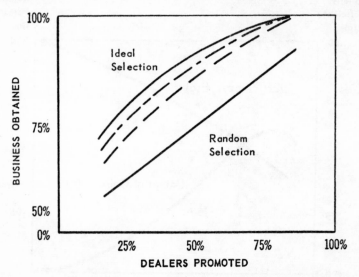

Figure 4. Relation between business obtained and number of dealers promoted.

This new method of selection was applied throughout the company's operations and tested simultaneously in an experimental program. The analytical methods used made it possible to focus attention in the test on the types of dealers where an improvement in business was expected. Consequently, the size of the test could be cut by a factor of 20 compared with that required by the experimental methods previously used by the company. The tests confirmed almost exactly the predicted results.

The results described were important, but even more rewarding results were obtained when the work was combined with a detailed study of the effect of business volume on manufacturing and distribution costs. An explicit statement concerning the relationship between promotional effort and volume, combined with equally detailed information on the relationship between volume and operating costs, made it possible to set the level of promotional effort on a rational basis. In short, a new measure—the effect of promotional effort on profits—could be used as the basis for establishing the level of promotional activity. It was shown that an increase of 50 per cent in the amount of promotional activity was possible. Briefly, the construction of this measure proceeded along the following lines.

Let it be assumed that a minimum desirable return on capital, i, has been set either as a matter of policy or because of alternative uses for capital. Then, the "profit" from a volume $B(a)$ is given by

$$P(a) = B(a) - C(B) - C(a) - i\{I(B) + I(a)\}, \qquad (18)$$

where $C(B) =$ the cost of producing and distributing a volume B of product;

$C(a) =$ the cost of promotion of a fraction a of the dealers;

$I(B) =$ the capital required to support production of a volume B of output;

$I(a) =$ the capital required to support a level of promotional activity represented by a.

The rate of change of "profit" with respect to the level of promotional activity a is given by

$$P'(a) = Nsv(1-a) - \frac{d}{da}\{C(B) + C(a)\} - i\frac{d}{da}\{I(B) + I(a)\}. \quad (19)$$

The "profit" will be maximized when $P'(a) = O$, or when

$$a = 1 - \left(\frac{1}{Nsv}\right)\left[\frac{d}{da}\{C(B) + C(a)\} + i\frac{d}{da}\{I(B) + I(a)\}\right]. \quad (20)$$

The computation of what is normally meant by profit typically does not include an imputed interest charge on capital employed. Maximization of profit as conventionally defined may well be erroneous, however. It is only correct in the very special case when the minimum acceptable return on capital is zero, hardly the typical case today. Neglect of imputed interest is sometimes based on the appeal to the fixed volume of capital employed in "the short run." Experience suggests that the exceptions to this idea have been more numerous than the applications.

The limitations of a model such as that discussed here are, of course, numerous. The model is static; it does not account for time changes introduced by promotional effort. These dynamic consequences are probably small, however, in comparison with short-run effects in an established enterprise. The model does not indicate the reason why the promotional effort has the effect it does, to provide a basis for improvement of the quality of this effort; this is a separate question. Finally, the model is not directly applicable to the analysis of new types of promotional activity completely outside the scope of the usual promotional effort. It does provide a solid starting point for such an analysis.

This development of a functional relationship between sales and promotional effort is useful in directing sales promotional activities. It is also of fundamental importance in any general model of the business as a whole. Such a model can be extremely valuable in providing quantitative guides to planning the basic strategy of the business.

Operations Research
in the Printing Industry

ROBERT H. ROY

Late in the 1930's, Waverly Press Incorporated proposed to launch a new development in hand composition,[1] a procedure which would have required new equipment and a relatively long-term experiment involving a sizeable segment of the Press's working force. The advent of war and the consequent shortages of materials prevented the adoption of this plan and it was put aside until after the war. Though we at the Press did not realize it during those early postwar years, the war had brought a new research procedure upon the scene. Operations research was unknown to us and it was only after our work in a new method of hand composition was well along that we became aware that we were, in effect, performing a kind of operations research. This was in no way an unpleasant revelation, since it indicated that our rather eccentric new approach to a very traditional aspect of the printing industry was, in some respects, in line with the operations research procedures which had paid off so admirably during the war years.

The reader may wonder why a modern printing plant was seeking a new development in hand composition; there is scarcely anyone who does not know that most type today is set by machines, by the Linotype

[1] See also Mr. Roy's article, "A New System of Hand Composition," *The Inland Printer*, Vol. 121, Nos. 3, 4 and 5 (June, July and August 1948).

invented by Mergenthaler, and the Monotype invented by Tolbert Lanston. While machine setting does account for the majority of type, and hand composition has been reduced to an adjunct of the machine, a considerable quantity of hand operation remains necessary. In Monotype machine composition, the following functions require hand operation: the correcting and altering of machine-set type; the setting of small amounts insufficient to warrant machine make-ready; the composition of advertising material and of mathematical and chemical formulae; the ruling of tables; and the assembly operations of collation and page make-up. In an establishment which does any quantity of composition, the payroll for hand composition is a significant item in the total expenses of operation. This was particularly true at the Waverly Press, which specializes in scientific books and periodicals. The hand-composition payroll was an item well worthy of some examination and study.

Evolution of the Modern Type Case.

In order to understand some of the problems encountered in modern hand composition, it is necessary to trace, to some extent, its history. The printing industry is roughly five hundred years old. The official penta-centennial was celebrated in 1940, possibly a few years in advance of the actual anniversary. In any case, there has been a long history of the use of type, and trade practices have become somewhat hardened in tradition. In fact it seemed, until a few years ago, that the compositor, because he was performing a hand skill boasting a history of nearly five centuries, failed to realize that his uses of type and his needs in terms of equipment were vastly different from those of Gutenberg.

Figure 1 illustrates two type layouts of the year 1683. These happen to be the earliest layouts for which illustrations are readily available, but other sources indicate that they are essentially typical of earlier layouts as well, even those of the late sixteenth century.

As the drawing demonstrates, one case contained the capital letters, numerals, accent marks, zodiac signs and other miscellany. The lower-case letters, which received the greatest proportion of use, were in a separate case. There are two functional features of early type layouts which warrant attention. First of all, the compartments of the cases were roomy. This was essential because the compositor needed at his disposal a large volume of type, since everything was then hand-set, and also because space was needed for the distribution of used type back into the compartments after a printing was completed. Second, the amount of space set aside for each lower-case letter was more or less in proportion to its frequency of use. Thus, the lower-case *e* occupied a large compartment, whereas *q* and *w* were in small compartments. Frequency was not the only consideration in this allocation of space. The lower case *l*, for example, was and is a frequently used letter, but, because of its narrowness, it required less space and, therefore, a smaller compartment. The cases in Figure 1 show that, even by

A	B	C	D	E	F	G	à	ê	î	ô	û	♂	△
H	I	K	L	M	N	O	ä	ë	ï	ö	ü	*	8
P	Q	R	S	T	V	W	á	ć	í	ó	ú	□	
X	Y	Z	Æ	J	U		à	è	ì	ò	ù	♃	†
♄	♃	♂	☉	♀	☿	☽	♈	♉	♊	♋	♌	♍	•
1	2	3	4	5	6	7	♎	♏	♐	♑	♒	♓	
8	9	0			ft	k	ffi	ffi	ffl	ffl	R	⊕	§

j			æ	œ		s					fl	ffl
'	b	c	d	e	i	f	f	g	fh	ff	ff
&										fi	fi
ã	l	m	n	h	o	y	p	q	w		?
;										en	em
z	v	u	t	Spaces.	a	r	,	:		Quadr.
x							.	-		

Figure 1.

that early date in printing history, some small modifications had been made. *J* and *U,* letters which came into use much later than the invention of printing, were added to the end of the alphabet rather than inserted in their proper places. No major changes, however, were introduced until the invention of composing machines, for the old-style type case adequately met the needs of the compositor for the many years during which all composition was done by hand.

Once the bulk of type could be machine set, however, the hand compositor's problems became completely different. Obviously, the quantity of type he would require would be considerably less and this fact was, to some extent, recognized in the new type cases which were introduced in the last decade of the nineteenth century. The most widely used and popular of these cases was the " California Job Case " first introduced in 1891 and illustrated in Figure 2.

The need for a smaller quantity of type made it possible for the capital and lower-case compartments to be combined within one frame, which retained the familiar 16 by 32-inch overall size. As the drawing demonstrates, the arrangement of compartments for letters was not much changed, but followed that which had been used for nearly three centuries. The capital letters remained in alphabetical order, with the exception of *J* and *U* still tagging along at the end.

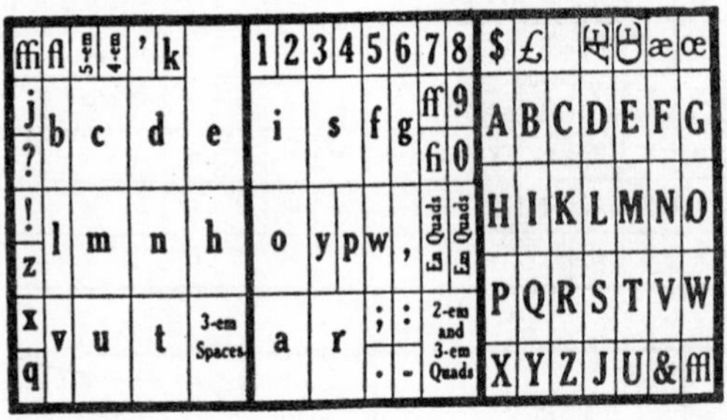

Figure 2.

The lower-case letters were in relatively the same positions, the long *s* being replaced by its modern equivalent. Although *q* was moved out to the left edge along with other signs of relatively infrequent use, and a few modifications were made in the placement of punctuation marks, the position of lower case letters was essentially unchanged; *b, c, d, e, l, m, n, h, o, y, p, w*, etc., all remained where custom had placed them. Even the same relative allocation of compartmental space to various letters was retained.

Disadvantages of the Conventional Case.

The " California Job Case " and its contemporaries made, in effect, only one major concession to the new role of hand composition in the age of machine-set type; they allowed for an overall smaller volume of type. What they failed to provide for was the fact that, whereas volume was no longer essential, variety of type was, since it was in the unconventional and special aspects of the printing operation that hand composition found its widest use. Figure 3, part of a page of a technical publication, provides an excellent example of the need for variety in modern hand composition. As the number legends indicate, a compositor correcting a quantity of pages of this kind might require as many as six varieties of type. While most pages are not so involved, jobs requiring three, four and five types are quite common.

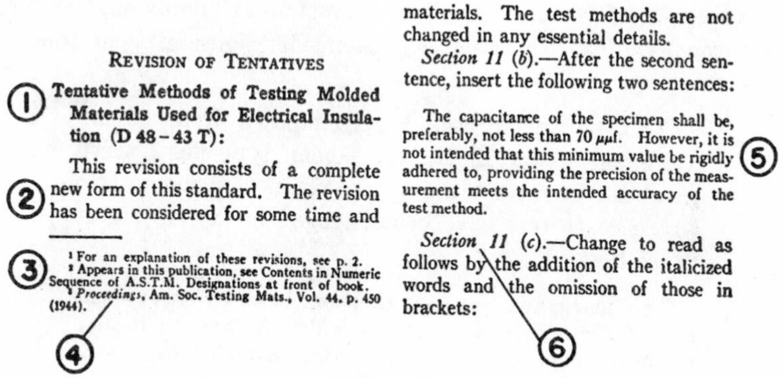

① Revision of Tentatives

Tentative Methods of Testing Molded Materials Used for Electrical Insulation (D 48 – 43 T):

② This revision consists of a complete new form of this standard. The revision has been considered for some time and

③ ¹ For an explanation of these revisions, see p. 2.
² Appears in this publication, see Contents in Numeric Sequence of A.S.T.M. Designations at front of book.
³ Proceedings, Am. Soc. Testing Mats., Vol. 44. p. 450 (1944).

④

materials. The test methods are not changed in any essential details.
Section 11 (b).—After the second sentence, insert the following two sentences:

⑤ The capacitance of the specimen shall be, preferably, not less than 70 μμf. However, it is not intended that this minimum value be rigidly adhered to, providing the precision of the measurement meets the intended accuracy of the test method.

⑥ Section 11 (c).—Change to read as follows by the addition of the italicized words and the omission of those in brackets:

Figure 3.

It is impossible, however, for the hand compositor to have conveniently before him more than two type cases of the conventional 16 by 32 inch dimensions. The size of these cases limits their usefulness in the composing room of a modern plant. The working surface of a composing frame can carry no more than two cases in addition to the galley of type being set and the proof from which the compositor reads. The cabinet beneath the frame holds forty cases, which by no means can encompass a compositor's needs.

Apart from its size, the conventional type case has other defects. It has already been mentioned that, in the days before machine setting, type which had been used was distributed back into the compartments of the type case. This process, undertaken for the sake of economy, not only required that the compartments be large enough to allow for this distribution but also resulted in having the individual pieces of type jumbled within the compartment. Consequently, the compositor was obliged to turn each piece of type so that the face would be up and the nick out before placing it in the line or stick. This, of course, involved extra time and motion.

Today, the conventional type case still contains jumbled type with its same requirements for extra time and trouble on the part of the compositor. Yet the very reason for type jumbling has disappeared, since used type is now generally melted down rather than distributed back into the compartments of the type case. Jumbling involves another disadvantage. As the supply of a particular sort becomes low in any one of the compartments, a new supply is dumped in from the sorts caster. The case is never emptied and never cleaned out. In the course of use and handling, characters inevitably spill over or are dropped into the wrong compartment; since all the type is

> **This paragraph was hand cimposed from a conventional 10 on 12 No. 9A Zoman type fflase weich has been in regular use in uee composing room. No wrang ceara*ters have been changed in the setting of twese lines.**
>
> Th2s paragyaph was han' cimposed from a fflonventional 8 on 10 No. 8A Raman type case whice has been in regular use in the composing room. No wring characters have fleen changed in the setting of ihese lines.

Figure 4.

jumbled, a misplaced piece is not easily visible and is "lost." Conventional type cases are normally "dirty"; that is to say that so many letters are misplaced that it is necessary for the compositor carefully to check each line in the stick as he works. He normally reads back the line, removing wrong characters and replacing them with new pieces of type from the compartments. Even with such inspection, errors in hand composition are three times as numerous per 1,000 ems as those in machine composition. Figure 4 vividly demonstrates the frequency with which characters are lost in the wrong compartment. The two paragraphs there pictured were set from a conventional case in regular use without subsequent correcting or discarding. In short, although California cases and others like them are in wide use throughout the country, the difficulties which they introduce into the composition process are an invitation to improvement. Efforts to effect such improvement have been undertaken at the Waverly Press.

Development of New Equipment.

It is necessary, at this point, to interject a personal note in order to provide background for the beginnings of innovation at the Waverly Press. In the 1930's, I became interested in setting type by hand as a hobby. After one mildly successful foray into this field, I decided to attempt something a little more ambitious. It was arranged that I participate in the setting, printing and publishing of what came to be called " The Leeuwenhoek Letter," a translation from the early Dutch by Professor Barnett Cohen of The Johns Hopkins Medical School, which contained the first recorded description of bacteria. I hand distributed the type from " dead " pages into a California case and then composed the script as translated by Dr. Cohen. Since this was an avocational effort, I turned to the job at odd moments, and allowed my mind to speculate freely on variations in the familiar type-setting operation.

As a matter of academic interest, I tried to see whether I could set type successfully with two hands. I practiced and, eventually, reached the point where I could perform this operation, not very well, but with reasonable adequacy. This random and idle experiment produced, however, an important by-product, namely the realization of how badly suited the California case was to modern composing room practice, at least in the plant with which I was familiar. The inadequate variety of the type available on the composing frame, the inconvenience caused by having to turn each piece of type into the proper position before its insertion into a line, and the inaccuracies and loss of time caused by " lost " pieces of type in " dirty " cases all seemed needless irritations which the professional compositor might be spared if certain changes were introduced.

Whether the changes would be immediately welcome at the Press was another consideration altogether. Since the industry is an old one, printing and hand composition have a strong, firmly-rooted tradition. Trade practices partake of the character of sacred dogma, so that attempts to change rigidly conventional methods are always likely to meet with strong opposition from those regularly engaged in the work. The human problems involved in any attempt to modify the type case loomed large from the first conception of the idea. The strategy and tactics of actually introducing the change after the war, even on an experimental basis, received careful attention from the

very start. One premise on which the entire experiment was introduced
was that a maximum of employee participation in the development
of improvement would be one of the best ways to minimize opposition

In the course of my attempts at two-hand type setting, I had
observed that a significant improvement in facility was achieved by
arranging all the letters in each compartment uniformly with each
piece lying on its side, the face away from the compositor, and the
nick to his left. Subsequent trials of various other type positions
indicated that this was the most convenient. This suggested that
some of the deficiencies in conventional equipment might be eliminated
if new cases were introduced, designed on the principle that sorts
of type would be kept in a uniform position just as delivered by the
Monotype sorts caster. It was obvious that any such attempt would
require some form of " package " sorts which could hold the reserve
supply in the desired position until placed in the case. This led to
questions about the best size and form for such a package which, in
turn, introduced the problem of designing a new case.

Compartments containing jumbled type were measured and the
results indicated that about half the volume of the typical container
was filled with air between the type bodies. It was readily apparent
that, if the type were uniformly laid out, a cubic inch of space would
contain many more pieces and, therefore, that the compartment for a
sort could be smaller and the case itself could be smaller. A reduction
in the size of the case would make it possible for more cases to be
readily available on the working surface and more to be stored within
a single frame.

The first approach to this innovation was the design of cases which
were, in size, fractions of conventional type cases so that they could
then be contained within conventional-size drawers. These attempts
were, for various reasons, unsuccessful and were abandoned in favor
of cases designed to fit into steel triple-column galley cabinets; these
are standard printing equipment with slides or " runs " made to hold
one hundred 8½ by 23½-inch galleys. When full advantage of one of
the clearance between uprights, these cabinets allow for type cases
measuring 8⅞ by 25 inches in size with retention of the full 1-inch
depth.

As a start, a few of these new cases were compartmented with
cardboard boxes and put into regular use in the composing room

A special effort was made to inform the workers of what was being considered and to elicit from them ideas about how the suggested design might be improved. The preliminary models were, in fact, used for approximately one year before any modifications were made on the design.

The new compartments, however, introduced another problem. It was necessary to devise some means for automatically casting sorts to the desired measure and for placing type into the boxes in the correct position. The solution to the first of these problems was provided by a company engineer, who designed an electric relay attachment for the sorts caster which allowed the machine to run automatically and then to be stopped mechanically when any required quantity of type had been cast. Once the measure for any particular character is properly adjusted, the machine functions without further attention, turning out type sorts in box-length units. The supervisor of the Monotype department devised a solution to the second problem in the form of a fixture for loading type into the boxes in the proper position. Although this device is operated by hand, the process is much more rapid than the machine-casting of the type, so that there is no bottleneck.

While the cardboard models of the new type cases were being used, attention was turned to the design of a work place. A wooden mock-up was constructed to be mounted on a standard galley cabinet. As originally installed in the composing room, it was made so that it could be altered as to reach, height, angle, and general dimensional characteristics. Every compositor in the department was asked to express preferences with respect to all these attributes so that some idea as to the optimum height of the lower edge, optimum angle of the slant, and the overall design limits could be obtained. After these preferences had been analyzed, a model of steel over plywood was installed and used for approximately one year. From experience with this prototype model, compositors and others in the plant were able to make valuable suggestions later incorporated into the finished product. Among these were some improvements in illumination, including a cowl on which two cases rest and in which there is a 40-watt fluorescent lamp shining through a glass diffuser, and a 20-watt fluorescent lamp for lighting the cases held in the frame below the working surface.

Eventually, the new composition frame was evolved, consisting of equipment strikingly in contrast to that used in more typical composing rooms. Each new type-case, 8¼ by 25 inches, now consists of plastic boxes in two colors, green and amber. A contrast in color was thought desirable in order to give the compositor some position cues since the familiar arrangement of letters was replaced by alphabetical order. Green and amber were selected for two reasons: the combination harmonized with the general decor of the room and, of more importance, consultation with a psychologist had revealed that this particular combination is one to which few people are color-blind. Figure 5 is a photograph of the new type case. The diagrams in Figure 6 illustrate three of the case layouts.

As the drawings roughly illustrate, the plastic boxes replacing the traditional compartments are molded in three sizes: those used for regular cap, lower case, and small cap fonts fit eighteen to a row along the case; those for thin terminals, twelve to a row; and those for hand-set fonts, thirteen to a row. All three sizes have a depth of 70 points, which is the measure to which sorts are cast, and a width of 1.360 inches. All cases contain six rows of boxes across the type case width. Each box carries an identifying label on the inside of the vertical surface facing the compositor as he works from the case. While this facilitates finding characters in composition, its principal function is for reordering sorts.

The new case differs from the conventional case in four important ways. Its overall dimensions are smaller. The box-compartments within the case are in aphabetical order and are smaller than the roomy compartments required by jumbled type. Finally, there is no attempt in the new case to apportion space according to frequency of use. (As a matter of fact, for the hand composition which is done as an adjunct to machine composition, differences in frequency of use are not standard. For those scientific and mathematical publications which include many formulae, such a generally infrequent letter as x may be used more often than e.)

Replacements of type for an empty box are obtained from reserve sorts, stored in trays similar to the new type cases, and centrally placed in the composing room so as to be available to all compositors. When a compositor has used all of a character contained within the case, he removes the empty box, tosses it into a special bin and procures a full box of the same character from the sorts storage galley cabinets.

Figure 5.

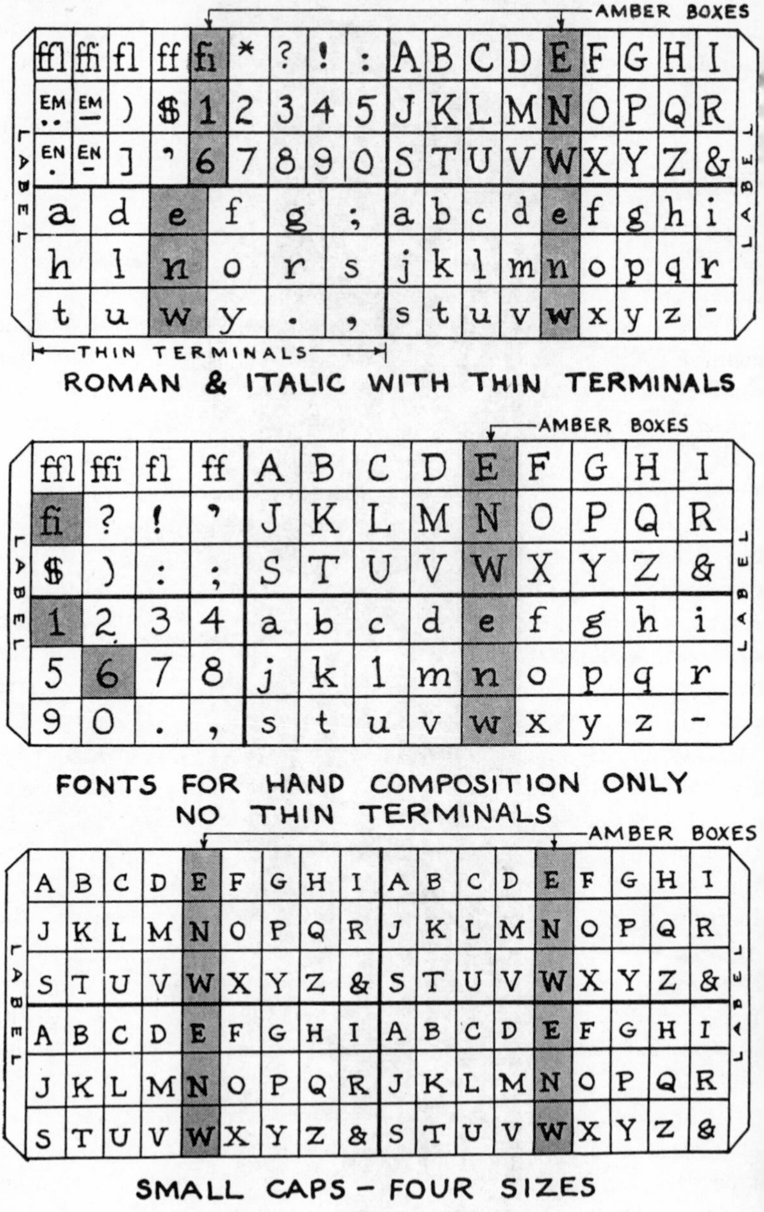
AMBER BOXES
LABEL
THIN TERMINALS
ROMAN & ITALIC WITH THIN TERMINALS
AMBER BOXES
LABEL
FONTS FOR HAND COMPOSITION ONLY
NO THIN TERMINALS
AMBER BOXES
LABEL
SMALL CAPS – FOUR SIZES

Figure 6.

The empty boxes, all bearing their appropriate labels, are placed daily in the sorts storage and their degree of accumulation serves to indicate the need or lack of need for new casting of particular characters. In the sorts storage cabinets, some attempt is made to apportion space to boxes according to frequency of use. Space is provided for a four-month supply of each character, with a minimum of two boxes for any particular character. The demands peculiar to certain classes of work make it impossible to fix rigid space allocations for all characters; experience in the composing room, however, provides certain guidelines upon which such allocation can be based.

While innovations were in progress it was decided that some changes could be made in respect to type spaces, and the new type cases incorporate two changes. Spaces are not included with alphabets in regular cases but are now separately contained. Formerly, spacing sorts were duplicated in all cases containing type of like size. Thus, if there were a dozen cases of 10-point in use, each of the twelve contained duplicate spaces. A new 10-point space case at each frame can now serve all 10-point character cases, thus avoiding this duplication. The compositor now has available a space case for each point size. Such cases are the same length as the type cases, but are much narrower, since they are subdivided by only one row of plastic box compartments; these dimensions make it possible for two cases to rest with the type cases on the working surface.

Traditionally, spaces for hand composition have been made in fractions of an em, in increments allowing for small variations in spacing and accurate justification; the mental arithmetic involved in their use has always proved cumbersome and difficult to learn. For this reason, the new space cases were designed for point spacing. The increments provided permit accurate justification as before, but the calculations involved are much less intricate. The "hair" spaces and large quads are jumbled in their compartments because they are, respectively, too small and too large to case in uniform rows. All the other spaces are cast, loaded, and sorted exactly like the regular alphabets.

A similar break with tradition was made in respect to punctuation characters. Previously, each font had its own punctuation, both in the type case and in the reserve sorts. There were separate periods, commas, etc., cast from separate matrices for each size of Modern

Number 8, Bruce Old Style Number 31, Scotch Number 36, and
Caslon Number 337. On the basis that the differences between such
characters were, in many cases, too small to be recognized, the practice
was adopted of casting punctuation sorts for different faces from the
same matrices and storing them together. Now the compositor who
seeks an 8 on 10-point light face semicolon procures a box from the
8 on 10-point light face storage area, without regard to the type face
he is using. Naturally, distinct punctuation sorts were retained for
those fonts characterized by unique alignment, weight, or design of
letter. The pooling of like characters wherever possible has resulted
in a large reduction in matrices and duplicate sorts and the Press's
customers appear to be entirely unaware of the change.

Triple-column galley cabinets form the bases for the new frames
at which the compositors now work. These are standard equipment,
except that the backs are removed so that the same file of type cases,
ninety-six cases in all, is available to two compositors working directly
across from each other. Upon the cabinets are the frame surfaces,
each mounted on a pair of jacks connected by a chain and sprockets.
By means of a crank, the jacks permit independent adjustment of
frame height by each person between limits of 41 to 49 inches from
the floor. The frame surface itself is of sheet steel over plywood, the
length and width determined to conform with the new type and space
cases. Each general purpose frame is 54 inches in length to accommodate two type cases laid end to end. The width of the main surface
is 22 inches, mounted at an angle of 20 degrees, designed to hold
three type cases and two space cases. Above the working surface is
a cowl, capable of holding two more type cases. Therefore the compositor now has available on open surface five type cases and two
space cases, in addition to the galley of type in work. By sliding out
type cases in the galley cabinet, the compositor can make a few
additional kinds of type available, although these will not be so conveniently placed as the cases on the surfaces. A special tilting device
to hold the galley in work and the new lighting arrangements are
additional features which add to the compositor's comfort. Figures
7 and 8 provide two views of the new equipment.

While the development of the new compositors' equipment was
underway, an independent but related innovation was introduced in
the type-casting operation. Word spaces on the Monotype, which may

Figure 7.

Figure 8.

vary in width by very small increments, had been produced on the caster as separate types, each requiring a pump stroke of the machine. At about the time the new case was being introduced, the Lanston Monotype Machine Company made "shoulder spacing" available, in which each word space is not a separate character but an integral part, or shoulder, of the first letter of the following word. This new development affords two advantages: it saves up to 16 per cent of caster pump strokes on text matter; and it reduces the chance of "work-ups" on press, since a shoulder space, not being separate, cannot ride up and print. When shoulder-spaced material is corrected, changes requiring an increase in the space between words present no new problems; a thin space providing the necessary increment may be inserted just before the shoulder space. Any changes requiring a reduction of the space between words, however, are troublesome, since such reduction would necessitate changing the first letter of the word together with the shoulder before it. If this procedure were followed, the economies of time achieved in shoulder-casting would be lost in the correcting process.

The problem was ingeniously solved by Wade H. Patton of the staff of the Monotype Company, who, from tabulations of the terminal letters of English words in common usage, ascertained that fifteen letters comprise approximately 98 per cent of word endings: these letters are those shown in the lower left quarter of the case layout in Figure 6a. Each of these characters has been cast two units thinner than normal, and such "thin terminals" are used whenever it is necessary to reduce word spacing in making corrections. While shoulder spacing has been independent of the new type case, there has been close correlation between the two. The use of shoulder spacing requires thin terminals, and thin terminals make necessary a change from conventional type case design. Full consideration was given to this development in changing to the new system.

Introduction of the new equipment and methods in the hand composing room could hardly have had fortunate results without the cooperation of those who would eventually use them. To facilitate the change, therefore, considerable effort was taken to keep the compositors and others informed of the plans being made at each stage of development. Employees' suggestions were solicited and all were carefully considered. A double gain was realized: the sympathy of the staff was achieved; and many good ideas were forthcoming, which were incorporated into the new system.

Performance with The New Type Case.

Once the transition from old to new system was nearly completed, initial assessments of the hand-composing operation under changed conditions could be made. Accordingly, time studies were conducted on hand-set lines from both the new type case and the old. With the exception of one study, made on a compositor with relatively little old-case experience, the results showed that composition from the new case was slower than from the old. In order to discover the reason for this, a motion picture was made of two compositors, each setting type first from an old case, then from a new. Analysis of this film produced the results shown in Table 1. The figures there tabulated represent the counts of motion picture frames during the setting of some twenty characters of type. The table indicates that the reach (first step) and carry (third step) required a longer time with the new case than with the old, despite the fact that the distances involved are shorter with the new equipment. The fourth step, the placing and releasing of a piece of type in the stick, took longer with the new case, although this phase of the operation is entirely independent of the case used. These factors pointed to a difficulty which had been suspected, namely that hesitation due to unfamiliarity with the new layout was slowing down composition.

The need for training to remedy this unfamiliarity was clearly indicated. The men were given daily practice sessions in composing from a new case specially prepared for the purpose by having the box-compartment labels removed. In reaching for a given character, therefore, the compositor was forced to rely only on position cues, instead of the combination of position and label. The test was based upon the sentence long familiar to typing students, " The quick brown fox jumps over the lazy dog." The compositor first pointed to the letters in succession with his eyes open, secondly with his eyes closed, and then set the line without justification; in the final step he distributed the type carefully and uniformly back into the case. Each of the first three parts was timed with a stop watch and plotted on a learning curve. The errors in setting the line were also counted and recorded. After some twenty daily lessons, a second film record was taken of the original subjects which provided the results shown in Table 2.

A quick comparison of the two tables indicates that each compositor made remarkable improvements in the speed with which he worked from the new type case. Compositor A, a relatively new man, had substantially exceeded his former speed for the new case, whereas he performed less quickly with the conventional case. Compositor B, a man with years of experience, had improved performance with both cases on the second test, except for some retarding in his *selecting and picking up type from an old case.* In general, Compositor B's speed

Analysis of First Film. Exposure rate: 16 frames per second.				
ELEMENT	**COMPOSITOR A**		**COMPOSITOR B**	
	New Case	Old Case	New Case	Old Case
	frames	frames	frames	frames
1. Reach for type	6.9	5.7	5.6	5.0
2. Select and pick-up	7.6	5.7	4.2	3.8
3. Carry to stick	11.6	8.0	7.2	6.3
4. Place and release	3.2	2.6	2.2	1.5
TOTALS	29.3	22.0	19.2	16.6

TABLE I

Analysis of Second Film. Exposure rate: 16 frames per second.				
ELEMENT	**COMPOSITOR A**		**COMPOSITOR B**	
	New Case	Old Case	New Case	Old Case
	frames	frames	frames	frames
1. Reach for type	5.4	6.1	5.1	4.8
2. Select and pick-up	6.7	8.5	3.9	4.5
3. Carry to stick	7.5	9.4	6.2	6.1
4. Place and release	2.0	3.0	1.6	1.2
TOTALS	21.6	27.0	16.8	16.6

TABLE 2

with the new case was nearly equal to his speed with the old. The improvement effected by the daily training was deemed sufficiently good so that similar training was given to all compositors. Figure 9 charts the striking improvements in both speed and accuracy achieved by nineteen compositors in the course of their training tests. Following the test, each newly trained compositor was timed composing the same line from a California case. Intensive daily practice with the new case, of course, stacked the cards somewhat against the old, but it was felt that the accumulation of years of experience on the California case somewhat balanced this effect. In any event, the results clearly indicated that the compositors were able to work more quickly from the new case. Average composition time was 1.17 minutes per line from the California case compared with 0.9 minutes per line from the new, an advantage of 23 per cent in favor of the new case. In the nineteen trials with the old case, a total of thirty-eight errors was made, an average of two per man; this was *ten times* the

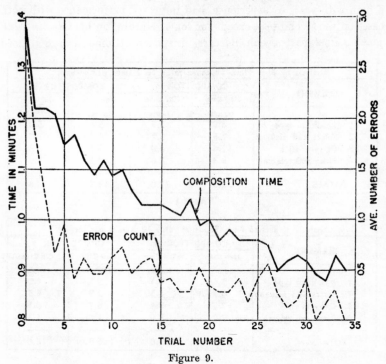

Figure 9.

number of errors made from the new case. This reduction in errors was expected, since so many errors formerly resulted from the mix-ups of jumbled type. To demonstrate the improvement in accuracy more vividly, the two paragraphs in Figure 4 were reset from a new case without correction after setting. As Figure 10 demonstrates, *there are no errors*.

Following the completion of the compositors' daily test series, each participant was asked to fill out a questionnaire designed to elicit his opinions on lighting, adjustability, frames, cabinets, galley tilters, cases, and layouts. The questions were framed to allow for responses ranging from approval to disapproval. In no instance were respondents obliged to identify themselves. The answers were, on the whole, strongly in favor of the new system. Of the detailed responses, 77 per cent were favorable and 23 per cent unfavorable. No single questionnaire contained responses which were all unfavorable. Probably the most gratifying response to the new system was a rise in the production index of the composing room from 107 in May, 1947, when the changeover was first introduced, to 126 in July, 1948.

This paragraph was hand composed from a new 10 on 12 No. 8A Roman type case which has been in regular use in the composing room. No wrong characters have been changed in the setting of these lines.

This paragraph was hand composed from a new 8 on 10 No. 8A Roman type case which has been in regular use in the composing room. No wrong characters have been changed in the setting of these lines.

Figure 10.

This, then, was the solution which the Waverly Press worked out to an operations problem which was not new, but which had arisen some half century previously, at the advent of machine type-setting; namely, how could the hand composition which remained necessary be performed more accurately and more speedily, and therefore at less expense in man-hours and money? To answer this question, it was necessary to examine the entire operation from the arrival of sorts from the type-casting department and of text material from the Monotype department through the completion of the hand composition process. The development of radically new equipment and techniques, consideration of time-and-motion factors, and careful attention to the human aspects of the problem all contributed to the system which finally evolved. For this job, the Press management, compositors, engineers, those involved in type-casting and operation of the Monotype machines, and others all pooled their ideas; and, when necessary, experts in other fields were called in for consultation. As the first paragraph in this chapter indicates, all this was undertaken without prior knowledge of operations research as a new way of attacking operations problems. Awareness of the similarity came after the fact; the successful solution which the Press has achieved to its operations problems, however, is a commentary on the effectiveness of operations research techniques, by whatever name they are called.

The Reliability of
Airborne Radar

DAVID M. BOODMAN

THE RELIABILITY of airborne radar equipment [1] is a subject which has, in recent years, been absorbing the attention of many people both inside and outside the Military Establishment. The problem has significance for the electronics design engineer and for the military operations analyst and requires the specialized techniques of both disciplines for its solution. The engineer is beset with the difficulties of building high-performance electronic equipment which will control, track, and guide planes and missiles, whereas the operations analyst is concerned with the effects of this increased complexity on operational reliability.

The operations analysis aspect of the problem centers around the question of what the added complexity of airborne radar costs in terms of reliability. Knowledge of how these quantities are related is needed in addition to an understanding of how to increase reliability should it prove to be less than satisfactory.

In the past, reliability has been treated as a materiel problem and approached from the engineering point of view. There have, for example, been numerous studies on relay reliability, resulting in recommendations of how relays should be built, installed and operated.

[1] See also Dr. Boodman's paper, "The Reliability of Airborne Radar Equipment," *Journal of the Operations Research Society of America*, Vol. I, No. 2 (February 1953), pp. 39-45.

Similar studies have also been made on vacuum tubes. While the information which these studies yield is valuable, it does not help to answer the question of more importance to the operations analyst, namely the relationship of reliability to complexity.

Although it is generally known that the complexity of electronic equipment has increased, it might be well to illustrate the magnitude of the increase. The average fleet destroyer provides an amazing but by no means unique example. In 1937, such a ship held fewer than sixty vacuum tubes in the few pieces of electronic equipment it carried. Since that time, the growth of electronics has been exponential, so that a single piece of equipment on a typical fleet destroyer now contains forty times that number of vacuum tubes. For certain aircraft types, these factors are still higher. It is readily apparent, therefore, that the effective employment of ships and aircraft depends heavily on the proper functioning of their electronic equipment.

Before further discussion of the subject, it will be necessary to define certain terms with more precision than ordinary usage implies. The term *reliability*, as here used, refers to the probability of survival, within a specified time interval. A *component* is the small functional unit of a system. The terms *system, machine, mechanism,* and *equipment* will be used interchangeably to refer to an aggregate of components interconnected for the purpose of performing a specific task or tasks. The term *complexity*, somewhat more nebulous than the others, is taken as a measure of the number of vital links necessary for the proper operation of a system. It should be emphasized that survival, i. e., proper equipment operation, is an on-off process. There is a distinction only between the "living" and the "dead," and no distinction between the "sick" and the "healthy." An equipment is considered as surviving if all its parts are functioning, regardless of how well they are functioning.

The Nature of Failures.

In order to determine the relationship between reliability and complexity, one must, on the one hand, understand the nature of failures in the system, and, on the other, establish a measure of complexity. In its work on airborne radar reliability, the Operations Evaluation Group has made use of a threefold categorization of failure types, proposed by the RAND Corporation a few years ago, and found to be applicable to a wide variety of failures including bus motor breakdown, ball and roller bearing collapse, and bank statement errors. The three broad categories are *initial failure*, *wear-out failure*, and *chance* or *random failure*.

An initial failure, as the name implies, is one which results from a defect present in a component at the time of its first being put into operation. Such defects arise because of an event in the preoperational life of the component, such as an error in manufacture or damage in transit or handling. Proper screening and testing procedures prevent

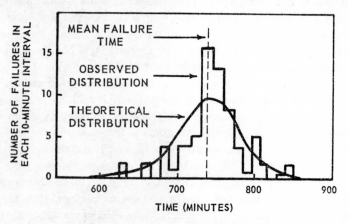

Figure 1. Observed and theoretical distribution of flashlight battery failure.

initially defective components from actually being put into operational use; therefore, such failures are rarely encountered.

A wear-out failure is one which results from the depletion of some material or property of the component which is essential to its proper operation. The depletion process may occur through abrasion, evaporation, chemical reaction, or through loss of such physical properties as fatigue or creep resistance. The failure of incandescent lamps, dry cells and the like are examples. It is characteristic of this type of failure that it can, to a large extent, be anticipated, since, generally, the life spans of a group of similar components, similarly employed, are normally or nearly normally distributed about a readily determined mean. Such is the case for a sample of dry cells tested and described in Figure 1.

This figure shows the times of failure for one hundred similar cells. The histogram represents the number of failures observed in 10-minute intervals during the test; the smooth curve represents a normal curve about the observed mean. The probability of a wear-out failure in an interval of time, dt, for a component of age t is $\phi(t)\,dt$, where ϕ is the usual Gaussian function

$$\phi(t) = \frac{1}{\sigma\sqrt{2\pi}}\, e^{-\frac{(t-\bar{t})}{2\sigma^2}}$$

and $\sigma^2 =$ standard deviation of the ages, with $\bar{t}$ the average age of components at time of wear-out.

The third failure category, namely chance or random failure, is the most interesting in its implications as well as the most important for purposes of studying the reliability-complexity relationship. Chance failures, such as tire punctures, capacitor breakdown, and fuse blowout, are generally the result of severe, unpredictable and usually avoidable stresses arising from such environmental factors as temperature, pressure, shock, vibration, humidity, etc. The rate of incidence of chance failures is determined by the severity of environmental conditions; the more severe the environment, the more frequent the occurrence of chance failures. In a given environment, however, the hazard of failure is constant. This is the fundamental characteristic of chance failures. For fixed environmental conditions, the probability of there arising a stress exceeding the failure resistance of a component is constant over all time. Since failure can be expressed as

$$\mu_t = \frac{1}{n_t}\,\frac{dn_t}{d_t},$$

and since, for chance failures, $\mu_t = c$, then the reliability of a chance failure system is

$$-\frac{n_t}{n_0} = P_t = e^{-\mu t}.$$

The density of failures follows a similar function and, as shown in Figure 2, vacuum tubes under certain conditions exhibit such random failure behavior.

The figure shows the times of failure of 903 aircraft radar vacuum tubes of a particular type. The number of failures in each 20-hour interval is plotted as a function of operating time of the tubes and, as the figure demonstrates, this density of failure follows the predicted exponential law.

The effects on reliability of these two different types of failures, then, are different. In systems experiencing wear-out failures, one can anticipate failure and can, therefore, prevent failure during

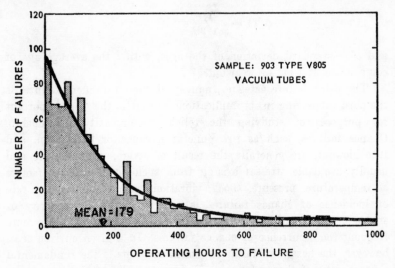

Figure 2. Distribution of failure of aircraft vacuum tubes.

operations by substituting new for old components at the appropriate time. Furthermore, if wear is serious, measures can be introduced for eliminating or reducing the effects of the wear-producing factors. This, in general, is the purpose of preventive maintenance. At present, techniques are being developed for the early detection of incipient wear-out failures in machines employing large numbers of vacuum tubes. It is claimed that as much as ten hours advance warning of failure in vacuum tubes can be obtained through the monitoring of their transconductance, grid current, and other characteristics. Chance failures, on the other hand, cannot be anticipated and forestalled by such measures. A new component is no better than one which has been successfully operating for a period of time, and one cannot tell a priori that one particular component will fail before any other. Furthermore, so little is known about the great variety of environmental factors which produce failure that there is little opportunity for instituting measures towards the reduction of failure rate.

Failures in Radar Equipments.

These general considerations were applied, by the Operations Evaluation Group, to the specific problem of the reliability of airborne

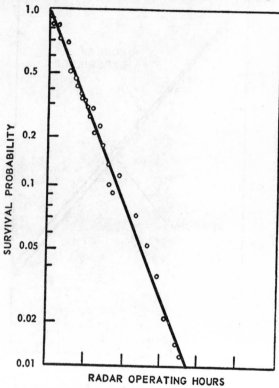

Figure 3. Survival probability of Type 1 radars.

radar. Observations were made of the failure behavior of several series of radars which were mounted in reciprocating engine aircraft of certain Marine and Naval squadrons in the United States and Korea. The primary data which were collected consisted of the identifications of the components and units which failed and their operating time to failure. From these data were computed the probabilities of survival to operating time t, which yielded the results shown in Figures 3 and 4.

Figure 3 indicates the fraction of Type I radars operating to time
t without failure requiring part replacement. Figure 4 gives similar
results for another type of radars under conditions of both training
and combat. The close agreement of the two is striking and indicates
that failure rate is more a function of the equipment itself and of the

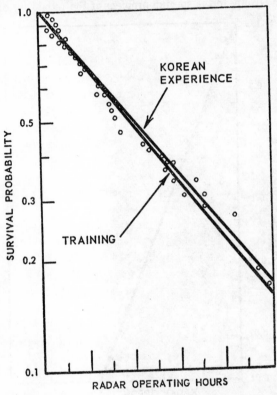

Figure 4. Survival probability of Type 2 radars.

environmental characteristics provided by the aircraft than of the
characteristics of external factors. Behavior similar to that demonstrated in the figures was found to hold for other airborne radar
types and for the sub-units of these radars, such as their power
supplies, modulators, indicators, and control units. In all cases,
survival probability was an exponential function of time and the total
equipment failure rate could be shown to be the sum of the failure
rates of these sub-units.

From the observed failure rates of these radars and their sub-units and their number of components, it was possible to compute the failure rates of their vacuum tubes and other electrical parts. The simplifying assumption was made that the total failure rate consisted of two parts—one due to vacuum tubes, the other due to all other electrical components. In short,

$$\mu \text{ total} = \mu_t T + \mu_c C,$$

where T and C represent, respectively, the number of tubes and of other components. For those equipments studied, it was found that vacuum tubes had a failure rate of 0.07 per cent per hour, while, for all other components, the failure rate was 0.02 per cent per hour. Therefore, the average service life of a vacuum tube in these sets was 1400 hours; that of the other components, 5000 hours. It must be emphasized that these values apply only to the particular class of radars being studied when installed in land-based, piston-driven aircraft. Any variation in these or in other environmental factors gives rise to another set of failure-rate constants.

At this stage of the investigation, the problem has resolved itself to this question: What can be expected of airborne electronic equipment which contains 1400-hour vacuum tubes and 5000-hour parts? The answer appears to be that not too much should be expected; with such components linked serially, that is, in such fashion that the proper operation of each is vital to the proper operation of the equipment, overall equipment reliability drops off rapidly with increasing complexity or number of components. This drop is clearly demonstrated in Figure 5.

In these radars, approximate component life is 4000 hours, since they employ parts and vacuum tubes in the ratio of about 10 to 1. Hence, a radar consisting of 1000 components has only a 60 per cent chance of surviving a two-hour mission and less than a 30 per cent chance of surviving a five-hour task. As the figures demonstrate, the survival probabilities decrease rapidly as either task-length or complexity increases.

Part of the problem, as presented by the Navy to the Operations Evaluation Group, was to provide conditional prediction of the reliability of two newer, advanced-design and high-performance radars of considerably increased complexity which the Navy was considering adopting for military use. The prediction was conditioned by the assumptions previously stated: that these newer radars would be used in environments similar to those of the earlier radars studied; and that they would be constructed of similar components. To the extent that these conditions would be met, it was shown that, as a result of increased complexity, the reliabilities of these two newer radars would be less than acceptable for missions of the duration required.

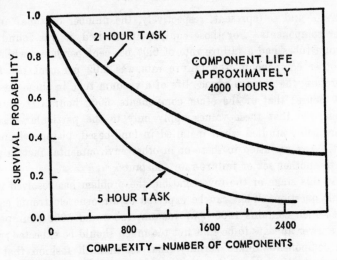

Figure 5. Reliability vs. complexity.

Problems of Improving Reliability.

It might be well to amplify somewhat the question concerning the value of maintenance as part of the larger question of what can be done to improve reliability. For wear-out failures, there is a simple and obvious answer: preventive maintenance and replacement, by means of age-telling devices built into the equipment or by running-time logs of the equipment. For chance-failure equipment, the answer lies in making components more rugged and in moderating the equipment environment wherever possible. OEG is not yet in a position to make such recommendations for airborne electronic equipment because, while it has been shown that the equipment as a whole follows a chance-failure pattern, it has not yet been proved conclusively that the components themselves are failing in random fashion. It can be shown mathematically or seen intuitively that large aggregates of components of mixed ages, each of which fails at a definite or nearly definite age, would, in effect, have a constant hazard of failure. It is virtually impossible to distinguish wear-out component failure from random component failure on the basis of the reliability pattern of the equipment as a whole. Mortality data on individual components are required.

There are strong indications, however, that the component failures which have been observed in these radars were pure chance failures for two reasons. The first is the growing body of data supporting the results shown in Figure 2. The second is the very low average life-times which have been found for the components. The same vacuum tubes which had an average lifetime of 1400 hours in airborne radars lasted for periods of from 10,000 to 80,000 hours in more static applications, such as electronic computers and ground-based radars. The research group at OEG which is studying the problem is presently gathering data on component failures in the hope that the results will indicate a more effective use of maintenance procedures or will show that such procedures are unnecessary and can be altogether eliminated.

The feasibility of increasing the reliability of individual components in chance-failure systems is of great interest to guided missile designers, who are currently using this component reliability approach to their problems. The complex gadgetry which missiles involve requires individual component reliability approaching 100 per cent for relatively short intervals of time after launching. Designers now believe that there exists some upper limit of component reliability, as yet unknown, beyond which it would be futile to attempt improvement; therefore, with the components now available, there is a corresponding upper limit to missile complexity. Missile designers now hold as axiomatic that: (1) the money and time required to increase component reliability rises rapidly with the level of reliability being increased; and (2) the difficulty of increasing the reliability of a complex system is roughly proportional to the square of the number of components. This implies that any attempt to raise component reliability above the upper limit would reduce the capacity to produce such missiles because of the huge loss in sorting, testing, and examining the super-high reliability components and the added effort and care which their production would require.

Utilization of Negro
Manpower in the Army

ALFRED H. HAUSRATH

ONE OF THE most pressing problems confronting the nation today
is the efficient and effective utilization of its manpower resources.
A *significant* segment of this manpower is Negro, and cases being considered by the Supreme Court and other evidences reported in the press
indicate that new patterns are emerging in the recognition and use
of the nation's Negro manpower.

There is a developing tendency to regard integration of Negro
with white manpower as one possible solution of this problem. The Navy
and the Air Force are working toward this solution, and so is the Army
—for which the problem is substantially different and much more
acute. It became especially acute after the outbreak of the Korean
conflict.

An operations research study of this problem (as differentiated
from earlier studies based on the considered opinions of "experts")
was completed by the Operations Research Office for the Army in
November, 1951.[1] This paper deals with the portions of that study

---

[1] This study was conducted by a team of ORO staff members, including
Dr. S. G. Billingsley, Mr. L. V. Naisawald, Dr. J. F. McCloskey, Mrs. Florence
N. Trefethen, and Miss Florence K. Nierman, with the author as team leader.
The team's work was augmented by temporary assistance from other ORO staff
members; by consultants from universities and research foundations; and by
special sub-studies conducted on a contract basis by the American Institute

which may be released without violating security regulations. Omitted parts comprise those which deal with strengths and distribution of forces, specific details of military effectiveness and combat performance, and similar data. This brief account is presented here as an example of the results which can be achieved in operations research where applied to problems in the social sciences. Some of the findings may be of value in industry, public institutions, and municipal governments.

Historical Background.

Late in March, 1951, the Department of the Army requested ORO to study this problem. A preliminary report was submitted on July 1, and the final report on November 1, 1951. The preliminary report included an intensive study of troops in Korea, a demographic analysis of the Negro population and the Negro component of the Army, a review of previous Army experience and studies, and consideration of the pertinent literature in the field. All of the preliminary study supported the hypothesis that segregation constituted a basic detriment to full, efficient, and effective utilization of Negro manpower in the Army.

Official Army policy from the time of the Civil War onward was to assign Negro soldiers to Negro units, which might or might not have Negro officers. This policy was set, in part, by an act of the Reconstruction Congress which, in 1869, had legislated segregated Negro units in establishing four colored regiments in the Army. This legislation remained in effect until the eve of the Korean conflict, when the Army Reorganization Act of 1950 restored to the Army the freedom to determine the composition of all its units.

So far as Army policy was concerned apart from this legislation, many minor changes and exceptions were made in the late 1930's and especially during World War II. The most noteworthy exception was made after the Battle of the Bulge, when platoons of Negro infantry volunteers were assigned to depleted white infantry companies. The performance of these volunteers was highly rated by the white soldiers with whom they fought and had some bearing on the postwar Army decision to assign one Negro battalion to otherwise

for Research, the Bureau of Applied Social Research of Columbia University, and International Public Opinion Research, Inc.

white regiments. The basic principle of segregation prevailed, however, until just before the Korean incident.

Such changes and exceptions as were made prior to early 1950 may be explained largely in terms of the changing position of the Negro *as manpower* in the United States since World War I. Six factors account for most of this change:

1. The increased education and job skills of Negroes following their broadscale introduction into the Nation's industrial economy at the time of World War I.

2. Restrictive immigration legislation, the effect of which is shown in Table 1.

3. The low birth rate, especially in the early 1930's, when young men now of military age were born.

4. The drying up of rural areas as a source of surplus population because of the reduction in farm population following extensive mechanization.

5. The manpower requirements of the Armed Forces during and

TABLE 1

NET INCREASES IN THE POPULATION OF THE UNITED STATES SHOWING THE RELATIVE CONTRIBUTIONS OF IMMIGRATION AND OF THE NATURAL INCREASE OF THE NEGRO POPULATION 1860-1950

Period	Net Increase in U. S. Population (in thousands) (a)	Total Immigration (in thousands) (b)	Net Increase, Negro Population (in thousands) (c)	Percentage of U. S. Increase from: (b)	Percentage of U. S. Increase from: (c)	Negro Percentage of Total Population
1861-1870	7,115	2,324	438	32.7	6.2	12.7 (1870)
1871-1880	11,597·	2,815	1,701	24.3	14.7	13.1 (1880)
1881-1890	12,792	5,293	908	41.4	7.1	11.9 (1890)
1891-1900	13,047	3,784	1,345	29.0	10.3	11.6 (1900)
1901-1910	15,978	8,835	994	55.3	6.2	10.7 (1910)
1911-1920	13,738	5,767	635	41.2	4.6	9.9 (1920)
1921-1930	17,064	4,057	1,428	23.8	8.4	9.7 (1930)
1931-1940	8,894	528	974	6.0	11.0	9.8 (1940)
1941-1950	18,831	1,035	2,029	5.5	10.8	9.9 (1950)

after World War II (relative to their requirements between World Wars I and II).

6. The phenomenal growth of the American economy during and after World War II.

This combination of factors, tending to restrict available numbers at a time of increasing demand for manpower, was creating a situation over a 15-year period, the full effects of which were not seriously felt until Korea added its demands. For example, in 1940, the mobilization effort could be cushioned by nearly 6,000,000 unemployed; in 1950, that pool had shrunk to just over 2,000,000, and was soon to shrink to about half of that.

This situation affected the Army as one of the nation's large manpower users, and provided much of the impetus toward its request for the ORO study of utilization of Negro manpower as well as for the many other manpower studies which have been conducted by other agencies over the last few years.

Some of the impetus, however, came from another source. In 1948, the President issued two Executive Orders directing that there should be equality of opportunity and treatment, regardless of race, color, or creed, in the Executive Branch of the Government, and in the Armed Forces.

A special committee, appointed to study the effects of the Executive Order on the Armed Forces,[2] recommended that the Army eliminate its all-Negro units by removing quotas and assigning men to units in terms of qualification rather than race. The quota concept had developed in the late 1930's, and had been applied after World War II, by which time enlistment in the Army at large had replaced the old system of enlistment in a unit. Its application after World War II was deemed necessary because a disproportionate number of Negro veterans sought to remain in the Army—more than the all-Negro units could absorb.

The Army responded to the report of the President's Committee by removing its quota on enlistments and virtually assured drastic future changes in policy by designating no additional Negro units.

[2] The President's Committee on Equality of Treatment and Opportunity in the Armed Forces (Fahy Committee), *Freedom to Serve: Equality of Treatment and Opportunity in the Armed Forces* (Washington: U. S. Government Printing Office, 1950).

The results were not long in coming. The training divisions which were receiving new recruits soon met the problem of very high Negro enlistment rates (running in the vicinity of 25 per cent of the total immediately after the quota was removed) by assigning white and Negro soldiers to the same units, rather than attempting to train overstrength Negro companies alongside understrength white companies, or rather than have groups of one race or the other sitting around waiting for companies to fill.

Later, especially after the retreat from the Yalu in 1950, the scarcity of white replacements and a surplus of Negro replacements in Korea led to the assignment of some Negro soldiers to hitherto white combat units. It was at this point that the Operations Research Office was requested to make its study.

Methodology.

Several techniques of the social sciences were used in developing the data and conclusions which were submitted to the Army:

1. *Demographic Analysis*: An extensive analysis of the white and Negro populations of the U. S. was conducted by experienced demographers. Comparisons were made of the white and Negro rates of population growth, their changing regional distribution, the age structure, the role of birth and death rates as factors in population growth, the patterns of internal migration, the shifting urban and rural distribution, and the relative frequencies in the different occupational categories and income levels. From Selective Service data and World War II Army samples, comparisons were made of such factors as health and physical fitness, educational background, and general achievement of Negro and white males of military age and of those men eventually accepted for service.

2. *Opinion and Attitude Surveys.* Question schedules were designed and administered by the research staff in order to elicit from Army personnel their views on the utilization of Negro troops, on the performance of Negro soldiers, on race relations in the Army and in civilian life, and on troop morale. Open-ended interviews were also conducted with a number of the respondents.

Opinion and attitude responses were gathered from Negroes in all-Negro units, from whites and Negroes in integrated units, and from whites in all-white units. The respondents were drawn from training units, service units, combat units, and combat replacement pools; of the men in combat units, some were in combat at the time of the investigation, others were awaiting their first combat experience, and still others had been returned from combat to the United States. In this way, it was hoped to ascertain the variations in opinions and attitudes which accompanied different types of personal experience.

The responses on question schedules were coded, put on machine tabulation cards, and statistically analyzed. A combination of question schedules and open-ended interviews was used in three separate studies, one on utilization of Negro troops in the Far East Command, one on their utilization in the United States, and a third on the performance of Negro troops in Korea.

3. *Content Analysis.* As used here, content analysis refers, essentially, to identifying and shifting out the principal concepts from a number of written statements on a given topic. These concepts are then sorted, classified, and counted. In this way, diverse and unstructured statements of opinion or descriptions of events were brought together in a quasi-quantitative summary.

Content analysis also was used in the preliminary review of the literature and in connection with transcripts of the interviews referred to in the section on opinion and attitude surveys. News stories and editorial comments reporting the end of segregation in the Far East Command of the Army, drawn from a nationwide sample of newspapers, also were subjected to content analysis so that public readiness to accept integration, as reflected in press reaction to the announcement, might be summarized. Content analysis was further used in connection with behavior descriptions gathered by the "critical incidents" technique.

4. *The Critical Incidents Technique.* The "critical incidents" technique was employed in an attempt to penetrate beyond the opinions and attitudes of respondents into the more objective area of observed behavior. The method consists, essentially, in gathering from competent witnesses their detailed descriptions of actual behavior incidents in situations which met certain specified criteria. A "critical incident" is an eye-witness account of a specific action or behavior

which he recalls and describes as an example of a particular type of situation, such as an attack on a machine-gun emplacement. After critical incidents were obtained, the descriptions were sorted, subjected to content analysis, classified, and quantitatively summarized.

This technique was used in a variety of ways in studies of Negro combat performance conducted in Korea. In one of these studies, platoon leaders in integrated units wrote descriptions of effective and ineffective behavior demonstrated by advancing and withdrawing combat squads which they had personally observed. The research team, without the knowledge of the respondents, was seeking to discover whether the adjudged competence of a combat squad was related to its racial composition. After the squad-behavior incidents were collected, the racial composition of each squad described was ascertained. A second study called for platoon leaders to write descriptions of effective and ineffective behavior by individual soldiers in combat; and, similarly, the race of each soldier described was ascertained later.

An elaboration of the critical incidents technique was used for another study. Descriptions of certain prototype behaviors, both effective and ineffective, were given to members of combat-experienced rifle squads. These men were requested to indicate, on a prepared form, whether they had ever observed each type of behavior, and, if so, how frequently, in each of their fellow squad members whose names were listed. Later, the race of each man rated was ascertained in order to determine whether specific behaviors could be related to the race of squad members.

Finally, in a different study, the critical incidents technique was used as a tool for identifying those types of interracial behavior which operate to the benefit or detriment of good relationships between the military post in the United States and the surrounding civilian community. Respondents, both military and civilian, white and Negro, provided written descriptions of directly observed interracial incidents which they felt had operated for or against a harmonious relationship between the military and civilian communities.

5. *Statistical Analysis.* Throughout the studies, data were subjected to statistical analysis. Standard techniques were employed. Frequency comparisons were made in per cents; distributions were compared in terms of both central tendency and dispersion; and various indices of concomitant variation among measured variables

were employed, as well as tests of reliability and significance for the various findings.

In systematizing the data obtained from several attitude questions, one study team applied the Guttman scaling technique [3] in the following manner. Questions concerned with various aspects of integration were arranged in order of the hostile responses to each question. At one end of the scale was the question with the highest frequency of responses unfavorable to integration; at the other end of the scale was the question with the lowest. Guttman scales recognize the characteristic that a person who gives an unfavorable response to any given question is likely to give unfavorable responses to all of the questions higher on the scale. This makes it possible to " score " respondents in terms of the scale and to rank them according to their degree of favorableness. Further analysis can be simplified by the use of scale scores instead of responses to individual questions. The position of various questions in the scale has the added value of revealing information about the structure of attitudes in the population of respondents.

6. *Community Surveys.* In considering the design of the study on relationships between the military post and civilian community, the research staff selected Army installations in different parts of the country and adjacent to civilian communities where varying patterns of interracial contact were practiced. The study team made partial sociological surveys in such civilian communities for each of the selected installations. In each community, the following information was obtained: the racial structure, the nature of the economic activity, the housing situation, customary patterns of interracial behavior, and the political and legal status of the different races. Such data made it possible to compare the pattern of race relationships on the military post with that existing in the surrounding civilian climate.

Findings.

One basic factor which emerged in this study as in other considerations of the Negro soldier was the limitation in the educational and economic opportunities represented in his background, as compared with those represented in the background of the white soldier. An

[3] L. Guttman, " The Cornell Technique for Scale and Intensity Analysis," *Educational and Psychological Measurement*, Vol. 7 (1947), pp. 247-79.

example of this difference is shown by a comparison of the scores achieved on the Army General Classification Test of World War II.

Table 2 shows that, of every hundred Negroes in the Army, nearly twice as many fall into the two lower categories (Groups IV and V) than is the case with white soldiers. Consequently, under a policy of segregation, Negro soldiers are often assigned to units where the level of all-around military adaptability is low. In general, these units are of the service type—construction battalions, port battalions, truck companies, and the like. It is difficult to find among Negroes alone the needed distribution of adaptabilities and background trainings to

TABLE 2

PERCENTAGE DISTRIBUTION OF AGCT SCORES OF MEN IN THE ARMY, 1941-1950:

AGCT Group	Mar. 1941–May 1946 White	Mar. 1941–May 1946 Negro	Mar. 1940 White	Mar. 1940 Negro	June 1950* White	June 1950* Negro
I	6	0	4	0	4	1
II	29	3	27	7	27	8
III	33	13	36	31	40	31
IV	26	48	30	58	28	54
V	6	36	3	4	1	6

* Regular Army Enlisted Men Only.

make possible the formation of artillery units, where mathematics is useful; of tank units, where mechanical aptitudes are important; or of infantry units, where there may be a lesser need for certain special skills, but where adaptability to training and the ability to improvise in tight situations become important.

There are many individual Negro soldiers who have had opportunities commensurate with those of the best-qualified white soldiers. But because there are relatively few all-Negro units, and most of these units require rather limited skills, there is frequently no place under a policy of segregation in which to assign the most highly qualified Negro soldiers so that full advantage can be taken of their special talents. Moreover, there is available an insufficient group of leaders to assist in training and directing the operations of an all-

Negro unit. As a result, a longer period is required and the level at which such units—especially larger units—may be expected to perform is usually lower than in the case of comparable white units.

In the aggregate, the Army has many more poorly qualified white than Negro soldiers, but these soldiers are scattered throughout the Army, so that they are "lost" in the 90 per cent of the units to which white soldiers are assigned. On the other hand, with segregated units, the poorly qualified Negro soldiers are concentrated in the 10 per cent of the units to which they may be assigned. In other words, all-white units are not reduced in adaptability to any considerable extent when they receive proportionate numbers of Negro soldiers, but all-Negro

TABLE 3

MEDIAN APTITUDE TEST SCORES, BY RANK
(for lettered companies, —th Infantry Regiment; Aptitude Area I Test).

Rank	1st Battalion (all-white) Median Score	2nd Battalion (all-white) Median Score	3rd Battalion (all-Negro) Median Score	Combined Median Score
M/Sgt	99	105	89	100
SFC	99	91	80	93
Sgt	89	91	85	89
Cpl	89	96	86	89
PFC	90	102	76	90
Pvt	90	98	71	81

units undergo a remarkable improvement in adaptability when they receive a proportionate number of white soldiers. Table 3 illustrates this point.

There is a corollary to the unfortunate concentration of low-scoring personnel in all-Negro units. While the officers of a Negro unit have difficulty in finding men with sufficient background to qualify as noncommissioned officers the commanders of white units are likely to find their units relatively rich in higher-scoring men.

These considerations become important when a commander who has under him both white and Negro units is called upon to use them. He can expect a higher level of performance from the white than from the Negro units; accordingly, he is likely to depend more upon his white units. On the other hand, if he has only integrated units under him, he can expect comparable performance from all and will tend to use all, thus achieving greater efficiency and equitability in the handling of his men.

On the administrative side, the maintenance of segregated units, with special provisions for housing and messing, special provisions for entertainment, and special provisions for operating the replacement system, requires extra time and personnel. Elimination of segregation permits the use of a single system of assignment and a single system of housekeeping facilities, with savings that are substantial.

Considerations such as these led to the preliminary conclusion that the basic detriment to efficient utilization of Negro manpower in the Army was segregation.

When the study was directed to the question, "Is integration feasible?" the answer could be obtained from the Army's own experience. Integration was already a fact, prima facie demonstration of its feasibility. The effects of integration on military effectiveness and morale, however, were somewhat more difficult to determine. Here, reliance had to be placed on the degree of consistency found among all of the approaches employed in the study. The answer to the question "Is integration working?" was first sought in the opinion and attitude surveys.

Responses in these surveys, before analysis, tended to cover the spectrum of all possible answers, with no apparent significant groupings; but as soon as they were ordered in terms of the respondents' familiarity with integration, a nearly perfect scaling of the replies was achieved. Contrary to widely held belief, geographic distribution according to the home state of the respondent had little influence. Thus, when attitudes, considered opinions, and professional judgments were brought together, the replies tended to scale from most favorable to least favorable toward integration, as shown in Table 4.

Similarly, the hostile attitudes toward Negro soldiers expressed by white soldiers in various units showed a strong correlation with the amount of experience each unit had had with Negroes. For instance, when 11 units were listed in order of their experience with Negroes, the percentages of hostile attitudes toward Negroes within each group were in the order: 58 per cent (for the unit with least Negro experience), 46, 44, 40, 38, 33, 26, 25, 15, 23 and 14 (the lowest for the unit with most Negro experience). In short, those who had seen integration in action agreed that it worked; those who had no basis for judging were in general agreement that it would not work.

The same general results were obtained with more specific questions about the effects of integration on individual white and Negro soldiers and about the effects on unit performance. In general, those experienced with integration stated that the Negro soldier, whose perform-

TABLE 4

EFFECT OF WHITE OFFICERS' EXPERIENCE WITH INTEGRATION ON THEIR RATINGS OF NEGRO SOLDIERS ON SPECIFIC ASPECTS OF PERFORMANCE

Specific Military Task or Duty*	Per Cent of Officers Rating Negro Soldiers Equal to Whites		
	72 with No Experience	78 with Some Past Experience	105 Commanders of Integrated Units
A	29	58	67
B	49	83	90
C	31	57	81
D	35	53	73
E	42	52	67
F	32	47	72
G	29	42	69
H	35	67	85
I	42	62	82
J	39	54	79

* Task descriptions are classified; items A through J include such military tasks as cleaning weapons, prompt reporting, etc.

ance in all-Negro units was in general considered poor, became a good soldier in an integrated unit, and that no adverse effects on the performance of the hitherto all-white unit were detected.

Limitations.

The next step was to determine how best to go about integrating Negroes into white units. Here the demonstrated relationship between experience with and attitude toward integration became very useful, especially in answering the question, " Is there a limit which should be placed on the percentage of Negroes in any particular unit? "

The most objective type of evidence, obtained by the critical incidents technique and shown in Table 5, indicated no correlation between Negro percentage in a squad and unit performance. In Korea, where much of the measurement of unit efficiency was conducted, examples of integrated units in excess of 15 or 20 per cent Negro were rare. There were sufficient numbers of such units operating, however, to suggest that the 10 per cent figure usually cited by experienced officers as the limit for integration was an overly cautious limit, probably carried over from the old quota-system pattern of thinking. Opinions of officers experienced with integrated units are summarized in Table 6.

TABLE 5

NUMBER OF EFFECTIVE AND INEFFECTIVE CRITICAL INCIDENTS
GROUPED BY RACIAL COMPOSITION OF SQUADS

	No. of Negroes in Squad			
	1	2	3	4
Effective in Advance	15	13	7	2
Ineffective in Advance	19	16	7	2
Effective in Withdrawal	21	5	6	2
Ineffective in Withdrawal	15	11	4	1

Any limitation on the level becomes important in effecting integration; e. g., if 10 per cent had been proved to be the maximum tolerable, complete integration would have been impractical inasmuch as the Negro percentage of Army strength was already in excess of 10 per cent. The demonstration that integration was working at levels in the vicinity of 20 per cent removed this obstacle, and the 20 per cent figure was used as the working basis in effecting integration in the U. S. Army in Europe when it was undertaken in 1952.

The question of how rapidly integration should be effected was also studied. Integration, and especially the breaking up of Negro units, involves some loss of unit time while individuals are being reshuffled and the newly constituted units are being trained to acceptable levels of unit performance. Thus a sudden program of integration throughout the Army could seriously reduce the Army's state of readiness. On the other hand, if integration were held up until the next crisis, it would be too late to put it into effect. Accordingly, the practical recommendation was to use every opportunity to move toward complete integration—toward greater efficiency in utilization of manpower—in as short a time as feasible.

Another reason loomed to support the recommendation for a

TABLE 6

PERCENTAGE OF OFFICERS AND NONCOMMISSIONED OFFICERS[a]
RECOMMENDING VARIOUS LEVELS OF INTEGRATION

Recommended No. of Negroes per Squad (9 Men)	105 Commanders of Integrated Units in Korea [b]	78 Officers with some past experience in Korea [c]	123 NCO's in Integrated Units in Korea [d]
1 Negro	14%	32%	11%
2 Negroes	48	33	36
3 Negroes	28	14	19
4 or more Negroes	6	9	18
"It makes no difference	4	4	10
No response	0	8	6

[a] All O's and NCO's had had experience in command of integrated units in combat in Korea.

[b] Officers currently in command in Korea.

[c] Officers in earlier command in Korea but now returned to the U.S. interviewed in the U.S.

[d] NCO's currently squad leaders in Korea.

gradual rather than a sudden integration. The factors that favored integration first in training divisions, later in combat units in Korea, and still later in units in Western Germany, do not all apply with equal force to units in garrison in the United States.

For, to a considerable extent in the States, no sharp line can be drawn between the professional or working life of the soldier, on the one hand, and his social life on the other. This truism was supported when the responses to opinion and attitude studies were scaled according to remoteness from combat. The consistent agreement that integration works at the front lines begins to diminish in questions regarding rear areas, and still further doubts arise when garrison situations in the United States are considered. Though no color line may exist among soldiers in foxholes, it may be an important factor at a social function involving civilians in an activity on or near an Army post in the States.

Myrdal pointed out, in *An American Dilemma,*[4] that underlying fears of miscegenation explain much of the white Americans' attitude toward interracial association. Supporting this conclusion, the attitudes expressed by the respondents in this study can be related, not only on the " remoteness from the front lines " scale, but also on the " proximity to the opposite sex " scale as applied by Myrdal, with allowance for the difference between U. S. social and cultural patterns as a whole and those found in the Army.

In this respect, local differences become important, largely because of interaction between military posts and the communities near which they are located. It is these considerations that show the difficulties of Army-wide integration.

Thus, ruling out those parts of daily life to which equal access has been established and those which have no direct relationship to Army operations, the study showed that difficulty in achieving acceptance of complete integration rises as one moves from one step to the next in each of the following social meeting grounds:

1. Post buses
2. PX shopping facilities
3. Post theaters
4. Athletic areas, except swimming pools
5. Service clubs
6. NCO messes, officers' messes, snack bars
7. Housing areas
8. Post schools
9. Swimming pools
10. Dance halls

This list reflects an attitude on the part of the soldier that he can accept interracial contact for himself, but does not want to be in a position of forcing such contact on his family. Obviously, too, these attitudes are a fairly realistic gauge of the persistence and difficulty of overcoming existing patterns of segregation in the United States—patterns which are by no means peculiar to the Army or to any one geographical area.

4 Gunnar Myrdal, et al., *An American Dilemma: The Negro Problem and Modern Democracy* (2 vols.; New York: Harper and Bros., 1944).

The scale of increasing difficulty in accepting integration at the social meeting grounds listed above provides a guide to commanders responsible for effecting integration. It serves to indicate the order in which they may proceed to build up the understanding, the cöoperation, and the familiarity with integration which is essential to its successful operation anywhere.

On July 26, 1951, newspapers carried the announcement of the discontinuance of the all-Negro 24th Infantry Regiment in Korea, and the ordering of complete integration as Army policy in the Far East Command as a measure to increase the efficiency of the Army. The news play and editorial comment on this news release was studied as a mirror of public reaction, and an indication of public readiness for an Army-wide policy of integration. A standard, national sample of 200 newspapers was analyzed. News and editorial comments were reported in an unemotional, matter-of-fact manner. These reports were generally favorable and free from adverse comment, save for one noteworthy exception, the Communist newspaper, *The Daily Worker*.

Conclusions.

In summary, this study provided policy-makers in the U. S. Army with objective evidence in support of integrated units of Negro and white soldiers. This evidence indicated: first, that integrated units allow more effective use of the manpower available through a more even distribution of aptitudes than is possible in segregated units; second, that performance of integrated units is satisfactory; and, third, that the resistance to integration is greatly reduced as experience is gained. The limit, if any, on the level of integration was shown to be above 20 per cent Negroes, and difficulties in extending integration to all parts of the Army were identified and arranged in a sequential order so that a program leading to Army-wide integration could be formulated.

Operations Research
in Agriculture

CHARLES WARREN THORNTHWAITE

S EABROOK FARMS is a giant farming enterprise in southern New Jersey. It is a completely integrated industry; vegetables are raised, processed, quick-frozen and stored at the Farms and, from there, are distributed to points along the eastern seaboard. The Seabrook Farms, trucks are constantly traveling between the warehouse and such places as Boston, New York, Philadelphia, Washington, Richmond, Charlotte, Miami, and other eastern cities, carrying millions of packages of frozen vegetables to local dealers. From the time the vegetable is planted nearly to the time that it is carried to the dinner table, Seabrook Farms controls all aspects of the operation. This large undertaking, including many links of activity, provides excellent opportunities for operations research.

Harvest Problems.

Eight years ago, I went to Seabrook Farms from the United States Department of Agriculture. I was engaged as a climatologist to advise on supplemental irrigation.[1] Upon my arrival at the Farms, however,

---

[1] Popular articles relating to Dr. Thornthwaite's work in agriculture include: "Invisible Drought," *Newsweek* (August 8, 1949); "Bottomless Forest?" *Newsweek* (November 6, 1950); "Science at Seabrook," *The Johns Hopkins Magazine* (October, 1951); "Don't Plant in the Dark of the Moon; Use the 'Climate Calendar' Instead," *Pathfinder* (February 6, 1952); "He Threw the Almanac Into the Ash Can," *News for the Seabrook Distributor* (June, 1952); "Seabrook Peas Outsmart Science—Featured Item for Septem-

I discovered that other problems involving weather and climate were much more urgent than the irrigation problem. It was late in May, 1946, and the men at Seabrook Farms were preparing for the pea harvest. There were, in that year, seven thousand acres of peas; these had been planted during the period from early March through the first part of April and all were approaching maturity late in May. The problem was to get these peas out of the fields and into the plant at the stage when they were just ready for freezing.

Seabrook Farms is divided into eleven geographical areas called divisions. Each of the eleven is more or less self-sufficient, with its own manager, headquarters, labor force, machinery pool, etc. As the zero hour for harvesting drew near, tension mounted among the personnel. Each division manager began deploying his harvest machinery, moving it to the edge of that field in his division which he though would first be ready for the harvest. Each of the division managers was harassed by the same question: When would the har-

ber," *News for the Seabrook Distributor* (September, 1952); "A Jungle Grows in Jersey," *The Johns Hopkins Magazine* (November, 1952); "Slide Rule Irrigation," *County Agent and Vo-Ag Teacher* (April, 1953); "Why Grow a Jungle in Jersey?" *Collier's* (May 2, 1953), "Klima-Kalender und Pflanzenwachstum," Die Umschau (No. 14, 1953).

Pertinent articles on agricultural climatology by Dr. Thornthwaite include: "El Agua en la Agricultura," *Irrigacion en Mexico* (Abril-Mayo-Junio, 1946); "Climate and Moisture Conservation," *Annals of the Association of American Geographers* (June, 1947); "Agricultural Climatology at Seabrook Farms," *Weatherwise* (April, 1951); "The Water Balance in Tropical Climates," *Bulletin of the American Meteorological Society* (May, 1951); "Climate in Relation to Planting and Irrigation of Vegetable Crops," prepared for presentation at the Seventeenth International Congress, Section of Climatology, Washington (August 8th to 15th, 1952); "Temperature Relations to Time of Maturity of Vegetable Crops," prepared for presentation at the 78th Annual Meeting of the New Jersey State Horticultural Society (December, 1952); "Operations Research in Agriculture," *Journal of the Operations Research Society of America*, Vol. I, No. 2 (February, 1953); "Climate and Scientific Irrigation in New Jersey" and "The Place of Supplemental Irrigation in Postwar Planning," *Publications in Climatology*, The Johns Hopkins University Laboratory of Climatology, 1953; "A Charter for Climatology," *WMO* (World Meteorological Organization) *Bulletin* (April, 1953); "Topoclimatology," prepared for presentation at the Toronto Meteorological Conference (September 15, 1953); "I Believe," *Country Gentleman* (January, 1954).

vest start? In what order would the fields be harvested? How could the work force keep up with the rate of the maturing of the crop?

In the course of the harvest season, they expended considerable effort in attempts to meet these problems. First, they needed to have some method for predicting when a field would be ready to harvest. Their means for determining the stage of crop maturity were rather primitive. For example, a field man would shell out some peas by hand and squeeze them to see if they felt " right "; or he would toss them up and let them drop on the hood of an automobile, listening to see how they rattled. Usually, however, the question of whether or not the crop was ready was more or less academic; the harvest would typically begin a little early, so that the work could get off to a good start, and would not end before some of the peas had already grown to overripeness.

When the peas began to mature at a rapid rate, the division managers tried to speed up the rate of harvest. If they were not able to keep pace by working twelve hours a day, they were prepared to work twenty-four, with double work crews spelling each other around the clock, and with giant floodlights illuminating the fields by night. Even this stepped-up activity, however, did not make it possible to harvest all the peas at the optimum time. During the harvest, there would be a period when the peas were just right: those harvested a little early were too young; and those which formed the backlog were too old.

The rapid harvesting itself introduced some additional problems. Peas tended to pile up at the factory, and the freezer capacity was overtaxed, with the result that many of the good peas had to be canned rather than frozen. Since canned peas are not so profitable as frozen peas, this represented an economic loss to the Farms. Still other peas were canned because they were not good enough for freezing; they had not been harvested and processed at the proper time. They too entailed economic loss, since it costs as much to can substandard as good peas, although those of poorer quality cannot be sold for a price high enough to pay the canning costs. One solution would be to throw away the substandards, but even disposal costs money. The best solution is to avoid having substandard peas altogether.

In short, the problem for which I was summoned to Seabrook

Farms was not that enterprise's most real and pressing problem. Though I was there to advise on supplemental irrigation with a view to increasing land yield, I soon observed that the current yield, at least in peas, was already overtaxing the work forces, the processing plant, and the freezer facilities. Clearly, the first problem was one of relieving, in some way, the harvest season's pressure.

Development of the Climatic Calendar.

Fortunately, the Seabrook Farms organization had some excellent records of planting and harvesting from past years and these provided valuable data to be used in reaching a solution. According to the seed catalogues, the Alaska variety of pea matures in fifty-seven days from planting to harvesting. I discovered, however, that in the year of my arrival, Alaska peas had been planted on March 4th and were ready for harvest on May 31, after an eighty-eight day interval. On July 15 of that year, I planted some Alaska peas, to the amusement of my friends. "You should know," they reminded me, "that you can't raise peas in the summer time." As a matter of fact, however, those peas were ready to harvest on August 25, after a lapse of only thirty-nine days.

This suggested something that farmers have always known in a general way, namely that, in the summer, things grow faster than in the spring or autumn because summer temperatures are higher. The rate of a plant's development is slow in the early spring, increases to a maximum in the middle of the summer, and drops off again to a minimum in the late autumn. Soon we had an experimental garden with a whole sequence of plantings at short intervals, from March 1 right on through the year. This made possible the measurement of the numbers of days required from planting to harvest throughout the growing season. In accordance with expectations, the rate of development was slow in the early spring, increased toward a mid-summer peak, and then began to decline.

The problems at Seabrook Farms indicated the need for a means for relating the rate of development with some climatic factor such as temperature, something independent of the plant which could be measured and which would provide a running indication of the stage of development and would signal the approach of full maturity. In short, the Farms needed a table which would indicate the probable harvest date for a crop of any given planting date. Actually, the usefulness of such a table lay mostly in the fact that it would make readings in the opposite direction possible; the intense pressures of harvest time could be drastically alleviated if it were possible to choose the dates when various fields should be harvested and then determine the appropriate planting dates for meeting this even schedule. In order to achieve such a table, the civil calendar was converted into a climatic calendar.

The pea plant seemed admirably designed for initial work toward this end, since it grows from a single growing point, extends upward and forms a node, extends farther upward and forms a second node, and so on through the course of its development. The plant, of course, grows from node to node more rapidly during the summer than in early spring or autumn. The growth curve for the pea plant has been well established. The nodes, which are the points where leaves eventually develop, are readily discernible; it is a simple matter to observe when a pea plant is six or seven or eight nodes high. The formation of each node indicates that a definite stage in the plant's development has been reached, and development within the space of a single day can be recognized and accurately recorded. For convenience, the interval between any two nodes can be regarded as encompassing one hundred growth units.

Although the number of calendar days required for the Alaska pea to reach maturity plainly depended on the time of planting, simple observation established the fact that optimum harvesting time was reached when the plant was 16.8 nodes old; when multiplied by the one hundred growth units encompassed in each internodal interval, this gave the Alaska pea a growth index of 1680. Calendar days might vary with the vagaries of season and temperature, but the growth index remained constant.

When the rate of node development expressed in growth units was extended through the year, it was found that, for the Seabrook Farms' area, the year comprised 7,500 such units. The number of accumulated annual growth units is, of course, a function of climatic factors. In northern Maine, there are only 4,500 growth units a year and, in Pensacola, there are 12,000. The Seabrook Farms annual quantity of growth units, 7,500, could then be divided among the calendar months. January and February are very "short" growing months; March is somewhat "longer"; April, May, June and July are increasingly "longer," since increasing numbers of growth units accumulate during these warmer months; after July, the months begin to "shorten" again. Stated another way, growth units accumulate at a rate of about ten a day at the end of March, thirty a day in the middle of May, and reach a peak of fifty-three a day on July 23; the rate falls to

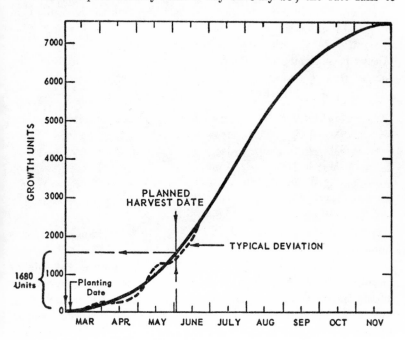

Figure 1. The growth curve at Seabrook, New Jersey.

forty a day on September 1, twenty-five a day on October 1, and six a day on November 6. The civil calendar of days, weeks and months can, thus, be converted into a climatic calendar. Expressed graphically, this relationship takes the form of a stretched-out S-shaped curve as in Figure 1. Any calendar span of time can be expressed in terms of growth units accumulating within that span; any calendar date can be designated in terms of the accumulation of growth units from the beginning of the calendar year to that date.

Again, the Alaska type pea can be used for simple illustration. The growth index for Alaska peas is 1680. If, by March 4, one hundred growth units have accumulated since the beginning of the calendar year, peas planted on March 4 will be ready for harvest when the year is 1780 growth units old on the climatic calendar. The approximate harvest date on the civil calendar can thus be calculated for peas planted on any calendar date; it is only necessary to add the growth index of the planting to 1680, then refer to the year's growth unit curve to check the date by which the resulting sum of growth units is likely to be accumulated. The following table illustrates the varying intervals between planting and harvesting for Alaska peas planted at different dates. Were there a fourth column labeled *Growth Units of Crop at Maturity*, the reading would be the same for every case, 1680.

Planting Date	Harvest Date	Days to Maturity
March 1	June 5	96
March 15	June 7	84
March 31	June 10	71
April 15	June 15	61
April 30	June 20	51
May 15	June 28	44
May 31	July 7	37
June 15	July 19	34

How could these facts be used in establishing a schedule at Seabrook Farms? One of the first steps would be to study the capacity of the factory to process peas. One might assume, for example, that the factory could process one million pounds a day. Next, it would be necessary to estimate the yield per acre in order to determine how many acres would have to be harvested to produce the one million pounds a day needed to keep the processing plant steadily busy at its maximum capacity. Then, it would be necessary to check on how many acres of peas a viner unit could harvest in one day; it so happens that a unit can, under ordinary conditions, harvest two and a half acres. A six-viner unit division, therefore, would be able to harvest fifteen acres a day, providing the vines were not too big. Whether or not the vines will prove to be too big cannot be predicted well in advance; this remains one of the chance elements in the planning system. The capacity of the processing plant, the yield per acre, and the capability of harvesting machinery must all, however, be introduced as factors in the overall plan.

Once these factors have been studied, a harvest program can be developed. One can assume, initially, that a decision has been made to begin the pea harvest on June 5, on which date a fifteen-acre field should be ready. The second fifteen-acre field should be ready on June 6 and a third on June 7, and so on through the schedule. It is advisable, when mapping out the harvesting schedule, to introduce an occasional holiday; this will give the plan sufficient flexibility to allow for contingencies. The harvest dates which are determined are tentative and are set down as calendar dates simply because of the long-established habit of thinking in terms of the civil calendar. Actually, the climatic calendar is of greater significance and is used exclusively in the laboratory, where the daily accumulation of growth units is closely watched by means of a complex of temperature readings. The first field will, in fact, be harvested when the growth index reaches 1780, whether this falls on June 5 or not. The second field will be harvested forty growth units later, the average climatological equivalent of a calendar day in early June, or when the growth index reaches 1820.

Once the schedule is drawn up in terms of growth indices for the harvesting times of successive fields, the planting dates can be readily determined. Thus the planting date for the first field will be the day on which the growth index has reached 100, for the second field, the day it has reached 140, and so on through the planting season. The first and second fields of Alaska peas will be harvested 40 growth units apart and, most probably, on successive days. They will, therefore, be planted 40 growth units apart. Growth units in early March, however, advance much more slowly, so that the two fields will be planted something like five days apart. All the peas planted at Seabrook Farms are not, of course, of the Alaska type, and the many varieties have different growth unit requirements. Among peas, there are the express and the freight-train types.

The planting season can be shortened if fast-growing and slow-growing varieties are planted at the same time, the slower growing ones for later harvest. A good arrangement would be, for example, to plant, on the same day in March, a field of Alaskas, a field of Glaciers, a field of Thomas Laxtons, and a field of Shastas. The growth index for Glaciers is 1720, just 40 growth units more than for Alaskas. Therefore, if the two are planted on the same day early in the season, it is likely that they will be ready for harvest on successive days in June. The growth index for Thomas Laxtons is 1790; if they are planted on the same day as the others, they will probably be ready to harvest two days following the Alaska harvest. The Shastas have a growth index of 2100, which places them quite late in the harvest schedule. Once the Shastas are planted, therefore, there are gaps in the harvest schedule which should be filled in. Considerable crisscross referencing from planting to harvesting and from harvesting to planting schedules is needed before the entire program falls into shape. And, unless it is well worked out, there is likely to be trouble at harvest time.

The Climatic Calendar in Action.

This, then, was the tentative solution which we prepared for solving the problems of when to harvest peas, which fields would first be ready for harvest, and how to keep the harvesting and processing in step with the maturation rate of the peas. The scheme was put into operation for the first time in 1947 on a very small scale. Mr. Seabrook called for volunteers among the division managers and received a favorable response from one. Since this was regarded as too small a test sample, two other division managers were specifically asked to cooperate; one willingly agreed and the other consented unwillingly. Their three divisions provided a fairly good experimental test group. The experiment was successful and has since been incorporated into the routine operation of Seabrook Farms.

There was ample opportunity, in that very first experimental year, to demonstrate the system's built-in flexibility. The schedule prepared in February of 1947 called for a first planting on March 20. The field was too muddy, however, on that date. The division manager started, therefore, to plant on the 21st. He got five acres in and then gave up because of heavy mud. The first planting wasn't finally completed until March 26. The dates of the planting schedule were altered and adjusted to allow for this delay and for other emergent weather peculiarities; the growth index for maturation, however, was fixed and it alone signaled the time when harvest was to begin. The only uncertainties for which allowance cannot be made in advance are those during the harvest season itself. Naturally, when a hot spell occurs during the harvest, the maturation rate of the crop will accelerate beyond the fifteen-acre-a-day rate, and the workers will be called upon to work harder during that period. Conversely, should a cool spell set in, the fields will reach maturity more slowly than planned, and the work can slacken accordingly. If rain should interfere with the harvest on a scheduled working day, one of the holidays can be substituted and the originally scheduled holiday can be redesignated as a working day.

The system, from the very start, clearly demonstrated that the peas could be gotten into the ground at the proper time and harvested at the proper time. It also resulted in cutting the labor force, in that night crews were no longer needed. In 1948, all divisions used such a schedule for peas. The results were extremely gratifying. The improvement in quality of the peas reaching the processing plant coincided with another innovation at Seabrook Farms. In 1949, after several years of development in the Engineering Department, electric-eye sorters were installed in the processing plant to pick out the off-color peas which had become pale and yellow. Ironically, since the fields were, by that time, being harvested at just the right stage of development, there were almost no off-color peas; what little sorting was necessary could be accomplished at other stages of the processing. The usefulness of the sorters for their intended purpose, therefore, was negligible. Fortunately, however, it was possible to adapt them to the sorting of lima beans, a vegetable in which it is normal for light and dark green beans to inhabit the same pod.

Sweet corn, snap beans, lima beans, and spinach have now been fitted into the master scheme. The growth of spinach can be described in terms of the growth of peas, the yardstick of the climatic calendar. Similarly, the nodes on a pea vine are an adequate, in fact a good means for describing the rate of development of sweet corn or lima beans. In the master plan, therefore, it can be arranged that, on the day following the end of the pea harvest, a field of snap beans will be ready for harvesting; that, on the day after the snap beans have all been gathered, the first field of corn will be ready, and so on through the crop year.

The data necessary for such scheduling have all been reduced to a simple slide rule which translates the civil calendar into a climatic calendar. A portion of this rule is illustrated in Figure 2.

On the upper scale of the slide rule, the days of the months are

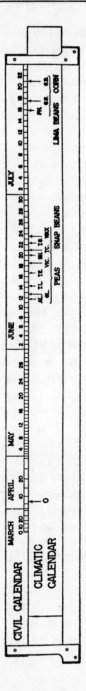

Figure 2. The climatic calendar.

plotted according to their climatic value. As the drawing illustrates, April is a very short month compared to June, although they are of equal length on the civil calendar. The first thirteen days of July are just as long on the climatic calendar as the months of March and April combined. On the sliding scale, the various crops raised at Seabrook Farms are plotted. The original working slide rule covers the entire growing season and gives indications for many other vegetable crops, including several varieties of potatoes and tomatoes, along with such fruits as apples, cherries and peaches. For greater working convenience, the slide rule has been reduced to a pocket-size dial chart which is, in effect, a circular slide rule. In half a minute, even an inexperienced person can set a pointer on the date he wishes to harvest a specific crop, and then read opposite a second pointer the planting date necessary to produce the harvest at the required time and with the required accumulation of growth units for the best quality.[2]

The usefulness of this slide rule can, perhaps, best be illustrated by a rather special example. If a farmer in southern New Jersey were planning to exhibit a variety of vegetables at the State Fair on September 15, he would need to know when to plant each variety so that it would be ready on time and so that each type of vegetable would have reached the proper stage of development to make a good showing. The slide rule would make it possible, within a few minutes, for him to set down the following planting schedule:

Golden cross bantam sweet corn	June 26
Fordhook lima beans	July 1
Detroit dark red beets	July 17
Brittle wax beans	July 25
Bountiful flat green beans	July 28
Victory freezer peas	July 29
Thomas Laxton peas	Aug. 2
Alaska peas	Aug. 4
Old Dominion spinach	Aug. 8

The year 1950 was the first in which everything at Seabrook Farms

[2] A circular slide rule having climatic calendars for all parts of the United States, and a manual containing growth indices for over 1,200 varieties of vegetables and flowers, may be obtained from C .W. Thornthwaite Associates, Seabrook, N. J.

was planted on the climatic instead of the civil calendar. Except for payroll purposes, the civil calendar has been largely abandoned. The system, however, cannot be considered as complete and firmly fixed. The relationship between climate and crops is full of complexities, and new data will undoubtedly produce modifications. The Farms has, at least, achieved a tentative solution which is currently yielding satisfactory results.

The master control will be developed as new charts build up year by year. Meanwhile, harvesting runs more smoothly. There may be all sorts of irregularities in the period between planting and harvesting. Unseasonably cool weather in April may slow the accumulation of growth units. This may be offset by a hotter than usual spell in May. By June, the line of accumulation may again have deviated from the mean condition. Formerly, the division manager would have relied on empirical tests and the hunches which accompany a " green thumb " to guide him through the weather's capriciousness. Now, however, whenever the accumulation of growth units reaches its proper point, he begins his harvest, confident that he is gathering in his crop at its best time.

Bibliography

Selected Bibliography

VERA RILEY

I. History and Methodology.

Abrams, John W., "Operational Research." *The Business Quarterly*, University of Western Ontario, Summer 1952, pp. 104-16.

Ackoff, Russell L., "Some New Statistical Techniques Applicable to Operations Research." *Journal of the Operations Research Society of America*, November 1952, pp. 10-17.

"American Committee on Operations Research." *Operational Research Quarterly*, September 1950, p. 43.

Batchelor, James H., *Operations Research—A Preliminary Annotated Bibliography*. Cleveland, Case Institute of Technology, 1952.

Blackett, P. M. S., "Obituary of Professor E. J. Williams." *Nature*, 1 December 1945, pp. 655-56.

———, "Operational Research." *The Advancement of Science*, April 1948, pp. 26-38.

———, "Operational Research." *Operational Research Quarterly*, March 1950, pp. 3-6.

British Association, "Operational Research in War and Peace." *The Advancement of Science*, February 1948, pp. 320-32; *Nature*, 15 November 1947, pp. 660-62.

Brown, Robert Goodell, "A Proposed Definition of Operations Research." *Operational Research Quarterly*, June 1951, pp. 21-24.

Case Institute of Technology, *Proceedings of the First Seminar in Operations Research Held 8-10 November 1951*. Cleveland, Case Institute of Technology, 1951.

Eddison, Roger T., "Social Applications of Operational Research." *Impact of Science on Society*, Summer 1953, pp. 61-82.

Goldsmith, Maurice, " What is Operational Research? " *Discovery*, January 1948, pp. 11-14.

———— and Roy Innes, " Operational Research." *Pilot Papers*, December 1947, pp. 8-21.

Goodeve, Sir Charles F., " Operational Research." *Nature*, 13 March 1948, pp. 377-84.

————, " Operational Research as a Science." *Journal of the Operations Research Society of America*, August 1953, pp. 166-80.

————, " Commentary: Operational Research." *Research*, 8 May 1948, p. 10.

———— and G. R. Ridley, " A Survey of O. R. in Great Britain." *Operational Research Quarterly*, June 1953, pp. 21-24.

Great Britain, The Working Party of the Committee on Industrial Productivity, Office of the Lord President of the Council. *The Principles and Practices of Operational Research*. 21 July 1948.

Hare, Van Court, Jr., " The Meaning of Operations Research." *The Journal of Industrial Engineering*, September 1954, p. 9 *et seq.*

Hedley, K. J., " Operational Research." *The Australasian Insurance and Banking Record*, 21 June 1950.

Hertz, David B., and Albert H. Rubenstein, editors, *Research Operations in Industry*. New York, King's Crown Press, 1953.

Hindle, Edward, " Zoologists in War and Peace." *Advancement of Science*, September 1948, pp. 179-86.

Hinrichs, Gerard, " Toward a Philosophy of Operations Research." *Philosophy of Science*, January 1953, pp. 59-66.

Hitch, Charles, " Sub-optimization in Operations Problems." *Journal of the Operations Research Society of America*, May 1953, pp. 87-99.

Horvath, William J., " Operations Research, a Scientific Basis for Executive Decisions." *The American Statistician*, October 1948, pp. 6-8.

Hurni, M. L., " Observations on Operations Research." *Journal of the Operations Research Society of America*, August 1954, pp. 234-48.

Johnson, Ellis A., " A Survey of Operations Research in the U. S. A." *Operational Research Quarterly*, June 1953, pp. 43-48.

Journal of the Operations Research Society of America. Published quarterly by the Operations Research Society of America (first issue, November 1952).

King, Gilbert W., " The Monte Carlo Method as a Natural Mode of Expression in Operations Research." *Journal of the Operations Research Society of America*, February 1953, pp. 46-51.

Kittel, Charles, " The Nature and Development of Operations Research." *Science*, 7 February 1947, pp. 150-53.

Knayer, Manfred, " Die Ablauf- und Planungsforschung " (Operational and Planning Research). *Rationalisierung*, October 1953, pp. 273-76.

Koopman, Bernard O., " New Mathematical Methods in Operations Research." *Journal of the Operations Research Society of America*, November 1952, pp. 3-9.

Lamm, Earl S., " Operations Research—Statistical Science Applied to Engineering." *Machine Design*, March 1952, pp. 102-07.

Levinson, Horace C., and Arthur A. Brown, " Operations Research." *Scientific American*, March 1951, pp. 15-17.

Marshall, A. W., " A Mathematical Note on Sub-optimization." *Journal of the Operations Research Society of America*, May 1953, pp. 100-02.

Massachusetts Institute of Technology, *Notes from MIT Summer Course on Operations Research, 16 June-3 July 1953*. Cambridge, Technology Press, 1953.

Meldin, Morley, " Operations Research—A Sharper Tool for Your Tougher Problems." *Factory Management and Maintenance*, October 1953, pp. 113-20, 238-44.

Menzler, F. A. A., " Operational Research: An Aid to Efficiency." *British Transport Review*, April 1953, pp. 263-83.

———, " Statistical Methods and Operational Research in Transport." *The Engineer*, 28 November 1952, pp. 737-40.

Morse, Philip M., " Mathematical Problems in Operations Research." *Bulletin of the American Mathematical Society*, July 1948, pp. 602-21.

——— and George E. Kimball, *Methods of Operations Research*. New York, John Wiley & Sons, Inc., 1951.

———, " Must We Always Be Gadgeteers? " *Physics Today*, December 1950, pp. 4-5.

———, " Of Men and Machines." *The Technology Review*, November 1946, p. 29 *et seq.*

———, " Operations Research." *The Technology Review*, February 1951, p. 191 *et seq.*

———, " Operations Research—An Application of Scientific Method." *The Technology Review*, May 1953, p. 367 *et seq.*

———, " The Operations Research Society of America." *Journal of the Operations Research Society of America*, November 1952, pp. 1-2.

———, " Operations Research—What Is It? " *Journal of Applied Physics*, February 1952, pp. 165-72.

———, " Trends in Operations Research." *Journal of the Operations Research Society of America*, August 1953, pp. 159-65.

" Operational Research." *The Economist*, 15 August 1953, pp. 465-67.

" Operational Research." *Scope, Magazine for Industry*, September 1948, p. 48 *et seq.*

Operational Research Quarterly. Published quarterly by the Operational Research Club, London (first issue, March 1950).

" OR : Weapon for Peace." *The Johns Hopkins Magazine,* October 1952.

" Peacetime Implications of Operations Research." *The American Statistician,* December 1948, pp. 1-17.

" Plan for Planners." *Chemical Week,* 25 April 1953, p. 32.

Rahman, A., and S. Husain Zaheer, " An Indian View." *Operational Research Quarterly,* December 1952, pp. 57-59.

Rios, Sixto, " Nuevas Aplicaciones de la Estadistica: La Investigacion Operacional." *Trabajos de Estadistica,* 1952, pp. 255-72.

Roy, Robert H., " Operations Research and Industrial Engineering: Contrast and Resemblance." *The Scientific Monthly,* September 1953, pp. 161-62.

Salzmann, C., " La Recherche Opérationnelle. (Introduction à Son Application Industrielle)." *Revue de Statistique Appliquée,* Université de Paris, 1954, pp. 57-68.

Sargeunt, H. A., " Operational Research Scientists." *Operational Research Quarterly,* June 1951, pp. 25-31.

Shainin, Dorian, " Quality Control Methods. Part 10—Operations Research." *Machine Design,* May 1953, pp. 176-80.

Smith, Nicholas M., Jr., Stanley S. Walters, Franklin C. Brooks, and David H. Blackwell, " The Theory of Value and the Science of Decision." *Journal of the Operations Research Society of America,* May 1953, pp. 103-13.

Society for the Advancement of Management, *Operations Research: Proceedings of the Society for the Advancement of Management Conference, January, 1954.* New York, The Society, 1954.

Solow, Herbert, " Operations Research." *Fortune,* April 1951, p. 105 *et seq.*

" Supply and Demand." *Operational Research Quarterly,* June 1951, pp. 37-38.

Swan, A. W., " Post-War Developments in Operational Research." *The Engineer,* 21 December 1951, pp. 812-814.

Tippett, Leonard Henry Caleb, " Operational Research." *Transactions of the British Ceramic Society,* 18 January 1949, pp. 153-60.

U. S. Department of the Navy, *Decennial Conference on Operations Research.* Washington, Office of Naval Research, 1953.

University of Illinois. *Proceedings of the Conference on Operations Research Held at the University of Illinois, 27 September 1951.* Washington, D. C., Committee on Operations Research, National Research Council, 1952.

Waddington, C. H., "Operations Research." *Nature*, 13 March 1948, p. 404.

———, "Operations Research." *Polemic*, 1945, p. 49.

———, "Operations Research." *World Review*, June 1945, p. 49.

Watson, Alfred N., "Operations Research." *Chemical Engineering*, February 1953, pp. 324-25.

Weaver, Wade R., *Operations Research and Its Relationship to Quality Control*. Cleveland, Republic Steel Corporation, 1952.

"What Operations Research Can Do." *Railway Age*, 16 November 1953, pp. 112-18.

Whitrow G. J., "Operational Analysis and the Nature of Some Physical Concepts." *Nature*, 15 July 1950, pp. 91-93.

Williams, Clyde, "Operations Diagnosis in Research Planning." *Science*, 26 December 1952, p. 3.

Williams, E. C., "Reflections on Operational Research." *Operational Research Quarterly*, June 1954, pp. 39-42.

Yates, Frank, "Operational Research." *Nature*, 15 April 1948, p. 609.

II. Military Applications.

"American War-Time Contributions to Statistical Methods." *Nature*, 2 October 1948, pp. 510-11.

Andrews, Thomas G., Denzel D. Smith, and Lessing A. Kahn, "An Empirical Analysis of the Effectiveness of Psychological Warfare." *Journal of Applied Psychology*, 1954, pp. 240-44.

Andrus, Edwin Cowles, and others, editors, *Advances in Military Medicine Made by American Investigators*. 2 vols. Boston, Little, Brown & Co., 1948.

Bailey, Robert A., "Application of Operations Research Techniques to Airborne Weapon System Planning." *Journal of the Operations Research Society of America*, August 1953, pp. 187-99.

Bartlett, Sir Frederick, "Planned Seeing: Some Psychological Experiments." London, HMSO, 1950.

Baxter, James Phinney, III, *Scientists Against Time*. Boston, Little, Brown & Co., 1946.

Bayly Pike, D. F., *Accidents Resulting in Injuries to Army Motorcyclists*. London, HMSO, 1949.

Blackett, P. M. S., "Operational Research—Recollections of Problems Studied, 1940-1945." *The Armed Forces Year Book, 1953* (Brassey's Annual). London, William Clowes & Sons, Ltd., 1954, pp. 88-106.

Boodman, David M., "The Reliability of Airborne Radar Equipment."

Journal of the Operations Research Society of America, February 1953, pp. 39-45.

Bready, James, "Putting the OR in VICTORY." *The Baltimore Sun,* 3 June 1951, Section A, p. 1.

Calder, Ritchie, "Clash of Ploughshares." *New Statesman and The Nation,* 13 September 1947, pp. 205-06.

Condon, Edward U., "Food and the Theory of Probability." *United States Naval Institute Proceedings,* 1934, pp. 75-78.

Crowther, J. G., and R. Whittington, *Science at War,* London, HMSO, 1947, and New York, Philosophical Library, Inc., 1948.

Cunningham, L. B. D., and W. R. B. Hynd, "Random Processes in Problems of Air Warfare." *Supplement to Journal of the Royal Statistical Society,* 1946, pp. 62-85.

Darcus, H. D., and A. G. M. Weddell, "Some Anatomical and Physiological Principles Concerned in the Design of Seats for Naval War Weapons." *British Medical Bulletin,* 1947-1948, pp. 31-37.

Davidson, Bill, "Why Half Our Combat Soldiers Fail to Shoot." *Collier's,* 8 November 1952, pp. 17-18.

Debeau, David E., and Robert A. Porter, "The Development of Planning Procedures at Air Proving Ground Command." *Journal of the Operations Research Society of America,* August 1953, pp. 200-07.

Eggleston, Wilfrid, *Scientists at War.* Toronto and New York, Oxford University Press, 1950.

"Evaluating Our Weapons. New Master Unit to Coordinate Defense." *Ordnance,* March-April 1949, p. 317.

Fitts, Paul M., "Psychological Research on Equipment Design in the AAF." *American Psychologist,* 1947, II, pp. 93-98.

Flood, Merrill M., "Application of Transportation Theory to Scheduling a Military Tanker Fleet." *Journal of the Operations Research Society of America,* May 1954, pp. 150-62.

Gordon, John E., "The Strategic and Tactical Influence of Disease in World War II." *Military Review,* March 1949, pp. 27-36, and April 1949, pp. 49-57.

Gray, George William, *Science at War.* London and New York, Harper Brothers, 1943.

Great Britain, Commonwealth Advisory Committee on Defense Science, "Operational Research and Defence in the Commonwealth." *Operational Research Quarterly,* September 1950, pp. 39-43.

Gringorten, Irving I., "The Verification and Scoring of Weather Forecasts." *Journal of the American Statistical Association,* September 1951, pp. 279-96.

Hankin, B. D., " Communication and Control of Military Forces." *Operational Research Quarterly*, December 1953, pp. 65-68.

Hausrath, Alfred H., " Utilization of Negro Manpower in the Army." *Journal of the Operations Research Society of America*, February 1954, pp. 17-30.

Hitchman, Norman A., " Today's Soldier—Porter or Fighter?" *The RCOC Quarterly*, October 1951, pp. 2-4.

Hoeber, Francis P., and Alvin Karchere, " Feasibility Considerations in the Allocation of Resources to Military Programs." *Journal of the Operations Research Society of America*, August 1954, pp. 306-15.

Hunter, Walter S., " Psychology in the War." *The American Psychologist*, November 1946, pp. 479-92.

Knight, Charlotte, " Ask Them Another." *Air Force*, December 1949, p. 30 *et seq.*

Lanchester, Frederick William, *Aircraft in Warfare, the Dawn of the Fourth Arm*. London, Constable and Co., 1916, and New York, D. Appleton and Co., 1917.

Lander, Max, " War and the Actuary." *Proceedings of the Centenary Assembly of the Institute of Actuaries*. Cambridge, Cambridge University Press, 1950, III, pp. 291-97.

Leach, W. Barton, " Lawyers as Operations Analysts in the Army Air Forces in World War II." *Boston University Law Review*, November 1952, p. 407-12.

LeGros Clark, W. E., " The Contribution of Anatomy to War." *British Medical Journal*, 12 January 1946, pp. 39-44.

Lew, E. A. and F. A. Weck, " Applications of Actuarial Techniques to Some Military Problems." *Proceedings of the Centenary Assembly of the Institute of Actuaries*. Cambridge, Cambridge University Press, 1950, III, pp. 298-312.

Liddell Hart, B. H., " The Development of the 'New Model' Army." *British Army Quarterly*, October 1924, pp. 37-50.

———, *Strategy: The Indirect Approach*. New York, Frederick A. Praeger, 1954.

Livesey, William E., *Mahan on Sea Power*. Norman, University of Oklahoma Press, 1947.

McDonald, John, " The War of Wits: Project RAND." *Fortune*, March 1951, p. 99 *et seq.*

Marshall, S. L. A., " The Mobility of One Man." *Infantry Journal*, October 1949, pp. 6-25.

" Men of Science and the War." *Nature*, 27 July 1940, pp. 107-08.

Murrell, K. F. H., " Fitting the Job to the Sailor: Review of Development of the Naval Motion Study Unit During 1947-1952." *Occupational Psychology*, 1 January 1953, pp. 30-37.

"Operational Research and Defence in the Commonwealth." *Operational Research Quarterly*, September 1950, pp. 39-43.

"OR: Weapon for Peace." *The Johns Hopkins Magazine*, October 1952.

"Operations Research—Weapons Systems Evaluation Group." *Infantry Journal*, March 1949, p. 38.

Parker, David B., "Our Greatest Secret Weapon." *This Week*, 5 August 1951.

Parker, Edward M., and David B. Parker, "Trial by Combat: Operations Research for the Army." *Combat Forces Journal*, May 1951, pp. 13-17.

Penton, J. C., "A Study in the Psychology of Desertion and Absenteeism in War-Time and Its Relation to the Problem of Morale." *Operational Research Quarterly*, June 1950, pp. 25-26.

Plymen, J., "Operational Research." *Proceedings of the Centenary Assembly of the Institute of Actuaries*. Cambridge, Cambridge University Press, 1950, III, pp. 313-28.

"Putting the OR in VICTORY." *The Baltimore Sun*, Sunday, 3 June 1951.

Richardson, Lewis F., *Mathematical Psychology of War*. Oxford, William Hunt, 1919.

———, "The Number of Nations on Each Side of a War." *Journal of the Royal Statistical Society*, 1946, pp. 130-56.

"Science Against War." *Newsweek*, 28 November 1949, pp. 49-50.

Seldon, M. R., and D. W. Pertschuk, "The Experimental Determination of Guided Missile Reliability." *Journal of the Operations Research Society of America*, February 1954, pp. 31-37.

Shellard, Gordon D., "Actuaries in the Operations Research Group, U. S. Navy." *Institute of Actuaries Centenary Assembly, 1848-1948*. 1948, pp. 1-6.

Steinhardt, Jacinto, "The Role of Operations Research in the Navy." *United States Naval Institute Proceedings*, May 1946, pp. 649-55.

Steward, Irvin, *Organizing Scientific Research for War: The Administrative History of OSRD*. Boston, Little, Brown & Co., 1947.

Taylor, Lauriston S., "Operations Analysis." *Military Review*, September 1946, pp. 21-26.

Thiesmeyer, Lincoln R., and John E. Burchard, *Combat Scientists*. Boston, Little, Brown & Co., 1947.

Vosseller, Aurelius B., and Glenn Nixon, "Science and the Battle of the Atlantic." *Yale Review*, June 1946, pp. 667-81.

Watson-Watt, Sir Robert, "Radar in War and in Peace." *Nature*, 15 September 1945, pp. 319-24.

Weaver, Warren, *The Scientists Speak*. New York, Boni & Gaer, 1947.

Whitmore, W. F., " Edison and Operations Research." *Journal of the Operations Research Society of America*, February 1953, pp. 83-85.

Williams, E. C., " Communications." *Operational Research Quarterly*, December 1953, pp. 68-71.

Wolfert, Ira, " The Silent Invisible War Under the Sea." *Reader's Digest*, November 1945, pp. 116-28.

Wood, Marshall K., " Scientific Techniques for Program Planning." *Air University Quarterly Review*, Winter 1949, pp. 49-65.

Yahraes, Herbert, " The Mysterious Mission of ORO." *The Saturday Evening Post*, 23 February 1952, pp. 36-37.

III. Industrial Applications.

Ackoff, Russell L., " Operations Research in Business and Industry." *Industrial Quality Control*, May 1952, pp. 41-46.

————, " Operations Research—New Tool of Industrial Science." *Industrial Laboratories*, November 1953, pp. 64-67.

Adler, Max K., " A note on Forecasting Demand for Special Offers in a Magazine." *Journal of Industrial Economics*, November 1953, pp. 44-50.

Andlinger, Gerhard B., and others, *Operations Research: Challenge to Modern Management*. Boston: Operations Research Associates, 1954.

Baldamus, W., and Hilde Behrend, " Variations in Absenteeism During the Week: An Index of Employee Morale." *Nature*, 27 May 1950, pp. 831-32.

Barnes, Ralph M., and Donald S. Correll, " Industrial Application of the Ratio-Delay Method." *Advanced Management*, August 1950, pp. 10-12, and September 1950, pp. 15-18.

Baxter, John, " Operational Research in Retailing." *Operational Research Quarterly*, September 1951, pp. 39-43.

Bonebakker, J. W., " The Application of Statistical Methods to the Analysis of Service Performance Data." *Transactions of the North-East Coast Institute of Engineers and Shipbuilders*, April 1951, pp. 277-86.

Breakwell, J. V., " The Problem of Testing for the Fraction of Defectives." *Journal of the Operations Research Society of America*, February 1954, pp. 59-69.

Brisby, M. D. J., and Roger T. Eddison, " Train Arrivals, Handling Costs, and the Holding and Storage of Raw Materials. *Journal of the Iron and Steel Institute*, October 1952, pp. 171-83.

" The British Association Meeting at Birmingham." *Engineering* 13 October 1950, pp. 303-09.

The British Cast-Iron Research Association's Operational Research Team. London, The Council of Ironfounding Associations, 1953.

Bronowski, Jacob, "Operational and Statistical Research in Building." *The Architects Journal*, 29 March 1951, pp. 403-06.

"Business Statistics Going Ph. D." *Business Week*, 30 May 1953, p. 96 *et seq.*

"Can Scientific Sampling Techniques Be Used in Railroad Accounting?" *Railway Age*, 9 June 1952, pp. 61-64.

Charnes, Abraham, William W. Cooper and B. Mellon, "Blending Aviation Gasolines—A Study in Programming Interdependent Activities in an Integrated Oil Company." *Econometrica*, April 1952, pp. 125-59.

Charnes, Abraham, William W. Cooper, Donald Farr, and others, "Linear Programming and Profit Preference Scheduling for a Manufacturing Firm." *Journal of the Operations Research Society of America*, May 1953, pp. 114-29.

Case, S. L., D. D. Moore, C. E. Sims, and R. J. Lund, *Comparative Economics of Open-Hearth and Electric Furnaces for Production of Low-Carbon Steel.* Bituminous Coal Research, Inc., July 1953.

Churchman, C. West, Russell L. Ackoff, and Murray Wax, editors, *Measurement of Consumer Interest.* Philadelphia, University of Pennsylvania Press, 1947.

Cook, L. S., and T. A. Evans, "Costs of Underground Locomotive Haulage Systems." *Iron & Coal Trades Review*, 6 April 1951, pp. 787-92, and 13 April 1951, pp. 853-57.

"Co-Operative Research in the Steel Industry." *Statistical Bulletin*, June 1949, pp. 1-11.

Crawley, Blick, "The Servicing of Aircraft: Choice of Principle and Procedure." *The Journal of the Royal Aeronautical Society*, December 1949, pp. 100-04.

Davies, D. R. G., "Operational Research and Control." *R. T. B. Quarterly*, September 1951.

Denerly, R. A., "Some Effects of Paid Sick Leave on Sickness Absence." *British Journal of Industrial Medicine*, 1952, pp. 275-81.

Diamond, E. L., and A. M. Frankau, "Present Methods of Open-Hearth Furnace Charging." *Journal of the Iron and Steel Institute*, March 1949, pp. 191-211.

Easterfield, T. E., "Can Operational Research Help Industry?" *Transactions of the Institute of Engineers and Shipbuilders of Scotland*, 11 May 1951, pp. 7-30.

Eddison, Roger T., and D. G. Owen, "Discharging Iron Ore." *Operational Research Quarterly*, September 1953, pp. 39-50.

Eddison, Roger T., "Operational Research—Application of Peace-Time Industry." *Nature*, September 1950, pp. 550-51.

Eden, J. F., "Building Operations." *Operational Research Quarterly*, September 1952, pp. 39-50.

Evans T. A., and S. L. Cook, "Costs of Underground Locomotive Haulage Systems." *Iron & Steel Trades Review*, 6 April 1951, pp. 787-92, and 13 April 1951, pp. 853-57.

————, "A Method of Studying Underground Costs With Special Reference to Locomotive Haulage Systems and Drifting." *Transactions of the Institution of Mining Engineers*, April 1951, p. 405.

Fair, William R., "Analogue Computations of Business Decisions." *Journal of the Operations Research Society of America*, August 1953, pp. 208-19.

Farkas, J. J., "Time Study and Standards Aid Foundry Production Planning." *American Foundryman*, June 1950, pp. 45-47.

Furness, H. J., *The Cost of Labour Turnover*. London, Institute of Cost and Works Accountants, December 1950.

Gillman, Leonard, "Operations Analysis and the Theory of Games: An Advertising Example." *Journal of the American Statistical Association*, December 1950, pp. 541-45.

Glover, John G., *Business Operational Research and Reports*. New York, American Book Company, 1949.

Goodeve, Charles F., "Productivity Studies as a Science." *Journal of the Institute of Production Engineers*, September 1953, p. 387.

Gregory, Robert H., "The Frequency and Importance of Errors in Invoices Received." *Accounting Research*, 1952, p. 332.

Harper, Roland, "Psychological and Psycho-Physical Studies of Craftsmanship in Dairying." *British Journal of Psychology*, Monograph Supplements XXVIII. Cambridge, University Press, 1952.

Harris, K. E., "Technical Objectives in Pre-Planning Production." *British Kinematography*, January 1951, pp. 18-29.

Herrmann, Cyril C., and John F. Magee, "Operations Research for Management." *Harvard Business Review*, July-August 1953, pp. 100-12.

Hertz, David B., and Albert H. Rubenstein, editors. *Research Operations in Industry*. New York, King's Crown Press, 1953.

————, *The Theory and Practice of Industrial Research*. New York, McGraw-Hill, 1950.

Hicks, Donald, "Operational Research in the Coal Industry." *Operational Research Quarterly*, December 1951, pp. 55-60.

Hillyar, George, "The Back Room Boys Go Into Business." *The Director*, October 1951, pp. 2-4.

Hofman, H. W., "Planungsforschung." *Schweizer Maschinenmarkt*, 1949, pp. 14-18.

Industrial Engineering Institute, University of California. *Proceedings*

of the Fifth Annual Industrial Engineering Institute. Berkeley, The
Institute, 1953.

Jennings, R. F., "Applying Research to Steel Works Plant and Operation." *The Engineer,* 18 July 1952, p. 83.

Jensen, Arne, *Moe's Principle.* Copenhagen, The Copenhagen Telephone
Company, 1952.

Keen, Joan, and Denys J. Page, "A Study of Pots Used in Making
Glass." *Applied Statistics,* November 1952, pp. 163-68.

Kellogg, F. H., *Construction Methods and Machinery.* New York, Prentice-
Hall, Inc., 1954.

Knox, J., "Operational Research in the Building Industry." *Operational
Research Quarterly,* March 1951, pp. 5-10.

Krige, D. G., "A Statistical Approach to Some Basic Mine Valuation
Problems on the Witwatersrand." *Journal of Chemical Metallurgical
and Mining Society of South Africa,* December 1951, pp. 119-39.

Kusik, John, "Discussion on the Use of Mathematical Models in Business
Organizations." *Econometrica,* April 1953, p. 351.

Lathrop, John B., "Production Problems Bow to Operations Research."
SAE Journal, May 1953, pp. 46-49.

LePoole, L. H., "Establishing a Suitable Stoker's Premium." *Tydschrift
voor Efficiente en Documentatie,* 1953, p. 19 *et seq.*

Levinson, Horace, "Experiences in Commercial Operations Research."
Journal of the Operations Research Society of America, August 1953,
pp. 220-39.

Lloyd, I. S., "Operational Research—A New Tool for Management."
Journal of Industrial Economics, July 1953, pp. 175-86.

Lockspeiser, Sir Ben, "Commentary: The Study of Industrial Operations." *Research,* March 1952, pp. 97-100.

McAnally, Patrick, "Market Research and Operational Research." *Operational Research Quarterly,* December 1951, pp. 61-64.

Magee, John F., "The Effect of Promotional Effort on Sales." *Journal
of the Operations Research Society of America,* February 1953, pp.
64-74.

Malcolm, Donald G., "Operations Research—Widening the Horizon of
Industrial Engineering?" *Journal of Industrial Engineering,* September 1954, pp. 3-6.

———, and L. L. Sammet, "Work Sampling Application." *Journal of
Industrial Engineering,* May 1954, p. 4 *et seq.*

Marriott, Basil, "The House That Fact Built—A Case for Operational
Research in Housing." *The Builder,* 12, 19, 26 September 1952.

Masefield, Peter G., "Some Economic Factors in Civil Aviation With
Emphasis on Civil Aircraft and Their Prospective Trends of Develop-

ment." *The Journal of the Royal Aeronautical Society*, October 1948, pp. 575-716.

Mees, C. E. Kenneth, and John A. Leermakers, *The Organization of Industrial Scientific Research*. New York, McGraw-Hill, 1950.

Menzler, F. A. A., "Operational Research: An Aid to Efficiency." *British Transport Review*, April 1953, pp. 263-83.

——, "Statistical Methods and Operational Research in Transport." *Journal of the Institute of Transport*, January 1953.

Moross, Manfred D., and others, *Automation, Challenge to Management*. Cambridge, Harvard Graduate School of Business Administration, 1953.

Morrison, Herbert, "Operational Research in Industry." *Nature*, 26 February 1949, p. 315.

——, "Scientific Research and Manpower." *Nature*, 6 November 1948, pp. 711-13.

Morse, Philip M., "Must We Always Be Gadgeteers?" *Physics Today*, December 1950, pp. 4-5.

Munn, Mary S., and Sarah M. Haywood, "Purchasing: Optimum Size of Order ('How Much Shall I Buy?')." *The Purchasing Journal*, January 1951, pp. 11-16, and March 1951, pp. 99 *et seq.*

Murdoch, J., "Operational Research and Materials Handling." *Operational Research Quarterly*, June 1953, pp. 25-29.

Nadler, G., "p-Charts Improve Methods for Determining Downtime." *The Iron Age*, 27 November 1952, pp. 110-13.

National Institute for Industrial Psychology, *The Foreman: A Study of Supervision in British Industry*. London, Staples Press, 1951.

National Research Council, Committee on Operations Research. *Operations Research with Special Reference to Non-Military Applications: A Comprehensive Scientific Aid to Executive Decisions*. April 1951.

Nelson, R. T., and M. E. Salveson, "Mathematical Methods in Management Programming." *The Journal of Industrial Enigneering*, March 1954, pp. 9-15, and September 1954, pp. 17-19.

Office of the Lord President of the Council, The Working Party of the Committee on Industrial Productivity, Great Britain, *The Principles and Practices of Operational Research*. 21 July 1948.

"O. H. P.—The Labour Used at the Roving Frame in Producing American Type Roving." *Shirley Institute Bulletin*, 1948, p. 21.

"Operational Aspects of Marine Radar: A Symposium of Papers." *The Journal of the Institute of Navigation*, April 1949, pp. 94-158.

"Operational Research." *The Engineers*, 23 September 1949, p. 331.

"Operational Research and Building." *Discovery*, July 1947, pp. 199-200.

"Operational Research Club." *Nature*, 23 October 1948, p. 646.

"Operational Research in Building." *The Engineer,* 20 December 1948, p. 661.

"Operational Research in Industry." *The Engineer,* 11 August 1950, p. 134.

"Operational Research in the Research Associations." *Nature,* 17 April 1948, pp. 584-85.

"Operational Research: Meetings at Manchester." *Nature,* 24 September 1949, p. 520.

"Operations Research for Railroads?" *Railway Age,* 8 March 1954, pp. 75-77.

"Operations Research is Scientific Common Sense." *Business Week,* 1 December 1951, p. 62 *et seq.*

"Operations Research Ready for Industrial Applications." *Chemical & Engineering News,* 16 June 1952, p. 2503.

Parker, E., and L. S. LePage, "Operational Factors and Operational Yields." *Journal of the Institute of Navigation,* April 1949, pp. 95-104.

Passano, R. F., "Finished Steel Production: Possible Increase From Existing Equipment." *Year Book of the American Iron and Steel Institute.* New York, The Institute, 1949, pp. 192-220.

"Peacetime Implications of Operations Research." *The American Statistician,* December 1948, pp. 1-17.

Pickard, R. H., "The Application of Statistical Methods to Production and Research in Industry." *Journal of the Royal Statistical Society,* 1934.

Pocock, John W., "Operations Research and the Management Consultant." *Journal of the Operations Research Society of America,* May 1953, pp. 137-44.

Preuschen, G., "Operational Research in German Agriculture." *Research,* October 1949, pp. 455-58.

"Proceedings of the Conference on Operations Research in Marketing." Cleveland, Case Institute of Technology, 1953.

"Proceedings of the Conference on Operations Research in Production and Inventory Control." Cleveland, Case Institute of Technology, 1954.

Productivity Measurement in British Industry. London, Anglo-American Council on Productivity, 1950.

Railway Systems and Procedures Association, *Seminar on Operations Research.* New York, The Association, 1954.

"A Rational Approach to Productivity Measurement." *Operational Research Quarterly,* June 1952, pp. 21-23.

Rice, A. K., J. M. Hill, and E. L. Trist, "The Representation of Labour Turn-Over as a Social Process—Studies in the Social Development of an Industrial Community (The Glacier Project)." *Human Relations,* November 1950, pp. 349-72.

Rinehart, Robert F., " Threats to the Growth of Operations Research in Business and Industry." *Journal of the Operations Research Society of America,* August 1954, pp. 229-33.

Rivett, B. H. P., " Underground Communications." *Operational Research Quarterly,* December 1953, pp. 61-65.

Roy, Robert H., " Operations Research and Industrial Engineering—Contrast and Resemblance." *Scientific Monthly,* September 1953, pp. 161-62.

Schell, Erwin H., " Toward New Horizons—Management Reconstructs Its Thinking." *Dun's Review,* May 1948, p. 7.

Scott, J. R., " Operational Research in the Rubber Industry." *Journal of Rubber Research,* September and October 1951, pp. 63-70.

Shragah, S., " The Flow of Motor Spirit from Refinery to Consumer." *Operational Research Quarterly,* March 1954, pp. 26-30.

Simon, Herbert A., and Charles C. Holt, " The Control of Inventories and Production Rates—A Survey." *Journal of the Operations Research Society of America,* August 1954, pp. 289-301.

Solt, R., " Capacities in a Manufacturing Process." *Operational Research Quarterly,* March 1954, pp. 24-26.

Sparling, David M., and others, *Operations Research and Business.* Boston, the authors, 1953.

Sporn, Philip, *The Integrated Power System as the Basic Mechanism for Power Supply.* New York, McGraw-Hill, 1950.

Sternhell, Charles M., " The Use of Medical Examinations and Blood Pressures in Underwriting Industrial Insurances." *Proceedings of the Home Office Life Underwriters Association,* XXX, pp. 195-211.

Swan, A. W., " Human Relations in Industrial Operational Research." *The Engineer,* 25 July 1952, pp. 117-120.

————, " Statistical Methods in the Iron and Steel Industry." *Engineering,* 15 October 1948, pp. 379-80.

————, " Time Study on Cranes at Rail Bank, Workington." *The Engineer,* 14 September 1951, pp. 327-28.

————, " The Work and Organization of a Statistical Department in Heavy Industry with Particular Reference to the Steel Industry." *Journal of the Iron and Steel Institute,* 1948, pp. 1-20.

Thornthwaite, C. W., " Operations Research in Agriculture." *Journal of the Operations Research Society of America,* February 1953, pp. 33-38.

Thring, M. W., " The Influence of Heat Transfer on Open-Hearth Furnace Charging Rate." *Journal of the Iron and Steel Institute,* March 1949, pp. 212-21.

Tippett, L. H. C., "Application of Statistical Methods to Problems of Production in Industry." *Bulletin of the International Institute of Statistics*, 1949, pp. 19-29.

———, "Operational Research." *Transactions of the British Ceramic Society*, 18 January 1949, pp. 153-60.

———, "The Study of Industrial Efficiency with Special Reference to the Cotton Industry." *Journal of the Royal Statistical Society*, 23 January 1947, pp. 108-22.

"The Use of Mechanical Plant in House Building." *Discovery*, April 1947.

Tomlin, S. Stokes, "Productivity Standards—Warehousing." *Advanced Management*, March 1951, pp. 19-22.

"Top Management by Mathematics." *Business Week*, 30 May 1953, p. 86 *et seq.*

Valentine, A. B. B., "Standards of Service in Transport." *Journal of the Institute of Transport*, November 1951, p. 247 *et seq.*

van de Wetering, J. M., "The Human Factor in Relation to Operations and Machinery." *Tydschrift von Efficiente Bedrijfsorganisatie*, 1954, pp. 100-105.

Weaver, Wade R., "Quality Control Aids in Steel Processing Control." *Blast Furnace and Steel Plant*, February 1953, pp. 198-202, and March 1953, pp. 307-10.

Whitin, Thomson M., "Erich Schneider's Inventory Control Analysis." *Journal of the Operations Research Society of America*, August 1954, pp. 329-34.

Williams, D. A. S., "The Economics of Packaging Equipment for Export." *The British Packer*, April 1950, pp. 33-34; May 1950, p. 32; June 1950, pp. 32-33.

Yates, Frank, "Agriculture, Sampling and Operational Research." *Bulletin of the International Institute of Statistics*, 1949.

IV. Government Planning.

Adams, William Frederick, "Road Traffic Considered as a Random Series." *Journal of the Institution of Civil Engineers*, November 1936, pp. 121-31.

Bailey, Norman T. J., "Operational Research in Medicine." *Operational Research Quarterly*, June 1952, pp. 24-29.

Bell, G. E., "Operational Research into Air Traffic Control." *Journal of the Royal Aeronautical Society*, 1949, pp. 965-76.

Bowen, E. G., "Operational Research into the Air Traffic Problem." *Journal of the Institute of Navigation*, October 1948, pp. 338-41.

———, and T. Pearcey, "Delays in the Flow of Air Traffic." *Journal of the Royal Aeronautical Society*, April 1948, pp. 251-58.

Bronowski, Jacob, " Some Uses of Statistics in the Building Industry: An Investigation into the Erection Times of Nine Types of Non-Traditional House." *Journal of the Royal Statistical Society*, 1949, pp. 287-308.

Charlesworth, G., and Hilary Tadman, " Accidents and the Road Surface." *The Surveyor and Municipal Engineer*, 9 June 1950.

Chase, Stuart, " *Operation Bootstrap* " *in Puerto Rico.* Washington, The National Planning Association, September 1951.

Collier, John, " U. S. Indian Administration as a Laboratory of Ethnic Relations." *Social Research*, September 1945, pp. 265-303.

Conant, James B., " Science and Politics in the 20th Century." *Foreign Affairs*, January 1950, pp. 189-202.

Dobbs, H. A. C., *Operational Research and Action Research.* Washington, Institute of Ethnic Affairs, 1947.

——, " Administrator and Specialist." *Corona, The Journal of His Majesty's Colonial Service*, November 1949, pp. 7-11; December 1949, pp. 18-22; January 1950, pp. 27-31; and February 1950, pp. 64-66.

Edie, Leslie C., " Traffic Delays at Toll Booths." *Journal of the Operations Research Society of America*, May 1954, pp. 107-138.

George, Alexander L., " Communications Research and Public Policy." *World Politics*, January 1951, p. 251.

Glanville, William Henry, " Aspects of Modern Road Research." *Contractors Plant Register*, May 1947.

——, " Experiments in the Marking of Pedestrian Crossings." *The Surveyor and County Engineer*, 8 July 1949.

——, " The Influence of the ' Zebra ' Marking and of Propaganda on Behaviour at Pedestrian Crossings." *Roads and Road Construction*, July 1950, pp. 204-5.

——, " Road Safety and Road Research." *Journal of the Royal Society of Arts*, 12 January 1951, pp. 114-92.

Goodeve, Charles F., " Operational Research in the Research Associations." *Nature*, 17 April 1948, pp. 584-85.

Great Britain, *The Application of Scientific Methods to Industrial and Service Medicine.* London, HMSO, 1951.

Highway Research Board, Committee on Highway Capacity. " Highway Capacity Manual." Washington, GPO, 1950.

Hodgson, William C., " Echo Sounding and Pelagic Fisheries." *Fisheries Investigations*, 1950.

——, and I. D. Richardson, " The Experiment on the Cornish Pilchard Fishery in 1947-1948." *Fishery Investigations*, 1949.

Institute of Public Administration, New York, " The New York Police Survey." Prepared for the Mayor's Committee on Management Survey, 18 September 1952.

Jeffcoate, Grace O., "Effect of Motor Patrols on Accidents." *Nature*, 14 October 1950, p. 639.

Lewis, E. Aneurin, "Tse-tse Flies Carried by Trains in Kenya Colony." *Bulletin of Entomological Research*, February 1950, pp. 511-31.

Lewis, R. E. F., "Some Measures of Driver Behaviour." *Operational Research Quarterly*, March 1953, pp. 10-15.

London Transport Executive, "Luggage Accommodation in Buses and Coaches." *Operational Research Quarterly*, June 1952, pp. 29-30.

———, "Stanchions on Road Service Vehicles." *Operational Research Quarterly*, September 1950, pp. 47-48.

Loofbourow, John R., "Operational Analysis in Relation to Administration of Government Sponsored Research." *Science*, 8 August 1947, pp. 113-17.

Manning, J. R., "An Investigation into Accident Rates on Trunk Road A. 4 in Slough." *Roads and Roads Construction*, August 1949.

Masefield, Peter G., "Some Economic Factors in Civil Aviation with Emphasis on Civil Aircraft and Their Prospective Trends of Development." *The Journal of the Royal Aeronautical Society*, October 1948, pp. 575-718.

Mayor's Committee on Management Survey of the City of New York, *Modern Management for the City of New York*. Report of the Mayor's Committee on Management Survey, 2 vols., 30 March 1953.

Menzler, F. A. A., "London and its Passenger Transport System." *Journal of the Royal Statistical Society*, 1950, pp. 298-337.

———, "Operational Research: An Aid to Efficiency." *British Transport Review*, April 1953, pp. 263-83.

———, "Statistical Methods and Operational Research in Transport." *The Journal of the Institute of Transport*, January 1953, pp. 35-45.

———, "Statistics in Administration." *British Transport Review*, April 1952, pp. 34-53.

Millett, John David, *The Process and Organization of Government Planning*. New York, Columbia University Press, 1947.

Moore, R. L., "Pedestrian Choice and Judgment." *Operational Research Quarterly*, March 1953, pp. 3-10.

Moss, Louis, "The Government Social Survey." *Operational Research Quarterly*, December 1950, pp. 55-65.

———, "The Social Survey." *Nature*, CLX, p. 662.

"Operations Research and Public Health." *American Journal of Public Health*, October 1952, pp. 1306-07.

Pearcy, T., "Delays in Landing of Air Traffic." *The Journal of the Royal Aeronautical Society*, December 1948, pp. 799-812.

Reid, David, "A Quantitative Method for Determining Palatability of

Pasture Plants." *Journal of British Grassland Society*, December 1951, pp. 187-95.

Ricker, William Edwin, *Methods of Estimating Vital Statistics of Fish Populations*. Bloomington, Indiana University Press, 1948.

Road Research Laboratory. " Accidents to Pedestrians on Roads Without Footpaths." *The Surveyor and Municipal and County Engineer*, 13 October 1952.

Russell Sage Foundation, " *Effective Use of Social Science Research in the Federal Services*. New York, Russell Sage Foundation, 1950.

Schiller, P., " Operations Research in the Electricity Industry." *Proceedings of the Institution of Electrical Engineers*, 1951, pp. 229-38.

" Scientific Research and Manpower." *Nature*, 6 November 1948, pp. 711-13.

Smeed, Reuben Jacob, " Some Factors Influencing the Road Behaviour of Vehicle Drivers." *Operational Research Quarterly*, December 1952, pp. 60-67.

——, " Some Statistical Aspects of Road Safety Research." *Journal of the Royal Statistical Society*, 1949, pp. 1-34.

Smith, Percival, " Twenty-five years of Research in Vocational Guidance." *Occupational Psychology*, January 1951, pp. 35-43.

Stansfield, R. G., " The Accuracy of Wind Finding by the 3-Course Drift Method: A Statistical Analysis." *Journal of the Institute of Navigation*, 1949, pp. 165-179.

Stein, Harold, *Public Administration and Policy Development, A Case Book*. New York, Harcourt, Brace & Co., 1952.

Stone, Marshall H., " Science and Statecraft." *Science*, 16 May 1947, pp. 507-10.

Tanner, J. C., " Sample Traffic Census, August 1949." *The Surveyor and Municipal and County Engineer*, 7 July 1950.

Tippett, L. C. H., " Operational Research at the Shirley Institute." *Operational Research Quarterly*, June 1950, pp. 19-23.

Valentine, A. B. B., " Standards of Service in Transport." *Journal of the Institute of Transport*, 7 November 1951, p. 247 *et seq.*

Wardrop, J. G., " The Capacity of Roads." *Operational Research Quarterly*, March 1954, pp. 14-24.

——, " Some Theoretical Aspects of Road Traffic Research." *Proceedings of the Institution of Civil Engineers*, June 1952, pp. 325-378.

Welch, J. D., and Norman T. J. Bailey, " Appointment Systems in Hospital Out-Patient Departments." *The Lancet*, 31 May 1952, pp. 1105-08.

Weston, J. C., and W. F. B. Shaw, " Fuel Economy—The Home Fires." *Research*, October 1951, pp. 455-62.

Index

Index

405